Advances in
Analytical Chemistry and Instrumentation
Volume I

Advances in Analytical Chemistry and Instrumentation

Edited by
CHARLES N. REILLEY
Department of Chemistry, University of North Carolina, Chapel Hill, North Carolina

VOLUME I

INTERSCIENCE PUBLISHERS INC., NEW YORK
INTERSCIENCE PUBLISHERS LTD., LONDON

Interscience Publishers, Inc.
250 Fifth Avenue, New York 1, N. Y.

For Great Britain and Northern Ireland:

Interscience Publishers, Ltd.
88/90 Chancery Lane, London W. C. 2, England

PRINTED IN THE UNITED STATES OF AMERICA BY MACK PRINTING CO., EASTON, PA.

INTRODUCTION TO THE SERIES

The scope, and even the purpose, of analytical chemistry has grown so amazingly in the last decade that even the dedicated analyst with time on his hands cannot follow the significant developments which appear now in ever increasing numbers. If analytical chemistry is to grow into its new and wider role and gain its rightful prestige, these new developments must become everyday working knowledge and be translated into practice. At present a serious time lag still exists between evolution and practice. This new venture aims to bridge the hiatus by presenting a continuing series of volumes whose chapters deal not only with significant new developments in ideas and techniques, but also with critical evaluations and the present status of important, but more classical, methods and approaches. The chapters will be contributed by outstanding workers having intimate knowledge and experience with their subject.

It is the hope and belief that *Advances in Analytical Chemistry and Instrumentation* will offer a new medium for the exchange of ideas and will help assist effective, fruitful communication between the various disciplines of analytical chemistry.

These volumes will probably appear annually. Each will contain articles covering a variety of topics presented from the standpoint of the nonspecialist but retaining a scholarly level of treatment. Although a reasonably complete review of recent developments is given, a dry and terse cataloguing of the literature without description or evaluation is avoided. The scope of the *Advances* is flexible and broad, hoping to be of service to the modern analytical chemist whose profession each day demands broader prospectives and solution of problems with increased complexity. The periodical literature is too specialized and the appearance of suitable monographs take place only after many years. Reviews are often directed to the specialist and often lack adequate description or evaluation. *Advances* hope to fill in the resulting need for critical, comprehensive articles surveying various topics on a high level, satisfying the specialist and non-specialist alike.

THE EDITOR

CONTRIBUTORS TO VOLUME I

FRED C. ANSON, *Division of Chemistry and Chemical Engineering, California Institute of Technology, Pasadena, California*

A. J. BARNARD, JR., *Director, Technical Information Service, J. T. Baker Chemical Company, Phillipsburg, New Jersey*

HERMANN FLASCHKA, *School of Chemistry, Georgia Institute of Technology, Atlanta, Georgia*

FORREST L. GAGER, JR., *Research Associate, Philip Morris, Inc., Richmond, Virginia*

ROBERT F. GODDU, *Analytical Division, Hercules Research Center, Hercules Powder Company, Wilmington, Delaware*

CHARLES A. HORTON, *Oak Ridge National Laboratory, Union Carbide Nuclear Company, Oak Ridge, Tennessee*

CHARLES N. REILLEY, *Department of Chemistry, University of North Carolina, Chapel Hill, North Carolina*

WILLIAM H. REINMUTH, *Department of Chemistry, Columbia University, New York, New York*

WOLFGANG SCHÖNIGER, *Microanalytical Department, Sandoz Ltd., Basel, Switzerland*

ROBERT B. SELIGMAN, *Manager of Development, Philip Morris, Inc., Richmond, Virginia*

ERNEST H. SWIFT, *Chairman, Division of Chemistry and Chemical Engineering, California Institute of Technology, Pasadena, California*

CONTENTS

Tetraphenylboron (TPB) as an Analytical Reagent

H. FLASCHKA, *Georgia Institute of Technology, Atlanta Georgia*, AND
A. J. BARNARD, JR., *J. T. Baker Chemical Company, Phillipsburg,
New Jersey*

I. INTRODUCTION

A satisfactory chemical determination of potassium has long been a cherished goal of analytical chemists. Classical precipitants for potassium have such defects as low selectivity or formation of potassium compounds of uncertain composition or of nonnegligible solubility. The introduction of sodium tetraphenylboron, $NaB(C_6H_5)_4$, for the determination of potassium (and of certain other ions) stands as one of the truly significant reagent advances of the last decade. The tetraphenylboron ion for convenience and brevity can be written as "TPB," a practice which has already been adopted by a number of authors.

Following World War II Wittig undertook an extended study of complex formation and reactivity in organometallic chemistry. In 1947, Wittig and Keicher (224) reported, without details, the preparation of lithium TPB and its reactivity as compared with analogous organometallic compounds. In 1949, Wittig, Keicher, Rückert, and Raff (225) reported in detail on the preparation and reactions of various TPB salts. Some related studies by Wittig and co-workers also appeared during the period 1950 to 1956 (220-223,226-229, 231). Wittig and co-workers (225,229) recognized the possibilities for lithium or sodium TPB as analytical reagents. These salts are stable and water soluble. The corresponding potassium, rubidium, cesium, silver, thallium(I), ammonium, and tetraalkylammonium salts are relatively stable and very insoluble in water and lower alcohols. In 1951, Raff and Brotz (160) reported on the use of lithium or sodium TPB in the gravimetric determination of potassium. Potassium TPB was found to be exact in composition and to possess a most favorable equivalent weight (i.e., 358.34), excellent thermal stability, and very low water solubility. The precipitation could be accomplished quantitatively in the presence of substantial amounts of sodium and alkaline earth metals. Wittig and Raff (229) effected the gravimetric determination of rubidium, cesium, and ammonium as their TPB salts with satisfactory results. These findings, coupled with early commercial availability of reagent grade sodium TPB, prompted study by other workers.

The interest in TPB methods and compounds is reflected by the extensive bibliography of Barnard and Büechl (12,13). By the end of 1958 close to 300 discrete publications on TPB compounds (and closely related compounds) had appeared. Of these publications, possibly over 200 are of actual or potential interest for chemical analysis, as are at least 40 further papers that appeared subsequently. It is noteworthy that a number of reviews on the use of the TPB ion in chemical analysis have appeared (1,4,13a,15,25c,71,79,92,96,107d, 116,133,152,159,166,203,205).

At the present time TPB methods have been applied to the detection, identification, and determination of potassium, ammonium, rubidium, cesium, thallium(I), and of certain other metal ions, and of certain basic organic compounds, especially basic nitrogen compounds. It is the aim of the present chapter to consider briefly the preparation, properties, and reactions of analytical interest of the metal TPB salts; to present a full and critical treatment of the precipitation of potassium TPB; to provide the principles and working directions for the application of this precipitation to the gravimetric, titrimetric, and other determinations of potassium (and of other metal ions); and to summarize the application of TPB methods to the determination, identification, and detection of organic compounds.

II. PREPARATION AND PROPERTIES OF THE METAL TPB SALTS

An understanding of the reactions and properties of the TPB ion and its salts is necessary either for the development of new TPB methods or for the appreciation of known methods. The reactions of the TPB ion are considered in Section II-1 as well as the preparation of metal TPB salts. Some physical properties of these TPB salts that are of analytical interest are discussed in Section II-2.

1. Preparation and Reactions of Metal TPB Salts

Wittig and co-workers (225) initially prepared lithium TPB by the reaction of triphenylboron with phenyllithium in ether solution (Equation 1).

$$B(C_6H_5)_3 + C_6H_5Li \longrightarrow LiB(C_6H_5)_4 \tag{1}$$

Subsequently they found (229) that this TPB compound could be obtained more expeditiously by the reaction of boron trifluoride etherate with phenyllithium (Equation 2).

$$BF_3 + 4C_6H_5Li \longrightarrow LiB(C_6H_5)_4 + 3LiF \tag{2}$$

The lithium salt may be converted (229) to the sodium salt by isolating the water-insoluble ammonium salt and treating this under reflux with sodium methylate in methanol (Equation 3).

$$NH_4B(C_6H_5)_4 + CH_3ONa \longrightarrow NaB(C_6H_5)_4 + CH_3OH + NH_3 \tag{3}$$

A more direct and elegant synthesis of sodium TPB was developed by Wittig and Raff (229) involving reaction of boron trifluoride etherate with phenylmagnesium bromide, treatment with water and sodium chloride, and extraction with chloroform (Equations 4 and 5).

$$BF_3 + 4C_6H_5MgBr \longrightarrow B(C_6H_5)_4MgBr + 3MgBrF \qquad (4)$$

$$B(C_6H_5)_4MgBr + NaCl \xrightarrow{H_2O} NaB(C_6H_5)_4 + MgBrCl \qquad (5)$$

This synthesis was studied subsequently by Ieviņš and Gudriniece (102–104) and by Mýl and co-workers (138a). The latter workers isolated the ammonium salt and converted it to the sodium salt by refluxing with sodium methylate (Equation 3). In a variation of this synthesis Nesmeyanov and co-workers (141) treated sodium fluoborate with phenylmagnesium bromide (Equation 6).

$$NaBF_4 + 4C_6H_5MgBr \longrightarrow NaB(C_6H_5)_4 + 4MgBrF \qquad (6)$$

The grignardization of a boron halide and the subsequent steps for the isolation of high purity sodium TPB are the subject of process patents (93,230). Sodium TPB is commercially available and is the usual form in which the TPB reagent is employed for analytical purposes; lithium TPB was only employed in a few early studies. Nesmeyanov and co-workers (142) prepared potassium TPB by substitution of potassium fluoborate in the Grignard reaction with phenylmagnesium bromide (Equation 7).

$$KBF_4 + 4C_6H_5MgBr \longrightarrow KB(C_6H_5)_4 + 4MgBrF \qquad (7)$$

Wittig and Raff (229) prepared silver TPB by mixing under red light acetonic solutions of equivalent amounts of silver nitrate and lithium TPB. As the precipitate turned brown, even under diffuse light, it was filtered in the dark and dried at 20°C. over silica gel. Its silver content was in satisfactory agreement with theory. Silver TPB is also precipitated from aqueous or acetonic solutions in various analytical methods; whether or not the product is completely stoichiometric under these conditions has been questioned (31,113).

Wittig and Raff (229) prepared copper(I) TPB by mixing anhydrous copper(II) chloride with excess lithium TPB in absolute ether, shaking for some weeks under a nitrogen atmosphere, and working up the reaction mixture. The over-all course of the synthesis is given by Equations 8 and 9.

$$2LiB(C_6H_5)_4 + 2CuCl_2 \longrightarrow 2CuCl + 2B(C_6H_5)_3 + 2LiCl + (C_6H_5)_2 \qquad (8)$$

$$CuCl + LiB(C_6H_5)_4 \longrightarrow CuB(C_6H_5)_4 + LiCl \qquad (9)$$

Nesmeyanov and co-workers (142) reacted potassium TPB in pyridine solution with the copper derivative of acetoacetic ester and thus obtained the stable copper(I) TPB tetrapyridinate. CuB-

$(C_6H_5)_4 \cdot 4C_5H_5N$. This product could be converted to copper(I) TPB by careful acidification. This white compound darkened fairly rapidly on exposure to air and developed the odor of biphenyl. Sazonova and Nazarova (180) studied the reaction of this TPB salt (added as the pyridine complex) with α,β-unsaturated ketones and substituted acetoacetates, and with carbon tetrachloride. Sporek and Williams (200) found that addition of copper(I) chloride to an aqueous sodium TPB solution (strongly acidic conditions) led to the formation of a precipitate.

The potassium, rubidium, cesium, ammonium, and thallium(I) salts may be obtained by mere treatment of an aqueous solution of sodium (or lithium) TPB with a soluble salt of the relevant cation. Ammonium TPB, unlike potassium TPB, is somewhat soluble in $3M$ sodium hydroxide, especially if the solution is warmed (153c). The thorium(IV) salt was reported (184,200) as being insoluble in water, however, this finding has now been traced to an unexpected ammonium content in certain commercial thorium salts (185,199, 218).

The free acid, $HB(C_6H_5)_4$, has not been obtained in a solid form and for analytical purposes has only been obtained by passing a sodium TPB solution through a cation exchange resin bed in the hydrogen form. The solution is unstable and undergoes extensive decomposition within a few minutes (6,61,90,149,150a,225) (see Sections IV-8 and IV-11). The TPB ion by the action of acid may initially be converted to benzene and triphenylboron (225,229) (Equation 10).

$$B(C_6H_5)_4^- + H^+ \longrightarrow [HB(C_6H_5)_4] \longrightarrow B(C_6H_5)_3 + C_6H_6 \quad (10)$$

The latter undergoes hydrolysis to phenylboric acid (Equation 11),

$$B(C_6H_5)_3 + 2H_2O \longrightarrow (C_6H_5)B(OH)_2 + 2C_6H_6 \quad (11)$$

or under controlled conditions to diphenylboric acid (150a) (Equation 12).

$$B(C_6H_5)_3 + H_2O \longrightarrow (C_6H_5)_2B(OH) + C_6H_6 \quad (12$$

This latter acid may be isolated as its anhydride, tetraphenyldiboroxide (146,150). The structures $C_6H_5B(OH)_2$, $(C_6H_5)_2B(OH)$, and $(C_6H_5)_4B_2O$ in the present review are termed phenylboric acid, diphenylboric acid, and tetraphenyldiboroxide, respectively. In an alternative nomenclature these are termed, respectively, phenylboronic acid, diphenylboronous acid, and diphenylboronous anhydride.

The structure $NaB(C_6H_5)_4$ is termed sodium tetraphenylboron in this review, an unambiguous name adopted by many workers. The 1957 IUPAC inorganic nomenclature rules (105c) consider this salt as a coordination compound and name it sodium tetraphenylborate. The nomenclature problems and chemistry of organoboron compounds have been considered in a monograph by Rochow, Hurd, and Lewis (168) and in an extensive review by Lappert (120).

The metal TPB salts undergo decomposition on heating to an appropriate temperature (see Section II-2). In the case of lithium, potassium, rubidium, and cesium TPB, the ultimate product (if oxygen is present) is the metal metaborate (Equation 13).

$$KB(C_6H_5)_4 + 30O_2 \longrightarrow KBO_2 + 24CO_2 + 10H_2O \qquad (13)$$

Prolonged heating of sodium or potassium TPB in aqueous 2-ethoxyethanol (Cellosolve) leads to the formation of benzene, phenol, diphenylboric acid, and acetaldehyde (162). The analogous treatment of ammonium TPB proceeds similarly with no evolution of gaseous ammonia (162). The heating of ammonium TPB in methanol at 100°C. (sealed tube) yields benzene, phenol, and ammonium triphenylboron (162). The reaction of bromine and the TPB ion is not stoichiometric (172) (see Section IV-12). However, the addition of methanolic bromine to an agitated methanolic suspension of 0.01 mole of potassium TPB until no further decolorization occurs was reported (162) to yield 0.01 mole of bromobenzene, 0.007 mole of biphenyl, and 0.008 mole of phenylboric acid. Prolonged exposure of potassium TPB in chloroform to a strong light source causes photochemical decomposition to potassium chloride, benzene, biphenyl, and phenol (162). Heating of potassium TPB in acetone with anhydrous iron(III) chloride for 30 min. leads to substantial decomposition to these same products, iron(II), and to phenylboric acid (162). Agitation of potassium TPB with mercury in chloroform for 70 to 80 hr. produces diphenylmercury, potassium chloride, and triphenylboron; analogous reactions occur with lithium and ammonium TPB. The original papers of Razuvaev and Brilkina (161,162) should be consulted for details of these and related "radical fission" processes.

In addition to the formation of water-insoluble salts the TPB ion undergoes other reactions of analytical interest with certain metal ions. One such reaction is involved in the preparation of copper(I)

TPB (Equations 8 and 9). The decomposition reaction occurring with mercury(II) has been studied by many workers and under varied conditions (6,56,58,62,126–129,172,178a,225,229). The process has been termed "the mercurization of the TPB ion," and the expression is adopted in the present review (see Sections IV-10 through IV-14, and IX-6). The reaction was first studied by Wittig and co-workers (225) in both aqueous and methanolic solution by employing mercury(II) chloride, and may be formulated as in Equation 14.

$$B(C_6H_5)_4{}^- + 4HgCl_2 + 3H_2O \longrightarrow 4C_6H_5HgCl + 3H^+ + 4Cl^- + B(OH)_3$$

$$(14)$$

Montequi and co-workers (126–129) have established that a second reaction, which may be formulated as in Equation 15, also occurs to some extent.

$$B(C_6H_5)_4{}^- + 2HgCl_2 + 3H_2O \longrightarrow 2(C_6H_5)_2Hg + 3H^+ + 4Cl^- + B(OH)_3$$

$$(15)$$

Under appropriate conditions the mercurization proceeds quantitatively to produce three moles of hydrogen ion for each mole of TPB ion (see Section IV-10).

Rüdorff and Zannier (172) observed that addition of iron(III) to a weakly acidic sodium TPB solution leads to the formation of a dark-colored, iron-containing precipitate that is presumably associated with the formation of phenylboric acid, benzene, and iron(III) hydroxide. In contrast, Sporek and Williams (200) and Wendlandt (213) observed no precipitation on addition of iron(III) to an acidic sodium TPB solution.

Cerium(IV) oxidizes the TPB ion with the formation of a white precipitate that does not contain cerium (200,213). This oxidation has been studied (197) as the possible basis of a cerimetric determination (see Section IV-5).

Geske (78) in controlled potential electrolysis at 0.7 v. versus the silver electrode found that the TPB ion suffers two-electron oxidation to biphenyl and diphenylboronium ion; the latter reacts with the solvent producing hydrogen ion. This ion then decomposes the TPB ion in a secondary process to produce (initially) benzene and triphenylboron. The reaction scheme in water proposed by Geske (78) is given by Equations 16 through 18.

$$B(C_6H_5)_4^- \xrightarrow{\text{electrode}} (C_6H_5)_2 + B(C_6H_5)_2^+ + 2e \qquad (16)$$

$$B(C_6H_5)_2^+ + H_2O \longrightarrow (C_6H_5)_2B(OH) + H^+ \qquad (17)$$

$$B(C_6H_5)_4^- + H^+ \longrightarrow B(C_6H_5)_3 + C_6H_6 \qquad (18)$$

Wittig and Raff (229) reported that manganese(II), iron(II), cobalt (II), and nickel(II) do not form TPB salts or metal-phenyl compounds. In ether, these cations decompose the TPB ion to produce triphenylboron and biphenyl. In aqueous solution (assuming no excess acid is present), the metal hydroxide is formed. In essence, the TPB ion has been hydrolytically decomposed (Equation 19).

$$2B(C_6H_5)_4^- + M^{+2} + 6H_2O \longrightarrow M(OH)_2 + 2C_6H_5B(OH)_2 + 6C_6H_6 \quad (19)$$

where M = Mn, Fe, Co, Ni.

Sporek and Williams (200) found that various divalent and polyvalent metal cations failed to yield a precipitate on addition to an aqueous sodium TPB solution made $0.44N$ in hydrochloric acid. Ions that had no precipitating action included the alkaline earths, aluminum(III), cadmium(II), chromium(III), cobalt(II), copper(II), copper(I), iron (II), iron(III), lead(II), manganese(II), nickel(II), tin(III), tin(IV), and titanium(III). These workers were able to obtain satisfactory results in the precipitation from such a strongly acidic medium at $0°C$. and in the gravimetric determination of potassium as potassium TPB in the presence of many of these foreign cations (and without addition of ethylenediaminetetraacetate or other masking agents).

Wendlandt (213) has reported that zinc(II), zirconium(III), antimony(III), cobalt(II), nickel(II), manganese(II), and bismuth(III) react with a weakly acidic aqueous sodium TPB solution to produce, on prolonged standing, a white precipitate that does *not* contain any metal. He concluded that the acid-catalyzed decomposition of the TPB ion is involved in the formation of this precipitate (Equations 10, 11, and 19). Wendlandt emphasized that these precipitates only form slowly, in contrast to the rapid precipitation of potassium, rubidium, cesium, and ammonium TPB.

2. Physical Properties of Metal TPB Salts

The metal TPB compounds are white in color and ionic in nature. The sodium and lithium salts are soluble in water and lower alcohols. In contrast, the potassium, rubidium, cesium, thallium(I), silver(I), ammonium, and organically substituted ammonium salts are insoluble in water. On this exceptional behavior is predicated most of the applications of the TPB ion in analytical chemistry. Salts of some metals cannot be obtained at all (or at least with difficulty) because the metal ion reacts with the TPB ion to decompose it (see Section II-1).

The solubility of various metal TPB salts in water has been determined by radiometric (75,76), conductometric (175), potentiometric (87), and spectrophotometric (99,100,155) measurements, and for sodium TPB by direct analysis (25). The values reported are recorded in Table I. The solubility of potassium TPB was early calculated erroneously from dilution experiments (160). Geilmann and Gebauhr (76) found that the solubility of potassium and rubidium TPB was decreased in the presence of a reasonable excess of the precipitating reagent, namely, sodium TPB.

TABLE I
Molar Solubility of Metal TPB Salts in Water as
Determined by Various Measurements

TPB salt	Radiometric (20°C.)	Spectrophotometric (25°C.)	Potentiometric (20°C.)	Other (24 & 25°C.)
Na				ca. 0.88 (25)
K	15×10^{-5} (76)	18×10^{-5} (155)	13×10^{-5} (87)	18×10^{-5} (175)
Rb	4.5×10^{-5} (76)	2.3×10^{-5} (155)		
Cs	2.9×10^{-5} (76)	2.8×10^{-5} (155)		
Tl(I)	3×10^{-5} (75)	5.3×10^{-5} (155)		
NH$_4$		29×10^{-5} (100)		
Ag			2×10^{-7} (87)	

In view of the importance of the TPB ion as a precipitant for potassium, it may be of interest to contrast the solubility, in water, of potassium TPB (18×10^{-5} mole/l.) with that of potassium cobaltinitrite, picrate, chloroplatinate, and perchlorate, respectively, 2×10^{-3}, 2×10^{-2}, 1×10^{-2}, and 1.2×10^{-1} mole/l.

Lithium TPB, because of the small volume of the lithium ion, is fairly soluble in ether and chloroform, and crystallizes from ether with eight molecules of ether. Sodium TPB is less soluble in these solvents and the solubility diminishes with a rise in temperature associated with the increasing ionic solvation at lower temperature (225,229). A similar temperature inversion is shown by potassium TPB in pyridine (142). Ammonium, potassium, rubidium, and cesium TPB are relatively insoluble in ether and chloroform (225,229).

All TPB salts, regardless of water solubility, are insoluble in nonpolar solvents such as carbon tetrachloride and cyclohexane, and are relatively soluble in various polar organic solvents including acetone, dioxane, dimethylformamide, and acetonitrile. Thallium (I) TPB is less soluble than potassium, rubidium, cesium, and ammonium TPB in these polar solvents (155). Silver TPB is much less soluble in acetone than is the potassium salt; this fact is of importance for a number of analytical methods. Findeis and De Vries (41) found the solubility of potassium TPB insufficient in methanol, ethanol, formamide, and acetone–water to permit satisfactory polarographic measurements; dimethylformamide, however, proved an excellent solvent for this purpose and a $0.125M$ stock solution of the salt could be prepared readily.

Scott and co-workers (101,193c) found the solubility of potassium TPB in acetone–water at 28°C. to be only 0.6 mg./ml. in 25% acetone (by volume based on the combined volume of water and acetone). The solubility increases sharply from 1.1 mg./ml. in 33% acetone to a maximum of 59.8 mg./ml. in about 95% acetone. Earlier, Razuvaev and Brilkina (162) stated that the solubility of potassium TPB in acetone, 2-methoxyethanol, and certain other unspecified solvents increased on addition of water, reaching a maximum with the addition of about 20% water. These findings make clear the desirability of maintaining as high an acetone:water ratio as appropriate in those analytical methods requiring an acetonic solution of potassium TPB.

The *thermal stability* of metal TPB salts is of special importance for gravimetric analysis and discordant results appear in the earlier literature. Exact data are now available through thermogravimetric studies by Wendlandt (212–214,217). The minimum decomposition temperature is defined as the lowest temperature at which weight loss can be detected. The minimum decomposition temperatures of lithium, sodium, potassium, rubidium, cesium, and thallium(I) TPB are, respectively, 140, 200, 265, 240, 210, and 180°C. Thus, precipitates of the last four compounds are definitely stable under the usual drying conditions and a simple gravimetric determination is possible. With all these compounds, except thallium(I), pyrolysis at higher temperatures proceeds quantitatively to a well-defined metaborate stage. In the case of thallium(I) TPB volatilization begins at 700°C., and ignition to a pure metaborate or to thallium(III) oxide is impossible (213). Silver TPB has a minimum decomposition temperature of 65°C.; the metaborate stage is apparently contaminated with metallic silver (214). Wendlandt (214) reported thermogravimetric studies of mercury(I) TPB and mercury(II) TPB; however, the data reported now appear to be for decomposition products of these compounds (213,218).

Flaschka and co-workers (59), among early workers, found that if ammonium TPB is heated rapidly in an open crucible over a flame complete volatilization of the compound (and/or its decomposition products) occurs. If the heating is conducted less rapidly a boric oxide melt is obtained which gives a positive test for ammonium with Nessler's reagent. Wittig and Raff (229) observed that ammonium TPB decomposed under closed-flask distillation conditions at a minimum bath temperature of 240°C. yielding triphenylboron, benzene, and ammonia. Razavaev and Brilkina (161) heated ammonium TPB at 110 to 120°C. without solvent and reported decomposition to benzene and $NH_3 \cdot B(C_6H_5)_3$. They stated that this decomposition occurs slowly at room temperature.

Wendlandt found (212) in a thermogravimetric study a minimum decomposition temperature of 130°C. for ammonium TPB. Because of the rapid loss of weight at 130°C. and because the amount of boric acid left ultimately on the pan was low, he concluded that rapid sublimation occurs at 130°C. Howick and Pflaum (100, cf. 99) have confirmed this value for the decomposition temperature; however, they were only able to effect the sublimation of ammonium TPB at a temperature of 130°C. at a much reduced pressure. On the basis of a differential thermal analysis, these workers suggest that boron is lost in the form of a volatile intermediate in the stepwise thermal decomposition of the compound. This low thermal stability of ammonium TPB requires special care in the gravimetric determination of ammonium. The volatilization of ammonium TPB, however, may be applied to advantage in certain nongravimetric TPB methods (see Section IV-7).

The *storage stability* of most metal TPB salts, as far as is known, is not indefinite. Even the most stable undergo slow decomposition with the development of a phenolic odor and often a yellow to brown tint; if the salt is water soluble the solution shows some degree of turbidity. The storage stability is clearly associated with the purity of the material and the presence of decomposition products apparently hastens the decomposition. The storage stability of the potassium salt is good; this may be due to the high purity and freedom from soluble impurities effected by precipitation of the salt from aqueous solution. The ammonium salt shows low storage stability and may become brown in color after a few weeks (55,161).

Sodium TPB suitable for analytical use may show the first faint signs of decomposition only after storage for many months, and will be suitable for known analytical applications for a far longer period. The use of material that has undergone extensive decomposition is inappropriate in many analytical methods; the material, however, may often be salvaged by recrystallization from chloroform, chloroform–cyclohexane, acetone–water, or other appropriate solvent systems. Although at the present time the intrinsic factors affecting the stability of solid reagent grade sodium TPB are unknown, it appears appropriate to keep the product cool, dry, and in a tightly closed amber glass bottle, and to expose the bottle contents to laboratory air during removal of material for as brief a period as is expedient. (The stability of sodium TPB solutions is considered in Section III-1).

The *absorption spectrum* of the TPB ion in water was studied by Cooper (28,29) in the region 230 to 300 mμ, and by Pflaum and Howick (155, cf. 99) in the region 290 to below 260 mμ. Strong absorption occurs below about 280 mμ (28,29). Spectral measurements have been applied in following the stability of sodium TPB solutions (see Section III-1) and the solubility of metal and amine TPB salts (see above and Section IX-1). The absorption spectrum of the TPB ion has also been studied in acetonitrile and acetonitrile–water (73a,99,100,155,156a). Maxima were found at 266 and 274 mμ with molar absorptivities of 3225 and 2100, respectively. These findings permit a spectrophotometric determination of potassium (see Section VI-1) and of organic bases (see Section IX-7).

The equivalent *conductance* at 25°C. at infinite dilution of sodium TPB has been reported to be 71 mhos/cm., and the ionic conductance of the TPB ion to be 21 mhos/cm. (175). The conductance of sodium TPB solutions in acetic acid has been followed in a study of the decomposition of the TPB ion in that medium (120). The ionic nature of lithium TPB was early established by a study of the freezing point depression in aqueous solution (229).

Crystallographic data for sodium, potassium, rubidium, cesium, and ammonium TPB salts have been reported (9,33,105). These salts are definitely isomorphous (9,33,174); and hence, mixed crystal formation is possible. Lithium TPB is *not* isomorphous with these other salts (9). Davies and Staveley (33) have discussed the fine structure of these salts on the basis of crystallographic data and of calorimetric data (down to 20°K.). Wittig and co-workers (225), in a preparation of lithium TPB, isolated a crystalline double salt etherate, $LiB(C_6H_5)_4 \cdot LiBr \cdot (C_2H_5)_2O$.

III. PRECIPITATION OF POTASSIUM TPB AND THE GRAVIMETRIC DETERMINATION OF POTASSIUM

A sodium TPB solution is the usual form in which the TPB ion is employed as a precipitating reagent or as a titrant. Hence, the preparation of a stable solution of this salt, which is considered in Section III-1, is of great importance. The most important application for the TPB ion in chemical analysis is the precipitation of potassium. The conditions and procedures for this precipitation and the interferences encountered are discussed at length in Sections III-2, III-3, and III-4, respectively. Many of the observations are also relevant to the precipitation of other metal ions and to some extent to the precipitation of organic bases. Section III-5 considers the gravimetric determination of potassium based on precipitation of potassium TPB.

1. Preparation and Stability of Sodium TPB Solutions

An aqueous solution of sodium TPB is now generally employed as the TPB reagent, both as a precipitant and as a titrant. A few early studies were made with lithium TPB because at the time it was the only product commercially available.

The reagent solution can be prepared simply by dissolving the proper amount of sodium TPB in water. Such a solution may not, however, possess adequate stability. Special attention has therefore been paid to the mode of preparation, the composition, and the storage conditions in order to attain satisfactory stability. Hence, the stability of sodium TPB solutions may be conveniently discussed prior to any description of practical preparations.

The mechanism of the decomposition of this reagent solution has not been fully elucidated. The simple observations are that the solution becomes turbid after some time and progressively develops a strong phenolic odor. The elapsed time before these phenomena are noted can vary within a wide range (from days to weeks), and seems to be closely related to the purity of the product used. It also appears that the presence of the decomposition products may speed further deterioration. The extent of deterioration that can be tolerated in the reagent solution depends, of course, on the method for which the solution is intended.

Sometimes in the preparation of the reagent solution a turbidity is immediately apparent. This may be caused by the presence of traces of potassium in the water used, or more probably may be attributed to a slight degree of deterioration in the solid state. Therefore, a clarification was recommended even by early workers (115), involving addition of alkali-free high purity aluminum oxide and subsequent filtration. Cluley (27) found that aluminum oxide is ineffective and recommended addition of moist aluminum hydroxide gel. This discrepancy may be related to the fact that aluminum oxides of different types and from different sources were employed. Jander and Anke (107) employed the aluminum hydroxide clarification in the preparation of a sodium TPB solution for use in a titrimetric procedure and observed that the solution was stable for a period of "several weeks."

In the clarification with aluminum oxide or hydroxide the first portions of the filtrate are usually still turbid and must be refiltered several times. Hence, the concurrent and deliberate addition of a small amount of a potassium salt has merit (55). The potassium TPB precipitate serves as a carrier for the very fine particles causing the turbidity, and in the process the filtrate is saturated with potassium TPB.

Investigations have clearly established that the pH of the reagent solution is a critical factor in its stability, and that a pH *greater* than 7 should be maintained. The alumina treatment yields a solution of pH 5 to 6.

A thorough investigation of the influence of pH on stability was reported by Cooper (28,29) as well as a simple spectrophotometric stability test (29). His findings have been confirmed by Kirsten and co-workers (113). Cooper followed the decomposition spectrophotometrically in the ultraviolet range. The TPB ion absorbs strongly below about 290 mμ. The absorption of a $10^{-3}M$ aqueous solution at any wavelength below this value can serve as a measure of the degree of deterioration. The preferred wavelengths are 250, 262.5, and 270 mμ. If no decomposition occurs, the ratios of the absorbancies at the extreme wavelengths to that at 262.5 mμ remain essentially constant. Cooper studied the effect of the pH and the temperature of storage on the stability of the reagent solution and eventually established as an optimum, a pH above 7, and storage at a temperature not exceeding room temperature (about 26°C.) and in diffuse light.

Satisfactory stability at higher pH values have been confirmed by other authors. Gloss and Olson (80) early employed the alumina treatment and found that the resulting solution of pH 5 to 6 gave satisfactory results in gravimetric procedures over a period of many weeks. They indicated that a solution of pH 7 was equally satisfactory but did not study higher pH values. Kirsten and co-workers (113) found that a reagent solution of pH 9.9 after storage for nine weeks at room temperature showed only 0.8% reduction in titer and in a refrigerator, only 0.3%. Schmidt (184) obtained a reagent solution having a pH of about 8 by merely dissolving reagent grade sodium TPB in water; this showed satisfactory stability without special treatment. Cluley (27a) studied the stability of a 0.6% sodium TPB solution brought to pH 9 over a period of 59 days and observed no significant change in titer.

At the present time an alkaline solution of sodium TPB is obtainable by merely dissolving the reagent grade product from some commercial sources because the technical process is adjusted in such a way as to yield this result. In this way the attainment of stability has lost much of its previous difficulty.

To obtain and to maintain the desirable high pH in the reagent solution the addition of sodium hydroxide, sodium carbonate, or a borate or phosphate buffer (170,171) has been recommended. Of course, the added salts must be potassium free or any resulting turbidity must be filtered off. Various workers, including Schall (183), recommend application of the alumina treatment followed by alkalinization of the solution with sodium hydroxide.

Epps and Burden (37) have delineated an obviously important observation that may partially account for some of the contradictory findings in earlier stability studies. A sodium TPB solution used as titrant in the procedure of Schall (see Section IV-4) failed to give satisfactory results unless it was aged by mere standing for at least 48 hr. After that period of time the solution was found to be stable for at least 17 days and reproducible results were obtained in standardizing the solution and applying it to titrations. Rüdorff and Zannier (173) early recognized that a solution of sodium TPB should be allowed to stand overnight before standardization. A small amount of potassium TPB is present even in reagent grade sodium TPB (minimum assay 99.5%) and it can be observed that solutions of this salt even after clarification will slowly deposit potassium TPB on the vessel walls (25). It is probable that in this process the titer of the solution will change. It is thus desirable to employ an aging period of possibly 48 hr. before standardization of a freshly prepared sodium TPB solution for use as a titrant.

The concentration of the reagent solution for use in precipitation procedures recommended by most workers is 3% by weight. This corresponds to a molarity of about 0.1. Some authors recommend a more dilute reagent for precipitation procedures. It should be appreciated, however, that with the use of too dilute a reagent the dilution effect may become so great that incomplete precipitation results. The concentration of a sodium TPB solution suitable for use as a titrant depends on the method employed and may vary from 0.001 to $0.1M$.

Taking all of the considerations discussed above into account, a generally suitable procedure for the preparation of a 3% sodium TPB solution having adequate stability for use as a precipitating agent, has the following details.

Procedure 1. Preparation of 3% Sodium TPB Precipitating Reagent. Dissolve 3 g. of reagent grade sodium TPB in about 80 ml. of distilled or deionized water. Add about 1 g. of aluminum hydroxide (freshly precipitated and thoroughly washed) and stir vigorously for 1 min. Add 1 drop of a $0.1M$ KNO$_3$, stir briefly, and allow to settle for a few minutes. Filter through retentive, quantitative filter paper. If the first portions of the filtrate are turbid, refilter through the *same* paper. Adjust the pH of the clear filtrate to about 8 by addition of potassium-free NaOH. Dilute to a volume of 100 ml. Store at, or below, room temperature and in diffuse light. If a turbidity develops after prolonged standing the solution may be salvaged by refiltration, but only for use in certain procedures.

Where it is necessary or desirable to avoid the introduction of sodium in the precipitation of an insoluble TPB salt, the free acid may be used in place of sodium TPB. For example, Hegemann and Pfab (90) have employed the filtrate from the precipitation of potassium TPB for the flame photometric determination of the sodium content of the original sample. Because the free acid is very unstable it must be generated as required. This is accomplished by passing the sodium TPB reagent solution through a strongly acidic cation exchange column in the hydrogen form. The effluent containing the free TPB acid is allowed to drop directly into the sample solution.

Economic considerations led Reimers (165) to the development of a regeneration procedure for sodium TPB. This involves dissolution in acetone of potassium TPB precipitates remaining from gravimetric procedures or obtained by adding potassium chloride to filtrates, supernatants, etc. The acetone solution is passed through a strongly acidic cation exchange column placed in the sodium form and especially treated with an acetone–water mixture. The effluent contains sodium TPB and may be used again as the reagent, if appropriate, or the solid salt may be obtained by evaporation followed by recrystallization from acetone. A recovery of better than 90% is claimed.

Mevel and Lacruche (124) have described another method of regenerating sodium TPB for use with their titrimetric procedure of determining potassium (see Section IV-2). A filtrate from the precipitation of potassium TPB containing excess sodium TPB is treated with ammonium chloride and the ammonium TPB is filtered off. The acetonic solution of the potassium TPB precipitate has been titrated with silver nitrate to the thiocyanate end point and hence contains insoluble silver TPB and thiocyanate. This precipitate is filtered off and treated at an elevated temperature with ammonium chloride and aqueous ammonia to produce ammonium TPB, which is then filtered off. The ammonium TPB residues from both sources are suspended in water and a calculated amount of sodium hydroxide (which provides a slight excess) is added. The solution is then boiled until the removal of ammonia is complete. The clear solution (filtered if necessary) is used again as a precipitating reagent after proper pH adjustment.   Obviously, the principles of this procedure are applicable to the regeneration of sodium TPB from other procedures.

Wittig and Raff (229) early converted ammonium TPB to sodium TPB in 59% yield by refluxing the ammonium salt in methanol with sodium methoxide and recrystallizing the product from ether.

Hahn (82) regenerated the reagent by dissolving potassium TPB precipitates in acetone, adding an excess of lithium chloride in absolute ethanol, filtering off the insoluble potassium chloride, and evaporating the solution.   The lithium TPB (which contains some lithium chloride) is dissolved in water, clarified, and used in the same manner as a sodium TPB solution.

2. Conditions for the Precipitation of Potassium TPB

The conditions appropriate to the precipitation, washing, and filtration of potassium TPB are of importance for the gravimetric determination of potassium.   In addition, these conditions are important for any method involving prior separation of potassium TPB and manipulation of the redissolved precipitate.   Thus, a discussion of these conditions is warranted prior to the consideration of particular methods for the determination of potassium as well as of other metals.

In the initial study of the determination of potassium as the TPB salt Raff and Brotz (160) employed precipitation from weakly acidic medium (acetic acid) at room temperature.   Although under this condition a fine precipitate, that is rather difficult to filter, is obtained, the method was adopted by many early workers.   This fine precipitate shows a pronounced tendency to creep—an obvious source of difficulty.   Further, the high rate of re-solution of this precipitate coupled with the relatively high solubility of the compound necessitates special attention.   Thus, it is understandable that attempts were made early to modify this precipitation condition in order to obtain a coarser precipitate.   However, attainment of such a precipitate is *not* the only consideration in establishing optimum separation conditions.   Other factors of equal importance include interferences and their exclusion, solubility of potassium TPB in the medium, stability of the precipitate, etc.

In general, with increasing acidity coarser paritcles of potassium TPB are obtained; with increasing basicity, finer particles.   It would, therefore, appear desirable to effect the precipitation from a strongly acidic medium. Such a condition (as later established) offers the advantage that fewer metals interfere. However, the more acidic the medium, the more rapid is the decomposition of the TPB ion. For practical purposes this limits the acidity employed at room temperature to $0.1M$ mineral acid (115). At $0°C$. satisfactory results have been obtained even in $0.66M$ hydrochloric acid, but a $0.44M$ acid solution was selected for practical application (200). Cluley (27a) made a 0.6% sodium TPB solution $0.01M$ in nitric acid and followed the decomposition by titration of 10 ml. aliquots with a 1% mercury(II) nitrate solution (see Section IV-3). The titration results (namely, 0 min., 9.62 ml.; 15 min., 9.59 ml.; 60 min., 9.51 ml.) indicated that a small but detectable decomposition of the sodium TPB solution did occur within 15 min. (which should be appreciated in certain titrimetric methods).

Fortunately this decomposition in strongly acidic medium only involves the "free" TPB ion in solution; hence, the precipitate is relatively unaffected. Because of this decomposition some methods, including those in which the excess of TPB ion in the filtrate or supernatant is manipulated, cannot employ the precipitation from strongly acidic medium.

The precipitation of potassium TPB from alkaline medium has special merit even though the difficulty of filtration is thereby increased. For example, under such conditions the ethylenediaminetetraacetate (EDTA) ion can be added as a masking agent of broad application. Further, exclusion of the ammonium ion, which offers a serious and frequent interference, can be readily accomplished from alkaline medium.

In order to assure as complete precipitation of potassium as possible, an excess of sodium TPB reagent solution must be added. The exact amount of this excess seems relatively unimportant as the amounts recommended by various workers fall within a wide range. Even a huge excess has no noticeable effect on the results. Geilmann and Gebauhr (76) have shown that a concentration of at least 0.2% by weight of sodium TPB in the supernatant should be maintained for practically complete precipitation. The majority of workers recommend a 1.5- to 2-fold amount of the theoretical amount of sodium TPB; this is a reasonable compromise between an adequate amount of reagent and economic considerations.

Because of the solubility of the potassium TPB precipitate, precipitation from too dilute a solution should be avoided. The recommended concentrations for different methods are given, where known, in the consideration of particular methods.

Improved filterability can be obtained in the precipitation from acetic acid medium by performing the precipitation at an elevated temperature of 40 to 50°C. (76) or at about 70°C. (53). To avoid decomposition the precipitate should not be held at the elevated temperature for an extended period, and the filtration should be performed at room temperature. It should be emphasized that use of an elevated temperature in the precipitation from strongly acidic medium is impractical because the decomposition is thereby accelerated. In fact, for the precipitation from strongly acidic medium, a temperature of 0°C. has been recommended (200). In contrast to many analytical precipitations, that of potassium TPB proceeds rapidly and quantitatively. Digestion or prolonged standing is unnecessary and even undesirable when an elevated temperature or strongly acidic medium is employed. Many workers recommend filtration after a settling period of 5 to 10 min.

Another approach to improved filterability from acetic acid medium involves addition of a few drops of $0.1M$ aluminum chloride solution prior to addition of the sodium TPB reagent solution (172). The precipitate then settles more rapidly and a coarser filter can then be employed. This addition is not suitable for use with many analytical methods that may be subsequently applied and will obviously interfere in the gravimetric method. A similar effect is exhibited by the addition of chromium(III) chloride, but to a lesser degree; however, in certain procedures where the presence of trace aluminum is intolerable, chromium will not interfere (184).

The addition of a few drops of a 0.1% aqueous solution of an Aerosol (i.e., a sodium dialkylsulfosuccinate) has been recommended to improve filterability at least in the case of thallium(I) TPB (213).

Geilmann and Gebauhr (76), Sporek and Williams (200), Cluley (27), and Muraire (137) have reported extended and critical studies of the various factors in the precipitation of potassium TPB considered above and many of the generalizations given in this section are based largely on the results of these workers.

Berkhout and Jongen (19,20) resolved the filtration difficulty in a precipitation from alkaline solution by use of a filter bed of diatomaceous earth. The precipitate can be freed of the filter aid by solution in acetone on the filter. This technique is probably not restricted to the precipitation from alkaline medium and may possibly be applied generally.

Various workers, including Muraire (137), have reported that a more filterable precipitate is obtained by slow addition of the sodium TPB reagent. This approach is not of obvious usefulness in the precipitation from alkaline medium.

In the selection of washing conditions, the solubility of potassium TPB is the critical factor. This consideration was not appreciated by Raff and Brotz (160) as they estimated the solubility to be of a much lower order than it actually is. When the true solubility was recognized, close control of the washing conditions was considered. This was further necessary because the fine precipitate can undergo rapid dissolution during washing.

The use of water (often with a few drops of acetic acid added) as the wash liquid is possible in some nongeneral procedures where careful removal of the precipitate from the precipitation vessel is not essential and a filter crucible is used in place of paper. Of course, in this case (and in any analytical precipitation of potassium TPB), the basic rules for washing must be observed. Namely, make each addition of liquid small and drain it off completely before the next addition; further, keep the total volume of wash liquid as small as possible. The mere application of these rules is generally insufficient and the use of a special wash liquid is recommended.

Geilmann and Gebauhr (76) employed as a wash liquid 0.5% acetic acid made 0.1% in sodium TPB. For general purposes a 0.1% sodium TPB solution, obtained by simple 1:30 dilution of the 3% precipitating reagent, is suitable as a wash liquid.

A saturated aqueous solution of potassium TPB is also appropriate and its use is strongly recommended when only small amounts of precipitate are obtained. On the micro scale, even minute losses during washing can seriously affect the result. In using a saturated aqueous solution of potassium TPB, however, it is recommended that the mother liquor adhering to the precipitate be first diluted by an initial washing with a small amount of water in order to prevent some potassium TPB from being precipitated from the saturated solution. This precaution is especially important when a large excess of precipitating reagent has been employed. The requisite potassium

TPB solution can be prepared by prolonged shaking of distilled water with solid potassium TPB and then filtering.   A more expeditious approach not requiring filtration is to add dropwise to 100 ml. of water, 0.4 ml. of an acetone solution containing 15 mg. of potassium TPB/ml. (58).

Crane and Smith (32a), in a study of the precipitation of ammonium TPB, recommended the use of a 1% formic acid solution as a wash liquid in place of a 1% acetic acid solution because the higher volatility of the formic acid permits a briefer drying period.   This use of formic acid is probably applicable in the separation of potassium TPB.

It is noteworthy, that where small amounts of potassium (or other appropriate cations) must be precipitated, ammonium can serve as an effective carrier.   Filtration is thereby facilitated and washing losses are reduced.   Of course, this expedient is only of value as an enrichment step or in connection with particular methods (see Sections IV-7, V-5, and VIII-3).   The study of Ieviņš and Peinberga (105a) exemplifies this approach.

3. Procedures for the Precipitation of Potassium TPB

Based on observations and conclusions given in Section III-2 three general procedures can be presented for the precipitation of potassium TPB, respectively, from strongly acidic, acetic acid, and alkaline mediums.   In applying these procedures to practical samples, the observations given in Section III-4 on interferences and their resolution should be studied.   These procedures are directly applicable to gravimetric determinations and to most titrimetric procedures involving manipulations of the redissolved precipitate.   With some methods, however, slight modifications or special precautions may be appropriate or necessary.   These are mentioned in the discussion of the particular procedures.   The following procedures apply to amounts of potassium from 2 to 10 mg.   If the amounts of potassium range from 10 to 20 mg., adjust the solution volume to 100 ml. and double the specified volume for all reagents and wash liquids.

Procedure 2.   Precipitation from Strongly Acidic Medium.   Neutralize the sample solution (containing 2 to 10 mg. of potassium) and bring the volume to about 50 ml.   Add 0.3 ml. of concentrated nitric acid and stir.   Slowly add 5 ml. of 3% sodium TPB precipitating reagent (see Procedure 1) .   Allow to stand 5 to 10 min.

Filter through a dense porcelain or sintered glass crucible under the suction of a water aspirator. Wash 2 to 3 times with 3 ml. portions of wash liquid (i.e., the above precipitating reagent diluted with water, 1:30). Finally wash 2 to 3 times with 1 to 2 ml. portions of distilled water. During the washing, suck off each portion completely before adding the next portion.

Procedure 3. Precipitation from Acetic Acid Medium. Neutralize the sample solution (containing 2 to 10 mg. of potassium) and bring the volume to about 50 ml. Add 2 ml. of acetic acid. Heat to about 70°C., and with good stirring add 5 ml. of 3% sodium TPB precipitating reagent (see Procedure 1). Cool to room temperature and continue as in the second paragraph of Procedure 2.

Procedure 4. Precipitation from Alkaline Medium. Neutralize the sample solution (containing 2 to 10 mg. of potassium). Add 0.5 ml. of 50% NaOH solution and heat to boiling. (If ammonia is to be removed prolong the boiling and add formaldehyde; to mask various metals add disodium ethylenediaminetetraacetate.) With vigorous stirring, add dropwise 5 ml. of 3% sodium TPB precipitating reagent (see Procedure 1). Cool to room temperature and continue as in the second paragraph of Procedure 2.

4. Interferences in the Precipitation of Potassium TPB

The precipitation of potassium TPB is affected by a surprisingly few number of cations. Of course, those cations that form insoluble TPB salts themselves will interfere, and include rubidium, cesium, silver, thallium(I), and ammonium. The first two are seldom present in nonnegligible amounts. Silver and thallium(I) can be easily separated by well known classical methods. Ammonium is the most serious interference and its resolution is given extended discussion below. Under any conditions mercury(II) interferes because of its decomposition reaction with the TPB ion (see Equations 14 and 15). Cerium(IV) interferes because of its oxidation of the TPB ion, but is easily excluded by prior addition of a reducing agent such as ascorbic acid. Copper(I) interferes also; however, because it does not occur in the usual analytical procedures or samples this interference is not important.

Interference by other cations is naturally dependent on the conditions under which the precipitation is performed. If an acetic acid medium is used for the precipitation, hydrolysis of aluminum, iron-(III), and chromium(III), etc., can be expected. The hydroxides will contaminate the potassium TPB precipitate, and the degree of inter-ference will depend on the amount of such ions present and the method employed for the determination of the potassium. In a gravimetric procedure such coprecipitation is intolerable. If, how-ever, the TPB precipitate is redissolved and the TPB ion is titrated argentometrically, the coprecipitated impurities are without moment. For example, in such a case aluminum may even be added to im-prove filterability (172).

The smallest number of interferences occur when the precipitation is effected from strongly acidic mineral acid solution (115). Under this condition only mercury(II), cerium(IV), and the cations forming insoluble TPB salts must be excluded. Prolonged standing, however, should be avoided as the decomposition products of the TPB ion may precipitate. The decomposition may be catalyzed by certain metals (see Section II-1). In the precipitation of potassium TPB from weakly acid (acetic acid) solution as well as from alkaline solution, interferences are conveniently excluded by addition of EDTA which masks the interfering ions (53,172). In the determination of potas-sium in samples of undefined composition the addition of EDTA may well be made a routine. Of course, the use of EDTA does *not* resolve the interference by mercury(II), rubidium, cesium, ammo-nium, etc. The presence of EDTA also circumvents the formation of extraneous precipitates caused by foreign ions including insoluble phosphates, sulfates, etc. It may be noted that the masking spec-trum of EDTA is broader under alkaline conditions.

For masking iron(III) in the precipitation from weakly acidic me-dium, sodium fluoride has been recommended (172).

The most frequent and serious interference is presented by the am-monium ion and, consequently, resolution of this interference has been given much attention. The usual method for the removal of am-monium salts by evaporating the sample to dryness and igniting the residue is applicable, but tedious. Furthermore, Muraca and co-workers (136) found it difficult to remove the last traces of ammo-nium, especially as the sulfate, by such a method. Special care was necessary to assure that no sublimate remained on the upper, cooler portions of the porcelain casserole. Hence, a wet method for the ex-clusion of ammonium is preferable. This may be done by boiling off ammonia from a caustic medium.   However, in a qualitative analysis procedure, these workers found a hypobromite oxidation necessary in order to remove the last traces of ammonia remaining from the caustic treatment (see Section VIII-5).   Probably the simplest approach is to add formaldehyde to the alkaline sample solution. Ammonia and formaldehyde react to form hexamethylenetetramine (urotropine) which is inactive toward the TPB ion, but only in alkaline medium (18–20,35).   This reaction is also the basis of the determination of potassium in the presence of ammonium ion and the determination of both ions in a single sample (see Section VII-1).

It should be emphasized that the above information is relevant only when the interfering cations are present in moderate amounts, possibly 10 to 30 times that of potassium.   Where huge amounts of foreign ions are present special problems exist and more research in this direction is warranted.   Application of an appropriate ion exchange technique offers an excellent approach for the separation of alkali metals from even huge amounts of polyvalent cations.

Only the influence of huge amounts of sodium and lithium have been closely investigated to date (76).   Slightly higher results were obtained in a gravimetric determination at a potassium:sodium molar ratio of $1:300$.   The positive error increased with increasing amounts of sodium.   However, the percentage error decreased with an increase in the volume from which the precipitation is performed. For example, with a molar ratio of $1:1000$ and an amount of about 2 mg. of potassium, the error was 6.5 to 6.9% from a volume of 20 ml., but under the same conditions the error was only 1.4 to 1.7% from a volume of 50 ml.   Geilmann and Gebauhr (76) also found that with increasing concentration of sodium the solubility of potassium TPB is reduced.   They attributed this finding to a "salting out" effect. These workers recommend a reprecipitation to eliminate the coprecipitated sodium.   The precipitate is dissolved in acetone and is reprecipitated by adding water after addition of some more reagent solution; the acetone is then evaporated to effect a quantitative precipitation.

Lithium behaves in the same manner as sodium in the gravimetric determination of potassium (76).

All of the above findings on the effect of huge amounts of sodium and lithium were obtained for the precipitation from weakly acidic medium and in a gravimetric procedure.   It is quite possible that these findings *cannot* be applied without modification to the precipitation from either a strongly acidic or alkaline medium. Further, it is probable that in most titrimetric manipulations of the precipitate no interference will occur.

Correct results have been obtained in the gravimetric determination of potassium in sea water (both natural and a synthetic standard) (198) and in sodium chloride (167) by precipitating from strongly acidic medium $(0.44M$ hydrochloric acid) at 0°C.

Interference by huge amounts of alkaline earths has been resolved by a carbonate precipitation, precipitation of potassium TPB, and resolution of the carbonates with acetic acid (160). However, in this case the use of EDTA offers a more expeditious approach.

To date, no interfering anion has been reported in the precipitation of potassium TPB. The following anions have been tested by various workers and found *not* to interefere; halides, PO_4^{3-}, SCN^-, CN^-, CNO^-, SO_4^{2-}, SO_3^{2-}, ClO_3^-, ClO_4^-, S^{2-}, ClO^-, BrO^-, BO_3^-, IO_3^-, NO_3^-. It is probable that no anion will interfere with the possible exception of strong oxidizing reagents under special conditions. Of course, this statement is limited to the precipitation of potassium alone. Serious interference may occur if particular foreign cations are present which form insoluble compounds with any foreign anions present. However, possible resolution of such a problem has been mentioned above.

It must be emphasized that the facts and generalizations in this section are related to the precipitation of potassium TPB. They may be extended, however, to the other inorganic cations forming insoluble TPB salts. If organic components are present in the sample they may present an interference by forming insoluble TPB salts. Their interference can sometimes be excluded by proper choice of pH conditions (especially the use of an alkaline medium), by ion exchange separation, solvent extraction, or as a last resort by destruction by wet or dry ignition.

5.   Gravimetric Determination of Potassium

Gravimetric procedures are generally considered to be far more tedious and time-consuming than titrimetric methods. This is not the case for determinations employing the TPB ion because almost all of the titrimetric procedures are indirect and most require a prior separation of the insoluble TPB salt.   Only a few are based on a more direct approach, notably, the conductometric titration.   In the routine determination of potassium in many samples (e.g., in fertilizer), the gravimetric TPB method may be superior to a titrimetric TPB method as far as working time is concerned, especially if an automatic balance is employed.   Further, the conversion factor for the gravimetric method is especially favorable: K/KTPB = 0.1091; $K_2O/2KTPB$ = 0.1314.

The conditions for the analytical precipitation of potassium TPB as well as interferences have been discussed in previous sections.   The conclusions reached are fully valid for a precipitation undertaken to obtain a weighable product.   However, some special precautions and considerations should be observed.

In contrast to many of the titrimetric procedures, an extensively decomposed sodium TPB solution may still give acceptable results in the gravimetric determination.   This is only true if no solid deterioration products are present which would increase the weight of the potassium TPB precipitate.   The precipitating conditions must be adjusted so that no such products are formed during the precipitation itself and within the time the solution is allowed to stand before filtration.   The danger of such an event is only serious in the precipitation from strongly acidic medium.   In this case, the filtration must be performed within an hour (115).   When a weakly acidic or alkaline medium is employed the standing period may be extended.   This time factor is of practical importance only when a large number of samples are being analyzed concurrently, because the filtration in a single determination can be performed within a few minutes of the precipitation.

The largest amount of potassium determined in practical work will usually not exceed 20 mg. because it is difficult to filter and wash large amounts of the fine precipitate.   A lower limit is only defined by the increasing difficulty of avoiding losses in the washing of the relatively soluble precipitate.   The gravimetric determination has been successfully accomplished (53) on the micro scale and amounts as low as 40 μg. have been determined with an average error of less than 1%. The filtration may be effected by use of a sintered glass or porcelain filter crucible of low porosity and a water aspirator as the vacuum source.   On the micro scale, a sintered glass microcrucible or preferably a so-called Emich filter-beaker should be utilized.   The potassium TPB precipitate is usually dried to constant weight at about 100°C. This requires 30 min. to 1 hr. A higher temperature and a shorter drying period are possible as a minimum decomposition temperature of 265°C. has been established for this compound by Wendlandt (212).

Although many papers could be cited confirming the precision and accuracy of this gravimetric TPB method, it is especially noteworthy that Muraca and co-workers (135) reported that inexperienced students, without special indoctrination, obtained satisfactory results.

In the analysis of applied materials, especially silicates, high results may be obtained in the gravimetric determination because of the precipitation of silica (or possibly of decomposition products of the TPB ion). This difficulty may be overcome by filtering the "crude" potassium TPB precipitate through an untared filter crucible, drying and weighing, and then redissolving the potassium TPB on the filter in acetone, and reweighing the crucible after drying. The difference in the two weighings corresponds to the weight of "pure" potassium TPB. This expedient has been used successfully in the analysis of fertilizers by Ford (64) and in the analysis of glasses and silicates by Yankov (233a).

IV. TITRIMETRIC DETERMINATION OF POTASSIUM TO A VISUAL END POINT

The following sections consider first, some general observations about titrimetric methods for potassium involving the TPB ion. (Section IV-1), and second, those titrations in which the end point is detected visually (Sections IV-2 through IV-14). It may be noted that many of these titrimetric methods involve the mercurization reaction of the TPB ion (Sections IV-10 through IV-14).

1. General Remarks on the Titrimetric Determination of Potassium

Most of the titrimetric determinations of potassium involving the TPB ion are based on a manipulation of a separated potassium TPB precipitate; a few, on the titration of the separated filtrate from such a precipitation. Hence, the observations presented in Sections III-1 through III-4 and to some extent in Section III-5 are most important for the titrimetric methods. It is noteworthy that the precipitation and separation for a titrimetric procedure may differ in a few restrictions from those for a gravimetric finish. For example, in titrimetric procedures the presence of insoluble decomposition products of the TPB ion or the addition of aluminum or chromium ions to improve filterability may have no adverse effect unless a reaction occurs with the particular titrant.

In most of the titrimetric methods the precision is very high in the actual titration step and the results are often reproducible within a small fraction of a drop of titrant. The accuracy and precision of such methods depend essentially upon the separation step. In almost all titrimetric methods the TPB ion is attacked, and in these cases the accuracy and precision are limited by the possibility of removing the excess of precipitating reagent as completely as possible without inducing losses during the washing step because of the nonnegligible solubility of the TPB precipitate.

Because of the separation step, the titrimetric determination of potassium is not especially favored over the gravimetric determination from the standpoint of required working time, as is the case for most ions. This is especially true in the routine analysis of many samples. It is true that procedures involving a back-titration and no separation are not as time-consuming and are not handicapped by such reasoning. However, in comparison with methods involving a separation, the possibility of interferences is greater because constituents of the sample may interfere with the cation selected as the back-titrant.

2. Argentometric Titration of Redissolved Potassium TPB

Rüdorff and Zannier (172) based a titrimetric procedure, to a visual end point, on the fact that silver TPB is much less soluble than potassium TPB in a 50% acetone–water medium. Hence, the TPB content of potassium TPB redissolved in acetone can be titrated argentometrically. Because silver TPB is soluble to a certain extent in acetone, care must be taken to avoid too high a concentration of acetone. However, by the addition of the aqueous silver nitrate solution, the medium is progressively diluted with water, and there is danger that potassium TPB may precipitate, thus leading to a low result. Havíř and Křivánek (87b) concluded from a radiometric study that theoretical results are obtained in a medium containing 33% acetone. Rüdorff and Zannier (172) recommended a medium 50% in acetone at the end point. From the solubility data of Scott and co-workers (193c) it would appear that a medium 30 to 50% in acetone should be appropriate.

The TPB ion, probably due to its large size, is not adsorbed on the silver TPB precipitate to an appreciable extent.   Hence, an adsorption indicator such as eosin does not give a satisfactory end point. To improve the color change it is necessary to add bromide ion and to correct the result for the amount added.

Procedure 5.   Precipitate up to 25 mg. of potassium as potassium TPB by an appropriate procedure.   Filter through retentive filter paper and wash the precipitate.   Small particles clinging to the vessel walls need not be transferred.   Place the paper and precipitate in the precipitating vessel.   Dissolve the precipitate in 10 ml. of acetone. (Alternatively, a filter crucible may be used; the washed precipitate may be dissolved on it, and transferred to the precipitating vessel.) Add 5 ml. of $2M$ acetic acid, 1 ml. of $0.100M$ KBr (measured exactly), and 2 drops of 1% eosin solution.   Titrate with $0.05M$ AgNO₃. Stir vigorously near the end point and move the paper about to assure reaction with the last traces of TPB ion.   Correct the result for the amount of bromide ion added.   The calculation takes the form:

$$(\text{ml.}_{\text{AgNO}_3} \times M_{\text{AgNO}_3} - \text{ml.}_{\text{KBr}} \times M_{\text{KBr}}) \times 39.1 = \text{mg. of potassium}$$

Remarks.   The time required for a determination, including the precipitation step is 20 to 25 min.   Because of the solubility of silver TPB for amounts of potassium up to 25 mg., not more than 10 ml. of acetone should be employed.   For amounts greater than 25 mg. of potassium, $0.1M$ AgNO₃ is preferable.   In a series of 18 experiments an average deviation of 0.4% was found (172) in the determination of 8 to 50 mg. of potassium, with only two results having an error exceeding 1%.   In some of these experiments aluminum or chromium(III) was added; in others, iron(III) was added and masked with sodium fluoride.

The argentometric procedure of Rüdorff and Zannier was improved by Hahn (82,83) by the use of chromate ion as the indicator and of a silver nitrate solution in 50% acetone–water.   In this modification the addition of bromide is not required and the danger of reprecipitating potassium TPB by dilution with an aqueous solution is avoided. Because a special titrant must be prepared, the modification is of greater interest in the routine analysis of many samples.   This method has been further evaluated by Berkhout (19,20) and found to give satisfactory results.

Procedure 6. In the usual manner, precipitate potassium TPB and filter and wash by using a sintered glass or porcelain filter crucible. Place the crucible, after rinsing the outer walls with water, in the precipitating vessel. Dissolve the precipitate in 5 ml. of acetone. Wash down the walls of the vessel with 5 ml. of acetone. Add 10 ml. of water and 0.1 ml. of 0.5% $KCrO_4$ in 50% acetone–water. With vigorous stirring, titrate with $0.01M$ $AgNO_3$ (in 50% acetone–water) to a persistent pink color. The calculation takes the form:

$$\text{ml.}_{AgNO_3} \times M_{AgNO_3} \times 39.1 = \text{mg. of potassium}$$

Remarks. The method was evaluated (19) by precipitating and titrating potassium from 2 to 10 ml. of $0.1M$ KBr and calculating the titer of this solution from the results. An average deviation of 0.3% was reported for 11 experiments with only one result having an error exceeding 1%. In the precipitation step, Berkhout (20) has also used a simple suction filter assembly with a diatomaceous earth packing that may be used repeatedly. With this assembly, satisfactory results were reported for amounts of K as low as 0.5 mg.

Rüdorff and Zannier (173,176) established that the TPB ion could be determined by a Volhard titration.

Procedure 7. Dissolve a potassium TPB precipitate in 20 to 30 ml. of acetone. Add an excess of $0.05M$ $AgNO_3$ and dilute to about 100 milliliters of ether. Shake vigorously; the insoluble silver TPB passes into the ether phase. Titrate the excess silver in the clear aqueous solution with $0.05M$ NH_4SCN to the appearance of the red color of the Fe(III)–SCN complex. The calculation takes the form:

$$(\text{ml.}_{AgNO_3} \times M_{AgNO_3} - \text{ml.}_{NH_4SCN} \times M_{NH_4SCN}) \times$$
$$39.1 = \text{mg. of potassium}$$

Remarks. In five experiments involving 15.6 to 23.3 mg. of potassium, the error ranged from −0.05 to +0.05 mg.

Mével and Lacruche (124) described a further procedure for the determination of TPB ion by a Volhard titration. This is a simplification of the above procedure of Rüdorff and Zannier to the extent that removal of the precipitate into ether is avoided. Mével and

Lacruche presented no representative results but claimed a precision of 0.5% and detection of the end point within 1 drop.

Procedure 8.   Dissolve a potassium TPB precipitate in 30 ml. of acetone and wash the filter with 15 to 20 ml. of acetone. To the combined solution and washings, add 20 ml. of $0.100M$ AgNO$_3$, stir and dilute to a volume of about 100 ml. with water. With use of indicator paper, adjust to pH 1 by the dropwise addition of nitric acid. Add 2 drops of a 10% FeNH$_4$(SO$_4$)$_2$ solution and back-titrate the excess of silver with $0.100M$ NH$_4$SCN. The end point is marked by the appearance of the red color of the Fe(III)–SCN complex. The titration must be performed promptly and rapidly. The calculation takes the form:

$$(ml._{AgNO_3} \times M_{AgNO_3} - ml._{NH_4SCN} \times M_{NH_4SCN}) \times$$

$$39.1 = mg. \text{ of potassium}$$

Erdey and co-workers (37a) redissolved potassium TPB in acetone, acidified with acetic acid, and titrated with aqueous silver nitrate solution. The end point is established by use of the redox indicator Variamine Blue, N-(p-methoxyphenyl)-p-phenylenediamine. The dye is added as a 1% solution of the base in 20% acetic acid or of the hydrochloride in water. In the latter case, for highest accuracy the result should be corrected for the chloride content.

3. Argentometric and Mercurimetric Titration Involving Back-Titration of Excess TPB Ion

Rüdorff and Zannier (173) described another argentometric determination of potassium to a visual end point that avoids the tedious complete removal of the precipitate. Potassium is precipitated with a measured amount of a standardized sodium TPB solution. The volume is then brought to a definite amount. Only a part of the solution is filtered and the excess of TPB in the resulting filtrate is determined by precipitating it with a measured amount of standard silver nitrate solution. The excess of silver is then back-titrated with thiocyanate solution (Volhard method). The removal of the potassium TPB is mandatory because silver TPB is much less soluble than potassium TPB and thus the latter would react with the excess of silver.

Because the titration is performed in the presence of all foreign ions present in the sample solution, this method is of only limited value for practical analysis. Ions that interfere in the precipitation of potassium TPB cannot be tolerated (see Section III-4); neither can ions that interfere in the Volhard method. Thus, the common anions permitted to be present are restricted to nitrate, sulfate, acetate, and phosphate.

Procedure 9.   Make the sample solution $0.1N$ in HNO_3 or H_2SO_4 (halides, etc., must be absent). Place the solution in a 50 ml. volumetric flask and treat with $0.05M$ sodium TPB solution in slight excess. Shake and dilute to the mark. Shake again to assure thorough mixing and filter a part of the solution through a retentive, dry filter. Mix 20 ml. of the clear filtrate with a measured volume of $0.05M$ AgNO$_3$. Add 2 drops of 10% $FeNH_4(SO_4)_2$ solution. Titrate the excess of silver in the presence of the silver TPB precipitate with $0.05M$ NH$_4$SCN. The end point is marked by the appearance of the red coloration of the iron(III)–SCN complex.

Prepare the sodium TPB solution by dissolving 8.7 g. of sodium TPB in 500 ml. of water adding a few milliliters of $0.2N$ Al(NO$_3$)$_3$, allowing to stand overnight, and filtering through paper. Standardize this solution by mixing 10 ml. with 15 ml. of $0.05M$ AgNO$_3$, adding a few drops of $FeNH_4(SO_4)_2$ solution, and titrating the excess of silver with $0.05M$ NH$_4$SCN. The calculation takes the form:

$$[\text{ml.}_{\text{NaTPB}} \times M_{\text{NaTPB}} - (A/B)(\text{ml.}_{\text{AgNO}_3} \times M_{\text{AgNO}_3}$$
$$- \text{ml.}_{\text{NH}_4\text{SCN}} \times M_{\text{NH}_4\text{SCN}})] \times 39.1 = \text{mg. of potassium}$$

where A and B are, respectively, the total volume of the solution prior to filtration and the volume of filtrate employed in the titration.

Remarks.   In a series of 19 experiments involving 15 to 40 mg. of potassium, the average deviation was 0.4% with a slight tendency to positive errors. Only three results exceeded a deviation of 1%. Some of the analyses were conducted in the presence of 100 mg. of Ca, 250 mg. of Al, 700 mg. of SO_4^{2-}, and 150 mg. of PO_4^{3-}, and these ions were without influence (173).

Other argentometric procedures given in Section IV-2 can of course be modified to permit the titration of an excess of the TPB ion in a filtrate. Erdey and co-workers (37a) have thus applied the argentometric titration employing Variamine Blue as indicator.

Cluley (27a) precipitated potassium in a solution made $0.01M$ in nitric acid with a standard solution of sodium TPB, diluted the mixture to known volume, and back-titrated an aliquot of the filtrate with a 1% mercury(II) nitrate solution by using the iron(III)–thiocyanate complex as indicator.   Under vigorous stirring the titration is continued until the color remains discharged for an arbitrarily selected period of 1 min.   He applied this method to the determination of potassium in glass.   The results in the analysis of four glasses (7 to 14% K_2O) showed agreement better than 0.1% absolute between the gravimetric TPB method and this mercurimetric titration method.   Duplicate determinations of potassium in a single sample could be completed by this titrimetric method within 2 hr.

4. Determination Involving Back-Titration of Excess TPB Ion with a Quaternary Ammonium Ion

Schall (183) based a determination of potassium on the facts that quaternary ammonium ions give insoluble TPB salts and react with bromophenol blue to give colored salts.   Quaternary ammonium halides, $R_1R_2R_3R_4N \cdot X$, where R_1, R_2, and R_3 are methyl or longer chained alkyls and R_4 is benzyl or butyl, or a longer chained alkyl group, undergo this color reaction (10).   Cetyltrimethylammonium bromide (CTAB) and alkyldimethylbenzylammonium chloride are suitable titrants.   The latter compound is employed as a surface antiseptic and is available in U.S. pharmacies as a 12.8% solution (benzalkonium chloride, U.S.P.;   Zephiran chloride, Winthrop).   As the solubility of the quaternary ammonium TPB salt is lower than that of potassium TPB, a filtration is necessary.   The process is made more rapid by diluting to known volume before filtration and by using only an aliquot portion of the clear filtrate for the titration.   Care must be taken that not too high an excess of TPB ion is present; under such conditions an indistinct end point is obtained.

Where the potassium content is completely unknown, a rough experiment is advised to determine the correct ratio of reagents.   This fact may limit the application of the method somewhat and make it more appropriate to the routine analysis of samples of similar nature and potassium content.   Schall (183) devised this method especially for the determination of potassium in fertilizers and additional details and an evaluation study have been published (8,65).   Although the procedure is for use in the analysis of fertilizers (and with ammonium masked by the reaction with formaldehyde), the concentrations given are not critical and can be changed to suit other purposes.

Procedure 10. Place a 2.5 g. sample (containing up to 50% K_2O) in a 250 ml. volumetric flask, add 50 ml. of 4% ammonium oxalate solution, and 125 ml. of water. Boil for 30 min., cool, dilute to volume with water, mix, and pass through a dry filter or let stand until clear. Transfer a 15 ml. aliquot of this filtrate to a 50 ml. volumetric flask. (Alternatively, do not filter, allow to stand and transfer a similar aliquot of clear supernatant liquid.) Add 2 ml. of 20% NaOH solution and 5 ml. of 37% formalin. Add 1 ml. of standardized sodium TPB solution (see below) for each 2% of K_2O expected in the sample and 2 ml. in excess. Dilute to volume with water, mix thoroughly, let stand 5 to 10 min., and pass through a dry filter (e.g., Whatman No. 12). Transfer 25 ml. of clear filtrate to a conical flask, add 6 to 8 drops of bromophenol blue indicator (40 mg. of dye in 3 ml. of $0.1N$ NaOH diluted to 100 ml. with water; prepare freshly each week), and titrate the excess TPB with a 2.5% quaternary ammonium salt solution (CTAB or benzalkonium chloride).

The required sodium TPB solution is prepared by dissolving 24 g. of the compound in about 800 ml. of water, treating with 20 to 25 g. of $Al(OH)_3$, filtering and making alkaline by addition of 2 ml. of 20% NaOH solution, and diluting to 1000 ml. The 2.5% quaternary ammonium salt solution is compared with the sodium TPB solution by the titration step of the procedure and adjusted so that 1.00 ml. of it equals 1.00 ml. of the sodium TPB solution. The latter solution is used to precipitate a known amount of KCl and the full procedure is then followed in order to establish its titer. Under these conditions of standardization and by using the amounts specified in the procedure the following calculation applies:

$$\% \ K_2O \ in \ original \ sample \ = \ (ml._{NaTPB} \ - \ 2 \times ml._{quat. \ NH_4}) \times F$$

where F is the % K_2O equivalent of 1 ml. of sodium TPB solution, determined in the standardization.

Remarks. In the recovery of potassium from KCl solutions, the average error of the method was about 0.3%. The standard deviation of the differences of the results in the analysis of 11 fertilizers by the described method and the classical chloroplatinate method was 0.14% (183).   The accuracy and precision of the method have been confirmed in a collaborative study (65).

Epps and Burden (37) recommended certain refinements and modifications in the procedure of Schall.   They employ a sodium TPB solution of half the above strength and emphasize that it should be aged for at least 48 hr. before standardization and use.   Further, in the determination they add a 7 ml. excess of this solution.   They also recommend the use of Clayton Yellow (i.e., Titan Yellow, C.I. 19,450) in the titration of colored solutions, as this indicator gives a better color contrast, pale yellow to intense pink.

Bermejo Martinez and Goñalons Bori (20a) extended the procedure of Schall to permit the analysis of a 1 ml. sample containing 0.01 to 3.00 mg. of potassium.   An average error of 0.6% was reported in the analysis of potassium chloride samples.   They applied their micro procedure to the routine determination of potassium in blood serum (after tungstic acid deproteinization) and plant material.

Karrman and co-workers (108b) attempted the Schall procedure on an ultramicro scale (4 to 30 μg. of potassium), but found that no end point color change could be observed, even photometrically, in the presence of bromophenol blue.   A large change in transmittance occurred, however, at the equivalence point, due to the formation of cetyltrimethylammonium TPB as a finely divided suspension; hence, the procedure could be conducted as a turbidimetric titration by measuring the absorption at 700 mμ (see Section VIII-2).

5. Cerimetric Titration

Spier (197) published a cerimetric determination of potassium based on the reaction:

$$B(C_6H_5)_4^- + 51H_2O \longrightarrow B(OH)_3 + 24CO_2 + 119H^+ + 120e \quad (20)$$

The oxidation equivalent of 120 could not be obtained in practice, but under certain conditions a constant oxidation equivalent of 72 could be maintained.   Even this yields an extremely favorable conversion factor: 1 ml. of 0.01M cerium(IV) ammonium nitrate solution is equivalent to 5.4 μg. of potassium.   Spier developed the method by using a stock solution of potassium TPB in acetone and obtained amounts of this compound corresponding to 10 to 45 μg. of potassium by evaporating the acetone. Under this condition the method gave very satisfactory results.

Spier assumed the low value for the solubility of potassium TPB erroneously estimated by Raff and Brotz (160). Taking the actual, much greater solubility into account, it is doubtful that such microgram amounts of potassium can be precipitated and washed with the required accuracy and precision. In view of the separation errors, the reported value for the conversion factor becomes meaningless. The method might be applicable to larger quantities of potassium, but proof is lacking that a constant oxidation equivalent is obtainable under such conditions. Karrman and co-workers (108a) stated that they "have not been able to reproduce Spier's surprisingly good values and moreover the fact that the tetraphenylboron complex is oxidized to an undefined intermediate state makes the method rather unattractive."

6. Nonaqueous Acid–Base Titration

Flaschka (54) described the determination of potassium by titration of potassium TPB in nonaqueous medium with crystal violet as indicator and perchloric acid as titrant. The titration medium consists of acetone containing 10% acetic anhydride. Pellerin (154), in connection with the determination of organic compounds (72), published a study of the decomposition of the TPB ion in acetic anhydride. The decomposition is relatively rapid. Of 0.73 meq. of TPB ion taken, 0.14 remained after 30 min., 0.05 after 60 min., 0.005 after 120 min., and 0 after 180 min. Both the phenylboric acid formed in the decomposition and the TPB ion are only very weakly acidic in polar organic solvents; hence, the presence of the TPB ion or its decomposition products does not affect the titration of a cation of sufficient basicity.

The nonaqueous titration has the advantage of rapidity as no manipulation beyond rapid re-solution of the precipitate is necessary. However, the requirement of a special, standardized perchlorate solution makes the method advantageous only if many samples are to be analyzed. The molar conversion factor is only 1:1, which is not as favorable as that of some of the other titrimetric methods.

Procedure 11. Precipitate potassium as potassium TPB by an appropriate method, filter through a sintered glass filter and wash.

Dissolve on the filter in acetone containing 10% acetic anhydride. Collect the solution and washings in the precipitating vessel. Assure that all particles on the vessel walls are brought into solution. Add several drops of 0.2% crystal violet in anhydrous acetone. Boil for some minutes to assure reaction of any moisture with the acetic anhydride. Titrate with $0.01N$ $HClO_4$ (6 ml. 72% $HClO_4$ and 3 ml. of acetic anhydride in 250 ml. of acetic acid) until the solution color changes from violet to blue (disappearance of last red hue). The $HClO_4$ may be standardized against pure potassium TPB or potassium biphthalate. The calculation takes the form:

$$ml._{HClO_4} \times N_{HClO_4} \times 39.1 = mg. \text{ of potassium}$$

Remarks. In the titration of known amounts of pure potassium TPB, the precision is about 0.02 ml. of $0.01N$ $HClO_4$. In the precipitation and titration of 1.6 to 6.3 mg. of potassium, an average deviation of 0.03 mg. can be expected. Application of this procedure to other cations giving insoluble TPB compounds appears possible, provided that the basicity of the cation in acetone is sufficiently high. (The application of analogous titrations to TPB salts of organic compounds is considered in Section IX-5.)

Espersen (38a) has applied the above procedure of Flaschka to the determination of the potassium content of some pharmaceutical infusion solutions.

Howick and Pflaum (99,100), in connection with a study of the composition of various TPB salts of metallic cations and organic amines, studied nonaqueous titrations in various solvents and with detection of the end point by acid–base indicators and by potentiometric measurements. Ammonium TPB was titrated successfully by the above procedure of Flaschka and also in dimethylformamide with sodium methoxide in methanol–benzene as titrant and thymol blue as indicator. Potentiometric titrations of potassium and amine TPB salts were also accomplished in anhydrous acetone with perchloric acid in acetic acid as titrant (see Section V-2).

7. Acid–Base Titration After Ignition of Potassium TPB to Metaborate

Flaschka and co-workers (59) found that potassium TPB on ignition to a dull red heat is quantitatively converted into potassium metaborate, which can be determined by an acid–base titration.   As the heating is accomplished rapidly, ammonium TPB is completely volatilized.   Hence, this method is especially advantageous if potassium has to be determined in the presence of moderate amounts of ammonium ion.   If ammonia is absent, it may be added deliberately as a carrier and also to protect the potassium from losses during the washing of the precipitate.   This finding is especially important for the determination of very small amounts of potassium.   If small amounts of potassium are to be determined, it is expedient to perform the precipitation in a platinum crucible to which the acetonic solution of the potassium TPB is returned, evaporated, and ignited. A quartz crucible is also applicable, and even a porcelain one, if the ignition is performed at as low a temperature as possible.   It is unnecessary to completely ignite the carbon particles formed.   For large amounts of potassium an acid–base titration is conducted in the usual manner.   For small amounts of potassium the technique of Ballczo and Sinabell (11), for the titration of alkali metaborates, is recommended because indicator and titration errors are thereby excluded.   This technique is included in the following procedure.

Procedure 12.   Perform the precipitation by an appropriate method, expeditiously, in a platinum or quartz crucible (see above). If ammonium ion is added as a carrier for milligram amounts or less of potassium, use at least the equivalent amount of NH_4 ion in order to provide a precipitate that is easily filtered.   The required amount of precipitating reagent is calculated from the sum of NH_4 ion and potassium.   Filter and wash by using a sintered glass or porcelain filter crucible.   Dissolve the precipitate in acetone and transfer quantitatively to the crucible used for the precipitation.   Carefully volatilize the acetone and evaporate to dryness.   (Heating from above using an infrared lamp is recommended to avoid losses by spattering.) Heat over a small flame to an ash.   Ignite at a dull red heat.   Pipet a measured amount (A ml.) of 0.01 to 0.005N HCl into the cooled crucible.   Dissolve the precipitate and heat to boiling (to expel carbon dioxide).   Immediately titrate with 0.005 to 0.01N NaOH using methyl red–methylene blue mixed indicator.   The end point is marked by the appearance of a clear green solution color.   Under the same conditions titrate a blank of A ml. of HCl with the standard base.   If N_{NaOH} is the molarity of the NaOH solution, and B and

C are the milliliters of NaOH in the blank and the determination, respectively, then the calculation takes the form:

$$(B - C) \times N_{\text{NaOH}} \times 39.1 = \text{mg. of potassium}$$

Remarks. In experiments involving 1 to 5 ml. of $0.005M$ KBO_2 carried through the *entire* procedure, the average error corresponded to 0.02 ml. of $0.005N$ NaOH, thus showing the excellent recovery. In a further series involving 0.1 to 1.5 mg. of potassium, an average deviation of about 0.004 mg. was obtained (27).

8. Acid–Base Titration after Cation Exchange

Hegemann and Pfab (90) reported that if an aqueous solution of a TPB salt is passed through a cation exchange column in its hydrogen form, the free TPB acid appeared in the effluent. The same exchange was found to occur, as reported by Flaschka and Sadek (61), if a 50% acetone–water solution of a TPB salt is passed through the column. This offers a simple possibility for an acid–base titration. However, as the free TPB acid is extremely unstable, the titration must be performed as quickly as possible and not later than 10 min. after the exchange. The conversion factor is only 1:1 but the simplicity of the method seems to designate it for use in the routine analysis of many samples. This cation exchange technique has been coupled with the mercurization reaction of the TPB ion to give a conversion factor of 1:4 (see Section IV-11). It may be noted that an attempt to exchange the TPB ion for hydroxyl ion on a strongly basic resin has proved unpromising as no reproducible results were obtained in the acid–base titration of the effluent and on occasion turbid solutions emerged from the column (61).

Procedure 13. Use a strongly acidic, cation exchange resin (sulfonic acid type), preferably of particle size of 0.2 to 0.5 mm. (50 to 100 mesh), and a resin bed about 7 cm. in height and 0.5 sq. cm. in cross section. Place the resin in its hydrogen form by passing $4N$ HCl through the bed. Wash the column with water until the effluent is neutral. Precipitate up to 10 mg. of potassium as potassium TPB by an appropriate method; filter through a sintered glass or porcelain filter and wash. Dissolve the washed precipitate in acetone and collect the resulting solution and acetone washings in the precipitating vessel. Add water until the volume is doubled. If a turbidity appears, add acetone until the solution is clear. Pass the solution through the column at the rate of about 5 ml./min. Wash the column with 5 ml. portions of 1 : 1 acetone–water until the effluent is neutral (5 washings often suffice). Titrate the combined effluents with 0.01N NaOH using methyl red–methylene blue mixed indicator. The end point is marked by the appearance of a clear, stable, green color. The calculation takes the form:

$$\text{ml.}_{\text{NaOH}} \times N_{\text{NaOH}} \times 39.1 = \text{mg. of potassium}$$

If higher accuracy is required, a blank consisting of acetone–water should be run through the exchange and titration steps.

Remarks. In a series of 10 experiments involving amounts of potassium from 0.6 to 12 mg., an average deviation of about 0.02 mg. of potassium was obtained (61). It is essential to use completely neutral acetone; if necessary, stock acetone may be distilled from a few NaOH pellets. The method as described above is applicable to larger amounts of potassium because the exchange step requires that the titration be conducted in a rather large volume. For amounts of potassium less than 2 mg., use of a smaller ion exchange column is desirable. To avoid any difficulty with decomposition of the free TPB acid, the procedure can be modified by dropping the effluent into a measured amount of standard NaOH solution and by titrating the excess with HCl. However, the uptake of carbon dioxide by the caustic solution must be avoided by the use of a titration flask with a narrow neck (6,55).

Neu (150a) studied the hydrolysis of sodium TPB to diphenylboric acid by the action of cation exchange resins in the hydrogen form. His findings confirm the necessity of rapidly titrating the effluent from the column in the above procedure.

9. Acid–Base Titration after Reaction of Ammonium Ion with Excess TPB Ion and with Formaldehyde

Ieviņš and Gudriniece (102,103) based a determination of potassium on the precipitation of potassium TPB by employing a standard sodium TPB solution. The precipitate is filtered, and the excess TPB ion in the filtrate is precipitated with a measured amount of standard ammonium chloride solution. The ammonium TPB is filtered off. The resulting filtrate is exactly neutralized to methyl red, formalin is added, and the solution is titrated with a standard sodium hydroxide solution to the phenolphthalein end point. Because the method involves two precipitations and three standard solutions, it may only be appropriate to the analysis of many samples. However, if the solution after each TPB precipitation is made up to a definite volume and if only a part of the filtrate (use dry filter) is carried through the subsequent steps, it is possible that the tedious complete filtrations could be avoided and that washing losses could be reduced.

Procedure 14. Treat up to 20 mg. of potassium (in 5 to 10 ml. of sample solution) with 2 ml. of $0.05N$ HCl and 15 ml. of a 1.7% sodium TPB solution (i.e., $0.05N$). Filter after 10 min. and wash. To the combined filtrate and washings add 20 ml. of $0.03N$ NH_4Cl (1.9 g. of NH_4Cl/l.). Filter and neutralize the filtrate to methyl red. Add 5 ml. of 40% (neutralized) formalin, and titrate with $0.05N$ NaOH (carbonate-free) to the phenophthalein end point. The sodium TPB solution is standardized by carrying a known amount of KCl through the procedure. The calculation takes the form:

$$(\text{ml.}_{\text{NaOH}} \times N_{\text{NaOH}} + \text{ml.}_{\text{NaTPB}} \times N_{\text{NaTPB}} - \text{ml.}_{\text{NH}_4\text{Cl}} \times$$

$$N_{\text{NH}_4\text{Cl}}) \times 39.1 = \text{mg. of potassium}$$

The requisite NH_4Cl and sodium TPB solutions are standardized as follows: Neutralize 20 ml. of the NH_4Cl solution, with $0.05N$ NaOH, to methyl red. Add 5 ml. of 40% formalin (neutralized with $0.05N$ NaOH to phenolphthalein) and titrate with $0.05N$ NaOH to the phenolphthalein end point (persistent pink). The normality of the NH_4Cl solution is given by

$$N_{\text{NH}_4\text{Cl}} = \text{ml.}_{\text{NaOH}} \times N_{\text{NaOH}}/\text{ml.}_{\text{NH}_4\text{Cl}}$$

Treat a measured volume (15 ml. of sodium TPB solution) with a measured, excess volume of NH_4Cl solution as given above in the procedure proper. Filter and wash. Neutralize the filtrate to methyl red, and 5 ml. of 40% formalin (neutralized with $0.05N$ NaOH to phenolphthalein) and titrate with $0.05N$ NaOH to the phenolphthalein end point. The normality of the sodium TPB solution is given by

$$N_{\text{NaTPB}} = (\text{ml.}_{\text{NH}_4\text{Cl}} \times N_{\text{NH}_4\text{Cl}} - \text{ml.}_{\text{NaOH}} \times N_{\text{NaOH}})/\text{ml.}_{\text{NaTPB}}$$

Remarks. In the recovery of potassium from KCl solutions corresponding to 2 to 10 mg. of potassium, the percentage errors fell in the range -0.28 to $+0.41\%$. In experiments in which $MgSO_4$, $Ca(NO_3)_2$, or $BaCl_2$ was present, the percentage error had a larger positive value (102,103).

10. Acid–Base Titration after Mercurization

The decomposition reactions of the TPB ion with mercury(II) yields three hydrogen ions and one molecule of boric acid (see Equations 14 and 15, page 8). These reactions were first studied by Wittig and co-workers (225,229). They developed a simple method involving titration of the liberated hydrogen ion that was sufficiently accurate to establish the expected composition of the TPB ion. However, the accuracy of this method did not fulfill the requirements of an exact analytical procedure. Resolution of this problem was first investigated by Flaschka and co-workers (58).

The mercurization was found to be quantitative if the solution of potassium TPB in acetone is boiled with mercury(II) chloride in the presence of an excess of sodium hydroxide. However, the titration of sodium hydroxide in acetone proved difficult in the presence of mercury(II) which partially hydrolyzes and thus prevents a sharp end point. This hydrolysis could be excluded by complexing the excess of mercury(II) with thiocyanate or chloride ion. When these findings were applied to the mercurization of the TPB ion, incorrect results were obtained. Flaschka and co-workers (58) concluded that the phenylmercuric chloride formed during the mercurization also undergoes a reaction with sodium hydroxide to yield an indistinct end point. The addition of potassium iodide was tried and was found to lead to satisfactory results. The excess of mercury(II) is transformed into the complex HgI_4^{2-} which is inactive in the acid–base titration. In addition, phenylmercuric chloride might be transformed into the corresponding iodide which is less soluble and thereby does not react with the sodium hydroxide (cf. 126). Under these conditions satisfactory results are obtained on both the micro scale (58) and the macro scale (56) in the titration of the three equivalents of hydrogen ion produced in the mercurization reaction. Attempts to increase the conversion factor to 1:4 by further titration of the boric acid(addition of glycerin, etc.) have not been successful (58).

Since the mercurization is performed in acetone, the results of a study by Montequi and co-workers (126) are of interest. Two reactions were found to occur to some extent and were formulated in the following:

$$KB(C_6H_5)_4 + 2Hg(OH)_2 \longrightarrow 2(C_6H_5)_2Hg + KOH + H_3BO_3 \quad (21)$$

$$KB(C_6H_5)_4 + 4Hg(OH)_2 \longrightarrow 4C_6H_5HgOH + KOH + H_3BO_3 \quad (22)$$

However, since the phenylmercury bond is very strong three hydrogen ions are always released and thus, the analytical result is the same regardless of which reaction predominates. This is made clearer by recasting these equations in the form of Equations 14 and 15 (see page 8).

Montequi and co-workers (126) uncovered another important fact; namely, the role that acetone plays in the mercurization reaction. Fernandez and co-workers (40) found that acetone forms a complex with mercury(II) according to the equation

$$HgCl_2 + 2CH_3-\underset{\underset{O}{\|}}{C}-CH_3 \longrightarrow (CH_3-\underset{\underset{\vdots}{O}}{\overset{}{C}}=CH_2)_2Hg + 2Cl^- + 2H^+ \quad (23)$$

As found by Flaschka and Sadek (62), the stability of this complex is sufficiently high to affect the EDTA titration of mercury(II) if acetone is present at high concentrations (see Section IV-13). Montequi and co-workers (125) have based an acidimetric determination of mercury salts on this complex formation.

With this further information at hand, it is quite probable that contrary to the assumption of Flaschka and co-workers (58) the mercurization reaction of the TPB ion proceeds quantitatively even in aqueous solution and without an excess of sodium hydroxide being present. The boiling prescribed in their procedure may not increase the rate of the reaction, as presumed, but simply expels acetone. This seems probable as they obtained an obscured end point if too large an amount of acetone was present.

These theoretically interesting considerations, however, do not affect the practical suitability of the procedure of Flaschka and co-workers (58). The analytical results have been fully confirmed by Montequi and co-workers (128) and by other workers in applied analyses.

Procedure 15.   Perform the precipitation of 2 to 10 mg. of potassium as potassium TPB by any suitable method and filter the precipitate through a sintered glass or porcelain filter crucible. Disconnect the filter flask, discard the filtrate and washings, and clean the flask. Place 5 ml. of a saturated aqueous solution of $HgCl_2$ in the flask, reconnect it to the filter crucible (but unconnected to the vacuum source).   Place 5 ml. of acetone on the filter and stir with a glass rod.   When solution is complete apply suction.   Wash quantitatively with two 3 to 5 ml. portions of acetone and finally with a little water. (When the acetone solution drops into the $HgCl_2$ solution, heavy flocs separate out, or with small amounts of potassium a turbidity occurs.)

Quantitatively transfer the contents of the flask to a beaker, with water as the wash liquid.   Add 10 ml. of $0.1N$ NaOH and heat to boiling.   Add 5 ml. of 10% KI solution and a few drops of a 0.1% methanolic solution of methyl red.   Titrate with $0.1N$ HCl until the solution color changes to red.   Add 1 to 2 ml. more of the $0.1N$ HCl, boil off carbon dioxide, and titrate with $0.1N$ NaOH to a pure yellow solution color.

For amounts of potassium in the range of 10 to 20 mg. of potassium, double the amounts of NaOH, $HgCl_2$, and KI.   For micro amounts of potassium, decrease the specified amounts of these reagents, employ $0.01M$ NaOH and HCl, and preferably substitute a filter stick for the filter crucible.   The calculation takes the form:

$$(\text{ml.}_{\text{NaOH}} \times N_{\text{NaOH}} - \text{ml.}_{\text{HCl}} \times N_{\text{HCl}}) \times 13.033 = \text{mg. of potassium}$$

Remarks.   In 20 experiments involving 2.5 to 20 mg. of potassium an average deviation of 0.5% was obtained with only two results having an error exceeding 1% (56).   On the micro scale, in 17 experiments involving 34 to 1000 μg. of potassium, an average deviation of ± 2 μg. was found (58).

An interesting direct method has been developed by Montequi and co-workers (128).   They found that prior solution of the potassium TPB precipitate (in acetone) is unnecessary and that the mercurization action proceeds quantitatively if the precipitate is treated directly.   A solution of Na_2HgCl_4 is employed in order to avoid interference in the acid–base titration by an excess of mercury(II) chloride.

Procedure 16.   Precipitate potassium as potassium TPB by one of the appropriate methods.   Filter and wash.   Transfer the precipitate to a conical flask.   This is expedited by aggregating the precipitate by a tiny amount of water and transferring with a platinum wire.   The total volume should be of the order of 25 ml.   Add a glass bead and 5 ml. of a solution of Na_2HgCl_4 (6.80 g. of $HgCl_2$ and 4.35 g. of NaCl in 100 ml. of water).   Place the flask in a boiling water bath and agitate.   Titrate with 0.05N NaOH using methyl red as an indicator.   When the approach of the end point is signaled, return the flask to the bath and reheat.   Then continue the titration to the end point.   The calculation takes the form:

$$ml._{NaOH} \times N_{NaOH} \times 13.033 = mg. \text{ of potassium}$$

Remarks.   In a series of 13 experiments involving 1 to 10 mg. of potassium, the average deviation was 0.02 mg.   There appears to be a significant difference above and below 5 mg. of potassium; results for amounts above this amount show a positive error and those below, a negative error (128).   Bromophenol red may be substituted for methyl red as indicator.   It is also possible to employ an asbestos mat in the filtration step.

The mercurization reaction has been applied to the effluent from the cation exchange of potassium TPB (see Section IV-11).   Bromatometric, EDTA, and thiocyanate titrations have also been applied after mercurization of the TPB ion (see Sections IV-12, IV-13, and IV-14).

11. Acid–Base Titration after Ion Exchange and Subsequent Mercurization

Amin (6) has combined the cation exchange procedure of an acetone–water solution of potassium TPB developed by Flaschka and Sadek (61) (see Section IV-8) with mercurization of the TPB ion in the effluent and acid–base titration following the procedure of Flaschka and co-workers (58) (see Section IV-10).   For each equivalent of potassium TPB, one equivalent of hydrogen ion is produced in the exchange reaction, and three in the mercurization.   Hence, a total of four hydrogen ions are titrated for each potassium ion initially precipitated.

Procedure 17. Proceed as in Procedure 13 (Section IV-8) and finally pass the acetone–water solution of potassium TPB through the cation exchange column. Collect the effluent in a 100 ml. flask containing exactly 25 ml. of standard $0.01N$ NaOH and a few drops of methyl red indicator (0.1 g. in 100 ml. of ethanol). Wash the column with a little 1:1 acetone–water and with five 3 ml. portions of water. To the combined effluents immediately add 1 ml. of saturated $HgCl_2$ solution. Heat on a steam bath, allow to cool, and add enough 10% KI solution to dissolve the mercuric iodide that initially precipitates. Add exactly 25 ml. of $0.01N$ HCl. Then titrate the excess of acid in the warmed solution with the $0.01N$ NaOH until the solution color becomes yellow. The following calculation applies:

$$(\text{ml.}_{NaOH} \times N_{NaOH} - \text{ml.}_{HCl} \times N_{HCl}) \times 9.775 = \text{mg. of potassium}$$

Remarks. For additional information on the mercurization and titration steps, (see Section IV-10). In representative results reported for the analysis of 0.4 to 10 mg. of potassium, the average error was about 0.4%. Amin also determined ammonium, rubidium, and cesium by the above procedure (6).

12. Bromatometric Titration after Mercurization

Rüdorff and Zannier (172) reported that the reaction between the TPB ion and bromine is not stoichiometric and that the uptake of bromine depends upon the amount of bromine in excess and the reaction time; 3.3 to 4.8 equivalents of bromine were consumed per mole of TPB ion. These workers also reported that the iodometric titration in aqueous medium gave variable results in the range and that 3.3 to 4.1 equivalents of iodine were consumed per mole of TPB ion. Montequi and co-workers (129) found that if the TPB ion was first decomposed by mercuric acetate, a bromination then proceeded readily. The following reaction scheme applies (expressing the acetate group as Ac):

$$KB(C_6H_5)_4 + 4Hg(Ac)_2 + 3H_2O \longrightarrow$$
$$4C_6H_5HgAc + KAc + 3HAc + H_3BO_3 \quad (24)$$
$$4C_6H_5HgAc + 4Br_2 \longrightarrow 4BrC_6H_4HgAc + 4HBr \quad (25)$$

The mercurization is performed with mercury(II) acetate in glacial acetic acid. This offers the advantage that the potassium TPB and the phenylmercuric acetate are both soluble in this medium. In this process one equivalent of TPB ion corresponds to eight equivalents of bromine. Although this conversion factor is most favorable, it should be emphasized that in the determination of small amounts of potassium, the major problem is *not* the titration, but the precipitation and washing of potassium TPB.

Procedure 18. Precipitate potassium as potassium TPB by an appropriate method. Filter through a sintered glass crucible and wash. Suck off the last portion of wash liquid as completely as possible. Add 10 ml. of 5% mercury(II) acetate solution (3.4 g. of HgO in 100 ml. of glacial acetic acid) to the precipitate to dissolve it. Collect the solution in a dry flask and wash the crucible finally with 10 ml. of glacial acetic acid added in portions of 2 or 3 ml. Add 2 ml. of concentrated HCl. (A slight turbidity may appear.) With vigorous stirring slowly add $0.1N$ $KBrO_3$ (containing 15 g. of KBr/l.) from a buret until a slightly amber color solution indicates a persistent excess of bromine. Add 10 ml. of 10% aqueous KI solution, starch indicator, and titrate the liberated iodine with $0.1N$ $Na_2S_2O_3$. The $Na_2S_2O_3$ solution should be compared with the standard $KBrO_3$ solution in the presence of mercury(II) acetate and acetic acid and under conditions comparable to those in the actual determination. The calculation takes the form:

$$(ml._{KBrO_3} \times N_{KBrO_3} - ml._{Na_2S_2O_3} \times N_{Na_2S_2O_3}) \times$$
$$4.8875 = mg. \text{ of potassium}$$

Remarks. For amounts of potassium less than 5 mg., add only 5 ml. of the mercury(II) acetate solution. For amounts of potassium less than 1 mg. use $0.02N$ $KBrO_3$ and $Na_2S_2O_3$. Representative results reported (129) show a maximum deviation of about 0.05 mg. of potassium for amounts of potassium between 0.5 and 9 mg.

13. EDTA Titration after Mercurization

In spite of the extremely high stability constant of the mercury(II)–EDTA complex, the reaction between mercury(II) and the TPB ion takes place in the presence of EDTA in an acetone–water system. Flaschka and Sadek (62) established that Equation 14 (page 8) applied and that one mole of TPB ion reacts with the mercury(II)–EDTA complex to free four moles of EDTA. They found that the

EDTA liberated could be titrated in acetate buffer with zinc ion employing 1-(2-pyridylazo)-2-naphthol (PAN) as an indicator. The conversion factor of 1:4 is most favorable, and the end point (especially when screened with methylene blue) is extremely sharp.

Procedure 19. Precipitate potassium TPB by an appropriate procedure and filter. (Complete removal of the precipitate to the filter is unnecessary.) Dissolve the washed precipitate on the filter with small portions of acetone and rinse the precipitating vessel with acetone. Collect the acetone solution and rinsings in a 400 ml. beaker. Add Hg(II)–EDTA solution in excess (see below), and dilute to about 200 ml. with water.

Add 5 to 10 ml. of acetate buffer (prepared by addition of acetic acid to $2.5M$ sodium acetate until the pH reaches 6 to 6.3) and a few drops of a 0.1% methanolic solution of PAN. Titrate with $0.100M$ ZnCl$_2$ (dissolve 6.538 g. reagent grade Zn in HCl and dilute to 1 l. with water) until the solution color turns to orange or red. Back-titrate to a pure yellow color with a few drops of $0.100N$ EDTA (dissolve 37.23 g. of disodium ethylenediaminetetraacetate dihydrate and dilute to 1 l. with water). For a screened end point, employ a 0.05% aqueous solution of methylene blue. The amount required will depend on the purity of this dye and of the PAN; the color change of the screened end point is from violet to emerald green.

Prepare the required Hg(II)–EDTA solution in the following manner. Prepare an approximately $0.1M$ Hg(NO$_3$)$_2$ solution and titrate three 20 ml. portions, following paragraph two of the above procedure, thus comparing the Hg(II) and EDTA solutions. Mix equivalent volumes of the two and store. The calculation takes the form:

$$(\text{ml.}_{\text{ZnCl}_2} \times M_{\text{ZnCl}_2} - \text{ml.}_{\text{EDTA}} \times M_{\text{EDTA}}) \times$$

$$9.775 = \text{mg. of potassium}$$

Remarks. In eight representative experiments involving 0.55 to 10.8 mg. of potassium, and involving titrants of $0.1M$, the average deviation was about 0.04 mg. of potassium. As known amounts of potassium TPB were taken, this precision is for the titration step only.

Sadek and Reilley (178a) have applied the same principle to the determination of potassium and ammonium and their sum. It was found that if the least amount of dimethylformamide is used to dissolve the TPB precipitate (rather than acetone), Eriochrome Black T can be used as the metal indicator, and magnesium as the back-titrant. After the dissolution of the precipitate, additions are made of Hg(II)–EDTA, NaOH to neutrality, pH 10 buffer, and the indicator. The EDTA freed is then titrated with a standard magnesium solution to a color change of blue to the first appearance of a slight red hue. Although these approaches have only been studied with potassium (62,178a) and ammonium (178a) they are probably applicable to other cations forming insoluble TPB salts.

14. Thiocyanate Titration after Mercurization

Montequi and co-workers (127) have developed another finish to the mercurization of potassium TPB involving a back-titration of the excess of mercury(II), with ammonium thiocyanate with iron(III) as indicator. Because one TPB ion reacts with four mercury(II) ions (see Equation 14, page 8), a favorable conversion factor of 1:4 is obtained. However, a 50% excess of mercury(II) must be added in order to obtain satisfactory results.

Procedure 20. Precipitate 1 to 10 mg. of potassium as potassium TPB by an appropriate method. Filter, preferably on an asbestos mat, to facilitate transfer of the precipitate, and wash. Return the washed precipitate to the precipitation vessel and treat with 25 ml. (exactly measured) of $0.1N$ mercury(II) acetate solution (15.933 g. mercury(II) acetate and 2 ml. acetic acid dissolved and diluted to 1 l. with water). Heat to boiling (a clear solution is obtained unless asbestos fiber was used as a filter mat). Cool and dilute with water to 50 ml. Add 5 ml. of concentrated nitric acid and 5 ml. of FeNH$_4$(SO$_4$)$_2$ solution (10 g. of the salt is dissolved in 80 ml. of water and 5 ml. of concentrated HNO$_3$ is added). Titrate with $0.1N$ NH$_4$ SCN to the appearance of the red color of the iron(III)–SCN complex. The calculation takes the form:

$$(ml._{Hg(Ac)_2} \times N_{Hg(Ac)_2} - ml._{NH_4SCN} \times N_{NH_4SCN}) \times$$

$$9.775 = mg. \text{ of potassium}$$

Remarks. In a series of 14 experiments employing 1 to 10 mg. of potassium, the average deviation was about 0.04 mg. of potassium.

V. ELECTROMETRIC TITRATION AND POLAROGRAPHIC DETERMINATION OF POTASSIUM

Some general remarks on TPB titrimetric determinations of potassium have been presented in Section IV-1, and titrations to a visual end point have been considered in Sections IV-2 through IV-14. The following sections discuss the titrimetric determinations of potassium involving an electrometric end point. The subject is conveniently divided into conductometric and high frequency titrations (Section V-1), electrometric titrations employing nonpolarized and polarized electrode systems (Section V-2 and V-3, respectively), and amperometric titrations (Section V-4). Polarographic determinations of potassium are treated in Section V-5.

1. Conductometric and High Frequency Titrations

The possibility of a conductometric precipitation titration of potassium was initially investigated by Raff and Brotz (160), in water made acidic by addition of acetic acid with a standard solution of lithium TPB as titrant. During the titration the potassium ions are replaced by the less mobile lithium ions (mobilities at 25°C. are 74.8 and 41.7, respectively, and the conductivity decreases until the equivalence point is reached. The addition of further lithium TPB causes the conductivity to increase. Excellent results were obtained even when foreign ions were present in the following molar ratios: Na:K, 4:1; Mg:K, 3:1; Ca:K, 2:1; Sr:K, 1.5:1; and Ba:K, 2:1. The lithium TPB solution was standardized conductometrically using a standard potassium bromide solution.

Jander and Anke (107) made a thorough study employing the commercially available sodium TPB as titrant. Sharp breaks in the curves were obtained even though the mobilities of sodium (50.8) and potassium (74.8) are closer to each other than are those of lithium and potassium. The influence of foreign ions was studied and it was found that sodium, calcium, and magnesium could be tolerated up to a 10-fold molar amount, but iron(III) only to a molar ratio of K:Fe of 1:2. As the titration can be performed in alkaline solution with no change in accuracy and reproducibility, interfering ammonium ions may be removed by boiling with excess sodium hydroxide.

Satisfactory results are obtained in solutions up to $0.005N$ in acetic acid. Mineral acid is tolerable up to $0.0025N$, and then only by working rapidly because of the decomposition of the TPB ion.

The usual limitations of conductometric precipitation titrations apply. When the concentration of foreign ions becomes too high, no sharp breaks are obtained. However, the method has merit in special cases. For example, in a silicate analysis after the usual separation of potassium and sodium, and weighing as the sulfate, the fraction may be redissolved and the potassium titrated conductometrically. Sodium is obtained by difference. Further, the method may be applied to the analysis of potassium in compounds containing only a limited amount of foreign ions. Excellent results have been reported for the conductometric titration of potassium in feldspar (160) and carnallite (107).

The conductometric precipitation titration avoids the tedious prior separation of potassium TPB required in many other titrimetric procedures. Jander and Anke (107) stated that ammonium ion can also be determined by this titration. Wendlandt (215) has titrated thallium(I) conductometrically with sodium TPB.

Procedure 21. Employ the usual techniques for conductometric titrations. Standardize approximately $0.1M$ sodium TPB against a $0.02M$ KCl standard solution. Preferably, adjust the potassium concentration of the sample solution to about 1/20th of that of the titrant. The calculation takes the form:

$$\text{ml.}_{\text{NaTPB}} \times M_{\text{NaTPB}} \times 39.1 = \text{mg. of potassium}$$

Lane (119) described the design and construction of a 250 Mc. high frequency titrimeter and applied the instrument to the determination of potassium. Well defined titration curves were obtained in $0.05M$ acetic acid. The $0.1M$ sodium TPB solution used as titrant was standardized against potassium biphthalate or silver nitrate by a similar high frequency titration. In experiments in which 8.26 mg. of potassium were taken, recovery of 8.21, 8.28, and 8.26 mg. was obtained. The high frequency titration with sodium TPB as titrant has now been studied with potassium (119), with potassium, rubidium, cesium, and ammonium ion (207b), silver (131), and thallium(I) (131,207c).

2. Electrometric Titration Employing Nonpolarized Electrodes

The first intensive study of the application of a potentiometric titration to TPB systems was published by Crane (30,31). His method was especially developed for the determination of organic bases but it is equally applicable to inorganic cations. A cation is precipitated as the TPB salt, the precipitate is dissolved in acetone, and the TPB ion content is titrated with a standardized silver nitrate solution. Best results have been obtained when the solution is about 50% in acetone.

Special precautions must be observed in standardizing the silver nitrate solution. Pure potassium TPB or sodium TPB recrystallized from chloroform is a suitable primary standard. If sodium chloride were employed as the primary standard, Crane reported that the normality found was 5.4% lower than that obtained with potassium TPB. He attributed this to the nonnegligible solubility of silver TPB in the acetone–water. Kirsten and co-workers (113) suggested that the TPB ion does not precipitate with silver in an exact 1:1 ratio; hence, the deviation. These workers obtained a different titer when working in an acetone-free, aqueous medium. (In contrast, Mukherji and Sant (131) observed in a high frequency titration of silver nitrate with sodium TPB and also in the inverse titration that the end point corresponded exactly to the stoichiometric formation of silver TPB.) Karrman and co-workers (108a) found that the concentration of acetone in the titration medium influences the titer of the silver nitrate solution when either potassium bromide or potassium TPB is used as the standard. However, if the medium is 45 to 50% in acetone, the titer obtained by use of either standard is identical within the experimental error of the method. These somewhat discordant findings suggest that standardizations should be effected under the exact conditions prevailing in the actual determinations.

Crane (30,31) employed a glass electrode–silver electrode system with a pH meter. The silver electrode consisted of a 2 mm. diameter silver wire immersed to a depth of about 8 cm. Kirsten and co-workers have also found this electrode system suitable and apply a voltage of -500 mv. to the silver electrode (erroneously given as $+500$ mv. in the original paper). This electrode system reaches equilibrium rapidly except near the end point where a waiting period of about 1 min. is necessary. This difficulty can be overcome often by scratching the electrode with a glass rod during the titration in order to remove particles of silver TPB adhering to the wire. Crane recommended use of a shielded platinum electrode with the Malmstadt automatic titration assembly, because this electrode shows less tendency to produce erratic needle movement.   The end point is established in the titration in the usual manner.

In order to avoid reprecipitation of the TPB compound from the acetone–water during the titration, the medium must have a high content of acetone.   On the other hand, silver TPB has appreciable solubility in acetone.   A 1:1 ratio of acetone was therefore used wherever possible and was found to give good results.   Crane disliked the application of a silver nitrate solution containing acetone because the volatility of this compound might lead to changes in the titer.   The titration is performed in an acetate-buffered medium of a pH of about 5.

Procedure 22.   Precipitate the TPB salt by an appropriate method and wash.   Dissolve in 40 ml. of acetone, add 3 ml. of $3M$ acetic acid, 3 ml. of $3M$ sodium acetate, and 34 ml. of water.   (Place a ring of petrolatum jelly on the wall of the titration vessel just above the solution level in order to avoid creeping of the precipitate formed during the titration.)   Insert the electrodes, connect the pH meter or other instrument, and with vigorous stirring titrate as usual with the $AgNO_3$ solution.   The calculation takes the form:

$$(\text{ml.}_{AgNO_3} \times N_{AgNO_3}) \times 39.1 = \text{mg. of potassium}$$

Remarks.   Ten samples of 100 to 200 mg. of potassium TPB were used to calculate the normality of the $AgNO_3$ solution.   The titers calculated showed a relative standard deviation of 0.17%.   About the same precision can be expected in the titration step for the determination of potassium; the precipitation step will, of course, lower the over-all precision.

Similar results have been obtained by Havíř (87) by dissolving the potassium TPB precipitate in acetone and by titrating potentiometrically with the silver nitrate solution.   He found that the concentration of acetone in the final solution had no effect on the position of the potential break; however, it does affect the height of the break significantly.   The maximum potential change was obtained in neutral solution with an acetone concentration of 20 to 50%.   The titration was not influenced by the presence of sulfuric, nitric, perchloric, or acetic acid up to $0.002M$; however, any further increase in acidity resulted in the consumption of a greater amount of titrant.   The addition of foreign salts (namely, sodium nitrate and aluminum sulfate) did not change the results but did decrease the height of the potential break. The procedure applied by Havíř (87) is essentially similar to that described above. In the determination of 1.6 to 10.7 mg. of potassium, the error fell in the range of −0.51 to +2.25%. Havíř (87a) also applied this method to microgram amounts of potassium, rubidium, and cesium.

A potentiometric micro titration of potassium TPB redissolved in 40 to 50% aqueous acetone with silver nitrate as titrant was reported by Karrman and co-workers (108a), by using a silver wire electrode as the indicator electrode, and in a separate vessel a silver wire in 0.1N silver nitrate solution as the reference electrode. The two vessels were connected by a sodium nitrate–agar bridge. In a series of six determinations involving 150 μg. of potassium, the average error was 1.6 μg. of potassium.

Kirsten and co-workers (113) reasoned that because of the low solubility of silver TPB a silver electrode should respond directly to a change in the TPB concentration of a solution. Their experiments confirmed this expectation. In the direct titration of an aqueous solution of an organic base, potassium, rubidium, or cesium, well-developed inflection points were obtained and the recovery fell between 99.8 and 100.3%. On the micro scale excellent results were obtained by merely reducing volumes proportionately. This direct titration is, of course, impossible in the presence of halides. Kirsten and co-workers avoided this interference by passing the sample solution through a strongly acidic anion exchange column in the acetate form prior to the titration.

Procedure 23. To about 40 ml. of sample solution (containing about 1 meq. of substance to be titrated), add 5 ml. of acetate buffer (250 g. of sodium acetate trihydrate and 28 ml. of glacial acetic acid diluted to 1 l.). Insert the silver wire–glass electrode system and apply −500 mv. to the silver electrode. Under agitation titrate with a 0.1N sodium TPB solution (prepared by dissolving the reagent grade salt in water and filtering if a slight turbidity occurs). Standardize this solution against standard K_2SO_4 solution, potentiometrically. The calculation takes the form:

$$(ml._{NaTPB} \times N_{NaTPB}) \times 39.1 = mg. \text{ of potassium}$$

Remarks. No attempt has been made to clarify the actual electrode processes involved in the titration. The inflection point of the titration curve is taken as the end point. Espersen has studied this procedure and confirmed its satisfactory nature (38b).

Kirsten and co-workers (113) also developed a back-titration procedure. The sample solution is treated with a measured amount of sodium TPB solution, transferred to a volumetric flask, and diluted to the mark. A portion of the solution is filtered, and an aliquot of the clear filtrate is used for the back-titration of the TPB ion that is present. In order to avoid interference by chloride ion, instead of a silver nitrate solution, a solution of an organic ammonium salt is employed. For this purpose 3-oxapentamethylene-1-trimethylammonium-5-ethyldimethylammonium ditartrate, a drug used in hypertensive therapy (Oxaditon, Pharmacia), is well suited as it has a favorable equivalent weight (272.4), forms an insoluble TPB salt, and is easily purified. It can be readily dried at 100°C. without decomposition, but it is then slightly hygroscopic. Espersen (38b) applied this procedure buts ubstituted for the back-titrant pethidinium chloride, presumably ethyl 1-methyl-4-phenylpiperidine-4-carboxylate hydrochloride.

Pflaum and Howick (99,100), in the course of a study of the composition of TPB salts, accomplished acid–base potentiometric titrations of potassium and amine TPB salts in anhydrous acetone with perchloric acid in acetic acid as titrant. Their electrode system consisted of a glass electrode and a calomel half-cell, the latter being connected to the solution via a fritted glass disk and a bridge, 0.2M in sodium perchlorate. This titration could also be effected in acetonitrile medium.

3. Electrometric Titration Employing Polarized Electrodes

Franck (66) has described a potentiometric method termed a "polarization titration" that differs from a conventional dead-stop method by employing a low frequency alternating current for polarization instead of a direct current. The original papers should be consulted for the theory and instrumental details. The technique may have wider application than the dead-stop method because a greater choice of electrodes is permitted. Only a very small polarizing current is required and hence noninert electrodes are serviceable. The

Franck assembly employs a total of three electrodes. The method was briefly studied for the determination of potassium by precipitating the TPB salt and back-titrating the excess of TPB ion with silver nitrate. In this determination a silver wire serves as the working electrode.

Schmidt (184) has simplified the circuitry of Franck. Further, in the determination of potassium he employs only two amalgamated silver wire electrodes. Any changes in alternating polarizing current, due to depolarization, are amplified electronically and are indicated on a sensitive galvanometer. The original publication should be consulted for circuitry and assembly details. After each titration the silver electrodes need only be rinsed with water and cleaned with a soft cloth. After 30 to 40 titrations, they must be amalgamated again by dipping the silver wire into nitric acid containing mercury(II) nitrate and then into metallic mercury.

The use of thallium(I) as the titrant is advantageous as it allows application to solutions containing even considerable amounts of chloride or of other anions which form insoluble silver salts. Silver can serve as the titrant, but has the above disadvantage. Schmidt mentioned that some interfering cations can be masked by addition of EDTA, but gave no details or results. It was noted that the presence of EDTA in alkaline solution destroyed the amalgamation of the silver electrodes.

Some special precautions must be observed in this method. Use of alumina in the purification of the sodium TPB reagent solution is not allowed as this has an unfavorable influence. The use of aluminum chloride as a coagulating aid during the precipitation of potassium TPB is not recommended. If the coagulation must be promoted, addition of a few drops of $0.1M$ chromium trichloride is suitable. Chromium(III) has less flocculating action than aluminum, but a negligible influence on the titration.

The determination of potassium, for example, is performed by addition of an excess of standard sodium TPB solution. A filtration step is then necessary because thallium(I) TPB is less soluble than potassium TPB. The mixture is, therefore, brought to a definite volume and filtered. Schmidt recommended Schleicher and Schüll black ribbon paper for the filtration; he found that filter paper from some sources contained sufficient ammonia to influence the result. The first turbid portions of filtrate are discarded. An aliquot of the clear filtrate is titrated with thallium(I) nitrate. Schmidt performed the precipitation from acetic acid medium buffered to a pH of about 3.5; from stronger mineral acid solutions the decomposition of the TPB ion was too rapid. The titration as well as the precipitation can also be performed in alkaline medium. This offers the possibility of avoiding interference by ammonia by the addition of formaldehyde. In this case the precipitation is performed from hot solution and the cooled solution is made up to volume. Some magnesium oxide may be added as a flocculating aid. The filtration and further treatment proceed as in the acidic medium.

The required 0.02M thallium nitrate solution is prepared by dissolving 10.656 g. of dried, reagent grade thallium(I) nitrate and diluting to 2 l. with water. As a reference standard a 0.02M potassium chloride solution is employed. The 0.02M sodium TPB solution is prepared by dissolving 13.7 g. of sodium TPB and diluting to 2 l. with water. (Schmidt reported that sodium TPB from one commercial source gave a solution in this manner that was sufficiently stable over a period of several months, although a slight turbidity was noticed.) This sodium TPB solution is standardized by the titration procedure against the potassium chloride solution. It is noteworthy that Schmidt obtained different titers for the precipitation from acidic medium and from alkaline medium; the difference was small, but significant.

As this method shows a very pronounced end point, of high reproducibility in the titration step, and as no error is introduced by a washing step, the accuracy may be limited only by the accuracy of the volumetric glassware and measurements. In the quintuplicate determination of two samples of 15.64 mg. and 10.65 mg. of potassium, the maximal deviations reported were +0.03 and −0.02 mg. of potassium, respectively. One hundred fertilizer samples were analyzed for potassium by Schmidt by three methods, with the following average per cent deviations: perchlorate method, 0.20% K_2O; platinic chloride method, 0.12%; flame photometer, 0.26%; and the above method, 0.03%.

Esperson (38b) briefly studied a dead-stop method by using a potentiometer with a special adapter and two platinum electrodes, and with sodium TPB as titrant. However, no satisfactory results could be obtained in the titration of potassium or nitrogen-containing drugs.

4. Amperometric Titration

Three different types of amperometric titration for the determination of potassium have been studied. One involves precipitation and separation of potassium TPB and titration of the redissolved precipitate with a suitable titrant; the second, addition of an excess of standard sodium TPB solution and back-titration of the excess *without* separation of the precipitated potassium TPB; and the third, direct titration with sodium TPB solution with measurement of the anodic depolarization current at a dropping mercury electrode.

Findeis and De Vries (42) described a method involving solution of potassium TPB in such organic solvents as acetonitrile, dimethylformamide, and 2-(2-methoxyethoxy)ethanol (i.e., methyl Carbitol), and amperometric titration with silver nitrate. Acetonitrile was preferred because more water can be tolerated before potassium TPB reprecipitates.

Procedure 24. Precipitate, filter, and wash potassium TPB by an appropriate method. Dissolve the precipitate in 15 ml. of acetonitrile and add enough water (5 to 8 ml.) so that at the equivalence point the medium is 50 to 60% (v/v) in acetonitrile. Place in a 100 ml. beaker and add 6 ml. of mercury to serve as the nonpolarized anode. Titrate at −0.10 v. versus this electrode with 0.03 or 0.1M aqueous AgNO$_3$. Open the circuit before each addition of titrant in order to avoid excessive galvanometer deflections. After stirring and waiting 15 to 30 sec., place the galvanometer in the circuit and record the reading. Obtain the end point graphically by plotting current versus milliliters of titrant; extremely sharp breaks are obtained.

Remarks. In a series of about 20 experiments involving amounts of potassium in the range of 1.2 to 20.2 mg., most results were within 0.6% of the correct value and the greatest deviation was 1.3%. Because these experiments were performed starting with pure potassium TPB, the accuracy relates *only* to the titration step. Titrations can be performed in the same manner in dimethylformamide but at −0.20 v. versus the mercury pool. In this medium the results obtained were 2 to 5% high. In 2-(2-methoxyethoxy)ethanol at −0.10 v. versus the mercury pool, the results were 1 to 3.5% high.

A similar method employing acetone as solvent has been described by Heyrovský (97), but procedural details were not given.

Kemula and Kornacki (111) studied a back-titration employing thallium(I) as the back-titrant and developed the following procedure.

Procedure 25. Precipitate 0.01 to 1 mg. of potassium (at a concentration of not less than $0.0005M$) from acetate buffered medium of pH 5 to 6 and $0.1M$ in $NaNO_3$ by addition of a measured amount of $0.002M$ sodium TPB. After 10 min., add 0.5% gelatin solution until its concentration is 0.01% in the mixture. Back-titrate the excess of TPB ion amperometrically with $0.005M$ $TlNO_3$. The potential is maintained at -0.475 v. versus the calomel electrode. Standardize the sodium TPB solution under the same conditions with the $0.005M$ $TlNO_3$. The end point is obtained graphically by plotting current versus milliliters of $TlNO_3$ solution added.

Remarks. In a series of 12 experiments involving 0.1 to 1.6 mg. of potassium, the average error was about 4% (111).

Amos and Sympson (7a) studied a direct amperometric titration of potassium with sodium TPB solution in acetate buffer, involving measurement of the anodic depolarization current of a dropping mercury electrode at $+0.080$ v. versus the saturated calomel electrode. The relative error in the titration of 4 to 36 mg. of potassium at a concentration of 10^{-3} to $10^{-2}M$ is less than 0.81%, but the method is tedious. A long time is required to attain a steady current value after each addition of titrant and 17 to 25 current measurements must be made; hence, 2 to 3 hr. are required for a titration.

5. Polarographic Determination

Geske (78) established that it is not possible to oxidize TPB on a rotating platinum electrode in aqueous solution because of the interfering evolution of oxygen. In anhydrous acetic acid, the oxidation wave obtained is drawn out and ill-defined. In dimethylformamide, the oxidation occurs with a half-wave potential of 1.20 v. versus the saturated calomel electrode; however, the residual current is quite large in this potential region. In acetonitrile solution, the TPB ion gives a well-defined oxidation wave on a rotating platinum electrode at the same half-wave potential. A two-electron oxidation process is involved. The reaction scheme proposed by Geske is given by Equations 16 to 18 (page 9). At low TPB concentrations, there was some indication of a second wave at 1.4 v.

Amos and Sympson (7a) reported that aqueous solutions of the TPB ion give an anodic wave at the dropping mercury electrode and based an amperometric titration on this finding (see Section V-4).

The cationic part of a TPB salt can be used for a polarographic determination. This approach has been applied to potassium, but can, of course, be applied to other inorganic or organic cations giving a suitable polarographic wave. A prior separation of the insoluble TPB salt is necessary.

Findeis and De Vries (41) isolated potassium TPB by use of a standard method of precipitation and dissolved it in dimethyl-formamide containing tetrabutylammonium iodide. A mercury pool electrode was used. The half-wave potential of the potassium ion under these conditions was -1.55 v. The wave height was found to be directly proportional to the potassium concentration in the range 2×10^{-4} to $7.5 \times 10^{-3}M$ (i.e., 0.08 to 3 mg. of potassium in a 25 ml. cell volume). The polarographic measurement is standardized by employing known amounts of a $0.125M$ potassium TPB solution in dimethylformamide. The temperature coefficient is relatively high; hence, the temperature should be held constant. Water does not interfere with the determination provided that the amount does not exceed 3 ml. in 25 ml. of final solution volume. Due to the decomposition of the supporting electrolyte, an impurity wave must be corrected for by running a polarogram of the electrolyte alone. The correction so obtained is constant over a period of 3 to 4 weeks. The accuracy of this method is about 1%.

Heyrovský (94) has described a polarographic method involving ignition of the TPB ion to metaborate. The precipitation is effected from strongly acidic medium in the presence of ammonium as a carrier. The precipitation and ignition (in a platinum crucible) recommended by Flaschka (27) are employed (see Section IV-7). The potassium metaborate is dissolved in water, tetramethylam-monium or tetraethylammonium hydroxide is added as the support-ing electrolyte. The accuracy is about 4%. The method was applied to the determination of potassium in mineral water, chemicals, injection solutions, and to various biological materials including serum, erythrocytes, and urine. The application to blood serum after initial ashing or deproteinization with trichloroacetic acid has been described further by Heyrovský (95).

VI. DETERMINATION OF POTASSIUM BY OPTICAL METHODS

Both spectrophotometric and turbidimetric determinations of potassium as potassium TPB have been accomplished. These methods are considered in Sections VI-1 and VI-2, respectively.

1. Spectrophotometric Determination

Cooper (28,29) reported the absorption spectrum of sodium TPB in aqueous solution in the ultraviolet region, from 230 to about 300 mμ. The TPB ion was found to absorb strongly below about 280 mμ. These data allowed the stability and decomposition of 1×10^{-4} to $4 \times 10^{-5} M$ sodium TPB solutions to be followed spectrophotometrically, as Beer's law was found to apply at various wavelengths in the region of 240 to 272 mμ.

Pflaum and Howick (99,100,155) have reported the absorption spectra of cesium, ammonium, rubidium, potassium, and sodium TPB in acetonitrile and acetonitrile–water from above 290 to below 260 mμ. In acetonitrile–water, the spectral curves of these salts show a maxima at 266 and 274 mμ with molar absorptivities of 3225 and 2100, respectively. The shape and height of the curves obtained with any of the salts are identical; hence, the absorption is associated only with the TPB ion. Further, the presence of water had no significant influence on the general shape of the curve as obtained in pure acetonitrile in mixtures up to 40% in water. Beer's law was found to be obeyed by concentrations of potassium TPB in the range of 5.0×10^{-5} to $7.5 \times 10^{-4} M$. The solubility of the above TPB salts and of thallium(I) TPB in water was determined by spectrophotometric measurements at 266 and 274 mμ (see Table I, page 10).

Pflaum and Howick applied their findings to the determination of potassium by precipitation of potassium TPB, filtration, solution of the precipitate in acetonitrile–water, and spectrophotometric measurement. The effect of diverse ions on the determination was studied and rubidium, cesium, silver, thallium(I), and mercury(II) were found to interfere as they form insoluble TPB salts. The interference by additional cations is, of course, closely related to the precipitation step. Permissible amounts reported by the workers (99,155) for the procedure given below are as follows: Al^{3+}, Ca^{2+}, Li^+, Mg^{2+}, Na^+, NO_3^-, SO_4^{2-}, Cl^-, Br^-, and I^- can be tolerated up to 2000 p.p.m.; Co^{2+}, Cu^{2+}, Fe^{3+}, and Ni^{2+} to 1000 p.p.m. It is interesting that these workers found that alumina may be used to enhance coagulation of the potassium TPB precipitate at pH 3 to 4 and is coprecipitated; however, the aluminum content does not dissolve in pure acetonitrile, but does in acetonitrile–water. The precipitation step gives quantitative results if made between pH 1 and 9; the workers prefer pH 3 to 4.

Procedure 26. Adjust the sample solution to pH 3 to 4 with NaOH or H_2SO_4. To 5 ml. of this solution, in a 15 ml. centrifuge tube, add 5 ml. of 1% sodium TPB solution (1 g. sodium TPB and 0.5 g. of $AlCl_3 \cdot 6H_3O$ or $Al(NO_3)_3 \cdot 6H_2O$ in 100 ml. of water, filtered after standing). Centrifuge for 3 min. at high speed. Remove the supernatant liquid with a pipet. Wash three times with 3 ml. of a cold, saturated potassium TPB solution. Leave a constant volume of liquid (0.5 ml.) with the precipitate. Dissolve the washed precipitate in 5 ml. of a 3:1 mixture of acetonitrile and water. Quantitatively transfer to a 25 ml. volumetric flask and dilute to the mark. Measure the absorbance at 266 mμ. Compare with a blank prepared in the same way by using water instead of the original sample solution. The result is obtained from a calibration curve prepared by analyzing samples containing known amounts of potassium.

Remarks. The above procedure was reported (155) to be applicable to the determination of 2 to 30 p.p.m. (5×10^{-5} to $7.5 \times 10^{-4}M$) of potassium with an accuracy of 2%.

2. Turbidimetric Determination

Very small amounts of potassium can be determined by precipitation as potassium TPB and turbidimetric measurement. The method was first studied by de la Rubia and Blasco (170,171). The sample was initially evaporated and then dissolved in a buffer of pH 2. This step is necessary in order to obtain reproducible results and assures constant conditions in the precipitation. The sodium TPB reagent which is buffered to pH 8 to 9, is then added and the pH rises to about 5, and fine particles are thereby produced. Finally a buffer of pH 2 is added; the pH is thereby lowered avoiding interference by metal ions that hydrolyze at pH 5 or that form insoluble salts (e.g., phosphates). The absorbance of the turbid solution is then measured.

The procedure has been applied to potassium in salts (170).   The general procedure (171) is summarized below.

Procedure 27.   Place 1 ml. of sample solution in a 5 ml. cuvette and evaporate to dryness at 70 to 80°C.   Dissolve the residue in 0.1 to 0.2 ml. of the pH 2 buffer.   Stir until solution is complete.   Add 0.2 ml. of the buffered sodium TPB solution (see below).   Shake well for 1 to 2 min.   Add 1 ml. of pH 2 buffer, and dilute to 5 ml. with water.   Shake again to assure complete dispersion and within 10 min. measure the absorbance with white light and water as a reference.   The result is obtained from a calibration curve obtained by employing the above procedure and known amounts of potassium.

Reagents.   Prepare a buffered solution 3% in sodium TPB by one of the following alternatives: (1) Mix 85 ml. of a 1.91% borax solution with 15 ml. of $0.1N$ HCl; to 20 ml. of this pH 9 buffer add 3 g. of sodium TPB and dilute to 100 ml. with water.   Heat to about 70°C. for about 1 min. and then filter (refiltering the first portions if necessary).   (2) Alternatively, mix 19.45 ml. of $0.2M$ Na_2HPO_4 with 0.55 ml. of $0.1M$ citric acid to form a buffer of pH 8; add 3 g. of sodium TPB, dilute to 100 ml.; heat to 70°C. for about 1 min., and filter.   Also prepare a pH 2 buffer by dissolving 21.008 g. of citric acid in 200 ml. of $1N$ NaOH and diluting to 1 l.; then mix 30.9 ml. of this solution with 69.1 ml. of $0.1N$ HCl.

Remarks.   The method is applicable to amounts of potassium from 5 to 500 μg. of K_2O/ml. of sample solution; however, Beer's Law is followed only in the range 5 to 100 μg./ml.

Jančić (106), independent of the work of de la Rubia and Blasco, investigated the turbidimetric determination of potassium in micro amounts of serum.   His procedure involves addition of the sodium TPB reagent solution to the protein-free filtrate (trichloroacetic acid deproteinization) without further adjustment of the pH.

Procedure 28.   In a small tube treat 1 ml. of serum with 8 ml. of water and 1 ml. of 30% trichloroacetic acid solution; mix well by inverting the stoppered tube, and filter.   Place 1 ml. of filtrate in a tube, add 4 ml. of water and 1 ml. of a 2% sodium TPB solution.   Mix by inverting the stoppered tube.   The turbidity produced reaches a maximum in about 3 min. and then remains constant for at least 10 min.   A reagent blank should also be prepared.   The absorbance of the unknown and blank are determined.   As the absorbance obtained is influenced by temperature, all reagents should be brought to room temperature.

Remarks. In the range from 15.2 to 30 μg. of potassium/ml., Beer's Law was found to be fully obeyed. The presence of medicaments containing basic nitrogen groups in the blood may introduce errors.

Power and Ryan (158) failed to get reproducible results by the turbidimetric method of de la Rubia and Blasco (171) and reported that much more reproducible turbidity could be developed in alkaline medium. EDTA was added to mask calcium and magnesium, and formaldehyde to react with ammonia to form inactive hexamethyl-enetetramine. These workers have only reported their work in an abstract. In brief, 1 ml. of a solution containing about 0.008 to 0.030 mg. of potassium (i.e., tungstic acid filtrate of serum) is added, with shaking, to 2 ml. of an alkaline mixture containing sodium TPB, EDTA, and formaldehyde. The volume is adjusted to 6.0 ml. with 0.8% sodium chloride solution and the absorbance measured at 420 mμ. These workers state that results obtained in the analysis of diluted urine, serum (protein-free filtrate), and solutions of ashed food and feces were in good agreement with those obtained by flame photometric measurements.

Teeri and Sesin (204) have combined certain elements of the procedures of Jančić (106) and of de la Rubia (170,171) into a turbidimetric determination of potassium in blood serum (after deproteinization with trichloracetic acid). The results obtained by the procedure and by a classical cobaltinitrite procedure were in good agreement. In experiments in which potassium was added to serum, the recovery was complete within the precision of the method. Teeri and Sesin noted that use of a buffered precipitating reagent was essential and that precipitation at a pH as low as 2 led to a coarse precipitate unsuited to turbidimetric measurement. Although the following procedure is for potassium in blood serum, its application to other materials is possible.

Procedure 29. Pipet 1 ml. of serum, 8 ml. of water, and 1 ml. of 10% trichloroacetic acid solution into a 15 ml. centrifuge tube. Mix and centrifuge. Pipet 1 ml. of the protein-free filtrate (equivalent to 0.1 ml. of serum) into a colorimeter tube, add 4 ml. of water, 1 ml. 3% sodium TPB in citrate–phosphate buffer (i.e., reagent (2) of de la

Rubia, see above, Procedure 27). Mix by inverting the tube. Within 30 min. measure the absorbance in a filter photometer by using a filter with a transmittance at about 540 mμ. The result is obtained from a calibration curve obtained by carrying known amounts of potassium through latter steps of the procedure.

Sunderman and Sunderman (202) for the determination of serum potassium studied the above turbidimetric procedures and found that they yielded, in their hands, results that were not in good agreement with photometric and platinic chloride methods. Hence, they undertook an extensive investigation of the factors effecting the development of a satisfactory, stable turbidity. They concluded that the turbidity was greatest when a 5% sodium TPB solution (made alkaline by addition of sodium hydroxide) is employed as the precipitating reagent. If the pH of the final mixture was about 3.5, the calibration curve had the greatest linearity. The slope of the calibration curve diminished slightly with increasing temperature; however, any possible advantage of conducting the determination at 0°C. is outweighed by the convenience of employing room temperature. It was established that the TPB reagent should be added last and mixed instantaneously; use of a "blow-out" pipet (Ostwald–Folin) gave a far more linear calibration curve than did the use of a transfer pipet with slow draining. Variation in the ionic strength of the final mixture in the range, $\mu = 0.1$ to 0.3, did not have a significant effect on turbidity.

Under the conditions of the procedure finally evolved, the absorbance showed variation during the first 15 min. after addition of TPB reagent, was virtually unchanged in the interval from 15 to 30 min., and then underwent slow, but progressive, decrease. This decline was far less rapid if gum ghatti was present; further this additive had little effect on the initial slope of the calibration curve. Methyl cellulose and polyvinyl alcohol were less satisfactory as they decreased the initial turbidity. The calibration curves were linear at wavelengths throughout the visible range; a wavelength of 420 mμ was selected because the absorbance is greatest in the violet region of the spectrum.

Sunderman and Sunderman observed that the presence of calcium or magnesium at a concentration of 5 to 10 meq./l. had no effect on results in the procedure (precipitation at pH 3.5); neither did the addition of iron(III) salts and organic and inorganic phosphates. However, the results were significantly higher when EDTA was omitted from the reaction mixture, in the analysis of serum. It was also found that omission of formaldehyde led to high results and it was concluded that the formaldehyde bound not only ammonium ion but organic amines present in the serum. The following procedure is for potassium in blood serum (1 ml. sample); the principles, however, are probably applicable to other materials.

Procedure 30. Place 1 ml. of serum in a 10 ml. volumetric flask or calibrated tube. Add 5 ml. of 8% trichloroacetic acid. Dilute to the mark with water. Allow to stand 10 min. and filter through paper. Place 3 ml. of a freshly mixed EDTA–formaldehyde solution in a cuvette. (This solution is made by mixing one part of 37% formalin diluted 1:1 with water with two parts of a solution containing 7.5 g. of disodium ethylenediaminetetraacetate dihydrate and 44 ml. of 0.1N NaOH dissolved and diluted to 500 ml. with water.) Add 1 ml. of the trichloroacetic acid filtrate and 3 drops of gum ghatti solution (10 g. of gum placed in bag suspended in 400 ml. of water overnight), and mix. Now add 1 ml. of 5% sodium TPB solution (5 g. dissolved in 50 ml. of water in 100 ml. volumetric flask, 10 ml. of 0.1N NaOH added, and diluted to mark with water) rapidly by blowing vigorously with an Ostwald–Folin blow-out pipet. Mix the contents by swirling and allow to stand for 15 min. Determine the absorbance in a filter photometer at 420 mμ during the interval 15 to 30 min. after mixing. Prepare a calibration curve by carrying known volumes of a standard potassium chloride solution through the procedure (omitting the trichloroacetic acid treatment).

Remarks. By reducing the volumes appropriately the procedure is applicable to a 0.2 ml. serum sample (202). In duplicate analysis made on 33 serum samples by the TPB turbidimetric method and the referee platinic chloride method, the maximum deviation between results was ±0.6 meq./l. and the values were randomly scattered around the expected values. The scattering and range of deviations were virtually identical to those noted in a comparison of a flame photometric and a platinic chloride method.

It is well known that small changes in reagents may exert profound effects on results obtained in turbidimetric procedures. This may explain some of the divergent results reported. De la Rubia and

Blasco (170,171), and presumably Jančić (106), used crude sodium TPB, and the impurities present may improve the turbidity developed or stabilize it.   (Sodium TPB of low assay, and hence with impurities present, often gives low recoveries in gravimetric procedures and poor filterability.)   De la Rubia and Blasco (171) do not even filter the sodium TPB solution if a slight turbidity develops.   Power (157) noted that solutions made from freshly opened, reagent grade, sodium TPB gave more reproducible results than older material.   This behavior parallels the observations made in the manufacture of this compound that it is difficult to remove the last trace of organic solvent (often methylene chloride) by persistent exhaustion *in vacuo* (25). However, this trace solvent can be replaced by moisture on extended exposure to air (25).   Power (157) has suggested storage of the reagent material overnight in a vacuum desiccator filled with anhydrous calcium sulfate.   Sunderman and Sunderman (202) recommend recrystallizing the reagent material from methylene chloride and drying at 120°C.

Turbidimetric (108b) and heterometric (26) titrations of potassium involving the TPB ion have been studied (see Section VIII-2).

VII. DETERMINATION OF METAL IONS OTHER THAN POTASSIUM

Sections III-1 through VI-2 are concerned principally with the determination of potassium.   Of course, many of the methods and procedures are applicable to the determination of other metals forming insoluble TPB salts.   Many of the considerations presented in Sections III-1 through III-5 on the precipitation of potassium TPB are relevant to the precipitation of other metal TPB salts.   The following sections consider the determination of ammonium and of both ammonium and potassium in a single sample (Section VII-1), the determination of rubidium and cesium (Section VII-2), the determination of thallium (Section VII-3), and the determination of silver (Section VII-4).

1. Determination of Ammonium and Both Ammonium and Potassium

Ammonium ion can be determined as the TPB salt in the same manner as potassium.   Of course, a few special precautions must be observed.   To avoid possible losses of ammonia, especially at elevated temperatures, the precipitation should be effected from acidic medium. In the gravimetric determination, which was first described by Wittig and Raff (229), care must be taken to avoid drying at too high a temperature and for too long a time (115,161). Wendlandt (212) found that the minimum sublimation temperature of this salt is 130°C.; this value has been confirmed by Howick and Pflaum (100). All titrimetric methods that depend upon the determination of the TPB ion are probably applicable. Naturally, the method involving ignition to the metaborate and subsequent acid–base titration (Section IV-7) is impossible as ammonium TPB is completely volatilized. Howick and Pflaum (99,100) effected a nonaqueous acid–base titration of ammonium TPB (see Sections IV-6 and IX-5).

Crane and Smith (32a) made a thorough study of the gravimetric precipitation of 0.4 to 0.7 meq. of ammonium as ammonium TPB. They recommend precipitation at room temperature from a solution volume of about 60 ml. and at a pH of 1 to 3. The addition of sodium TPB should be controlled to provide a TPB excess of 0.003 to 0.006 meq./ml. The mixture is digested for 15 to 60 min., and the coarse precipitate is filtered through a sintered glass crucible. The precipitate is washed with 20 ml. of a 1% formic or acetic acid solution in 4 to 5 ml. portions, and then with 3 ml. of water or water saturated with ammonium TPB; it is dried to constant weight at 100°C. Under these conditions the recovery from 11 samples, precipitated at pH 1, is 98.3 to 103.2% with an average of 100.65% and a standard deviation of ±1.45%. If the precipitation is performed at a pH less than 1, high results are obtained even at 0°C., due to the decomposition of the TPB ion. At a pH value above 3, a fine precipitate is obtained that is less filterable and subject to greater washing losses; above pH 5, loss of ammonia through volatilization is possible. Formic acid is preferred as the wash liquid because it is more volatile than acetic acid, thus permitting drying to constant weight in a shorter time. The presence of an inert salt, such as sodium chloride or sulfate, helps to coagulate the precipitate and hence to improve filterability. These workers observed that if methyl orange or methyl purple is used for the pH adjustment, it will be adsorbed on the ammonium TPB precipitate and its color will disappear only after the precipitate is completely dry.

The determination of both ammonium and potassium ions in a single sample solution may be accomplished by the analysis of separate aliquots. In one, the sum of potassium and ammonium may be determined by a TPB method. In a second, ammonia may be removed by alkalinization and then boiling or treating with formaldehyde. Potassium may then be determined by a TPB method. Alternatively, ammonia may be distilled from the second aliquot and then be determined by a Kjeldahl procedure; in this case potassium is found by difference. Which of these methods is more appropriate may depend to a great extent on the ratio of the amounts of the two ions present. Simpler and more integrated procedures are possible, however.

Kohler (115) precipitated both ammonium and potassium (up to 5 mg. of nitrogen and 10 mg. of K_2O) from strongly acidic medium and then dried and weighed the washed precipitate. This was dissolved in 10 to 20 ml. of acetone and the solution was boiled on a steam bath after the addition of 20 ml. of 2.5% sodium hydroxide solution. Acetone and ammonia are thereby volatilized. The potassium TPB reprecipitated in this way was filtered off, dried, and weighed. Kohler (115) gave only four results of such a determination; these showed good agreement between the amounts taken and found. In a further publication (193), this method was applied to fertilizers, and the results were in agreement with values obtained by classical methods. Tendille (206) confirmed the satisfactory nature of Kohler's procedure for the analysis of fertilizers.

Vicaire (207e) reported that in Kohler's procedure it is advisable to evaporate the acetone prior to the removal of ammonia by addition of 2% sodium hydroxide solution. This avoids contaminating the precipitate with insoluble brown products resulting from the combined action of sodium hydroxide and ammonia on the acetone.

Rüdorff and Zannier (174) conducted a more detailed study of this method and concluded that good results are obtained only under certain conditions, and only if two sources of error compensate for each other. They held that in experiments performed by them involving boiling the potassium TPB salt in an alkaline medium, low results were obtained for potassium due to slight decomposition of the salt. In the presence of ammonium TPB, the TPB ion is in excess, and this decomposition does not play an important role. Further, they found that the reprecipitation of the potassium TPB may commence before all of the ammonia and acetone are volatilized; hence, some ammonium TPB may be coprecipitated. This is not unexpected as the two salts are isomorphic (9,33,174). These workers therefore recommend (174) a simpler approach, based on an initial formol titration of ammonia. The hexamethylenetetramine formed is inactive to the TPB ion in alkaline medium and an excess of formaldehyde is added to assure no ammonium ion can be regenerated. Potassium TPB may then be precipitated from the titrated solution. In the original paper, the argentometric titration procedure developed by these workers (172) is then applied (see Section IV-2, Procedure 5).

Procedure 31. Make the sample solution (containing not more than 10 to 20 mg. of potassium) neutral to methyl red. Add 10 ml. of 30% formalin (previously carefully neutralized to phenolphthalein). Titrate with $0.05N$ NaOH (carbonate-free) with phenolphthalein as indicator. One ml. of the $0.05N$ NaOH equals 0.902 mg. of ammonium.

Add more formalin so that for each milligram of ammonium ion about 2 to 2.5 ml. of formalin is present. Add sufficient solid NaOH to make the solution about $1N$ in NaOH. Warm nearly to boiling and add 0.2% sodium TPB solution slowly and dropwise with stirring. The appearance of the precipitate may be retarded, and turbidity may be observed only after a few milliliters of the precipitant have been added. Cool to room temperature. Filter the potassium TPB precipitate and proceed to determine potassium by an appropriate titrimetric method.

Remarks. In a determination (174) of 6 to 67 mg. of ammonium in the presence of 15 to 21 mg. of potassium, the deviations reported ranged from $+0.16$ to -0.73 mg. Potassium was titrated by an argentometric titration (Section IV-2, Procedure 5) and the deviations ranged from $+0.16$ mg. to -0.02 mg. This procedure is, of course, applicable to the determination of potassium alone in samples containing ammonium ion.

Erdey and co-workers (37c) described a method for the determination of ammonia involving the precipitation of ammonium TPB and the argentometric titration of the TPB content of the redissolved precipitate, with use of Variamine Blue as indicator (see Section IV-2). Alternatively, the excess of TPB in the filtrate may be titrated similarly (see Section IV-3).   This method was extended (37b) to the determination of nitrite and of organic nitro compounds via a prior reduction to ammonia.

Jander and Anke (107) applied the conductometric titration (Section V-1) to ammonium and potassium with satisfactory results. By addition of sodium hydroxide and then boiling, ammonia could be eliminated and potassium alone be titrated satisfactorily in the alkaline solution.   Veïs and Ieviņš (207b) have effected the high frequency titration of ammonium ion with sodium TPB.

Procedure 19, (Section IV-13), in the modification of Sadek and Reilley (178a), has been applied to the determination of ammonium as well as the sum of ammonium and potassium.   Ammonium can be determined in another aliquot of the sample solution by titration of the hydrogen ion liberated by the reaction of ammonium ion with the mercury(II)–EDTA complex.

2. Determination of Rubidium and Cesium

Rubidium and cesium TPB are more insoluble than potassium TPB; hence, they can be determined gravimetrically in exactly the same way as potassium (229).   Probably, most of the procedures developed for the determination of potassium are applicable.   However, the infrequent occurrence of the two metals has led only a few workers to study their actual determination.

Geilmann and Gebauhr (76) have presented some gravimetric results for both rubidium and cesium, using the precipitation from weakly acid medium.   The absolute deviations in terms of the TPB salts were the same as that for potassium.   Of course, the percentage error is greater, due to the greater gravimetric factors, namely, 0.2112 for rubidium and 0.2939 for cesium.   The thermal studies of Wendlandt (212) indicate a minimum decomposition temperature for rubidium and cesium TPB of 240 and 210°C., respectively. Hence, drying of the precipitate can be easily effected.

Kahn and co-workers (108) attempted the precipitation conditions employed by Geilmann and Gebauhr for the concentration of radioactive cesium using a cesium and/or potassium carrier prior to radiometric measurements.   However, as a rapid settling precipitate was not obtained, another approach was studied.   In contrast, Handley and Burros (83a) were successful in applying a TPB precipitation to effect the separation from fission products of radioactive cesium on a cesium carrier. The precipitation was carried out from a medium $1M$ in hydrochloric acid. The precipitate, after centrifugation, was redissolved in a minimum amount of acetone, hydrochloric acid and more sodium TPB was added, and the resulting precipitate after separation, drying, and weighing was employed for γ-ray spectrophotometry of the Cs^{136} and Cs^{137} content. Finston (42a) employed the procedure of Handley and Burros for the recovery of radioactive cesium from fission products in better than 75% yield, the determination being completed by either β-counting or γ-ray spectrophotometry.

Rüdorff and Zannier (172) accomplished the argentometric titration of redissolved rubidium TPB (see Section IV-2). The error in the determination compared to that for the corresponding determination of potassium is the same when expressed in terms of milliliters of titrant. However, the percentage error based on the weight of rubidium taken is, of course, slightly higher due to the higher equivalent weight of rubidium. Havíř and Křivánek (87b) applied a radiometric finish to this argentometric titration of redissolved rubidium or cesium TPB (see Section VIII-2).

The acid–base titration after cation exchange and mercurization (see Section IV-11) has been applied by Amin (6) to the determination of rubidium and cesium. The representative results reported are within the experimental error expected of such a procedure.

Kirsten and co-workers (113) titrated rubidium and cesium potentiometrically with sodium TPB as titrant (see Section V-2). The potentiometric titration of a redissolved tetraphenylboron precipitate in acetone–water with silver nitrate has been successfully applied, by Havíř (87,87a), to the determination of rubidium and cesium (see Section V-2). A high frequency titration with sodium TPB has been applied to the determination of rubidium and cesium (207b).

Fix (52a) extracted carrier-free radioactive rubidium and cesium with nitrobenzene from $0.1M$ aqueous sodium TPB solution at pH 9 (unbuffered or borate buffered). Under these conditions, the extraction coefficients for these alkalies have the values 1180 ± 120 and 8800 ± 1400, respectively. These values are relatively constant over the pH range 5 to 10, but are decreased if the sodium TPB concentration is increased. Nitroethane and 2,2'-dichlorodiethyl ether were also found to be suitable, but less efficient, extractants. Because of emulsion formation, the phases were separated by prolonged centrifugation. Addition of aluminum, chromium(III), and uranyl ions decreased emulsification, and only the last ion decreased the extractability of rubidium or cesium. This solvent extraction technique has been applied to the separation, prior to radiometric determination, of Rb^{84}, Cs^{136}, and Cs^{137} from carrier-free solutions and from the disintegration products of the cyclotron bombardment of uranium trioxide. Handley and Burros (83a) briefly studied the solvent extraction of cesium TPB. Tracer amounts of cesium could be readily extracted by various organic solvents, of which amyl acetate was the only one mentioned by the workers. The extraction of macro amounts of cesium was not found to be feasible. Finston (42a) also studied the TPB extraction of Cs^{137} with amyl acetate. The cesium activity could be stripped from the solvent phase by $3M$ hydrochloric acid, and determined by γ-counting. The procedure is suitable for the separation of carrier-free Cs^{137}, and over the range of 0 to 10 mg. of cesium, employed as a carrier, the recovery of Cs^{137} is quantitative.

3. Determination of Thallium

Wittig and Raff (229) observed that thallium(I) was quantitatively precipitated as thallium(I) TPB. Geilmann (75) first mentioned the possibility of thus determining thallium(I). No procedure was presented but only the statement that a very fine precipitate was obtained which had been used for a turbidimetric determination of thallium in concentrations under 1 mg./100 ml. Geilmann doubted that a suitable gravimetric procedure could be developed because of the fineness of the precipitate and hence the extremely poor filterability.

Wendlant (213), however, has developed such a gravimetric method and has overcome the filtration difficulties by addition of minute amounts of an Aerosol (i.e., a sodium dialkysulfosuccinate). The precipitation could be effected without significant error at a sulfuric acid concentration less than $1N$, but a concentration of $0.01N$ or the use of an acetate-buffered solution was preferred. The precipitation could be effected even in $5N$ sulfuric acid but the decomposition produced low results; nitric acid exerted an oxidizing action so that it could not be used in concentrations greater than $1N$. When compared with many other methods for thallium, the gravimetric factor of 0.3563 is favorable.

Procedure 32. To the acidic sample solution (containing about 15 to 45 mg. of thallium), add 20 ml. of $2M$ sodium acetate solution, and adjust to a volume of about 60 to 80 ml. with water. Add 2 drops of a 0.1% Aerosol solution and (at room temperature) add a slight excess of 2% sodium TPB solution (usually 3 to 8 ml. is required). Allow the flocculent precipitate to settle for about 2 hr. and then filter through a tared porcelain crucible. Wash with three 10 ml. portions of water and dry at 100 to 105°C. for 4 hr.

Remarks. In 18 experiments involving 17 to 42 mg. of thallium, an average deviation of about 0.1 mg. was obtained.

Yamaguchi and co-workers (233) have studied the separation and determination of thallium(I) and silver. Cyanide ion is used to complex silver during the precipitation of thallium(I) TPB from alkaline solution. The thallium salt is filtered off, dried, and weighed. The silver content of the filtrate after appropriate work-up is titrated with thiocyanate solution.

Procedure 33. To 10 ml. of a sample solution (containing in the experimental work 10 mmoles of silver and also of thallium) add 2 ml. of $1M$ NaCN, 7 ml. of dioxane, and an excess $0.01M$ sodium TPB. Filter off the thallium(I) TPB employing a tared porcelain crucible. Dry at 105 to 110°C. and weigh. Make the filtrate acid with nitric acid and heat. Collect the precipitated mass, heat with concentrated nitric acid, and evaporate to dryness. Dissolve in dilute nitric acid and evaporate to dryness. Dissolve in dilute nitric acid, and titrate the silver content with $0.01N$ KSCN.

Wendlandt (215) also determined thallium(I) by a conductometric precipitation titration with sodium TPB in acetic acid or neutral medium as the titrant. The considerations relevant to the analogous titration of potassium apply (see Section V-1). In a series of experiments involving 8 to 16 mg. of thallium, slightly high results were obtained, but well within the experimental error. The average deviation was $+0.02$ ml. of $0.00292M$ sodium TPB. This solution was standardized gravimetrically against potassium.

The potentiometric titration involving polarized electrodes developed by Schmidt (184) can also be applied to the determination of thallium (see Section V-3). Heyrovský (97) also described a potentiometric titration of thallium(I), but full procedural details are lacking.   Mukherji and Sant (131), and Veĭs and Ievin̦š (207c), accomplished a high frequency titration of thallium(I) even in very dilute solutions (100 ml. of 10^{-3} to $10^{-4}M$) with sodium TPB as titrant.

Alimarin and co-workers (3,195) described a radiometric titration of thallium involving sodium TPB as the titrant and Tl^{204} as the indicator.   After each addition of titrant a part of the solution is filtered and the radioactivity of the filtrate counted.   The counts are plotted versus the milliliters of titrant added and the curve thus obtained is similar to that of a conductometric titration.   In the determination of 0.1 to 6 mg. of thallium, the relative error ranged from -2.5% to $+2.6\%$.   Satisfactory results were obtained with industrial samples containing 0.01 to 0.1% of thallium in cadmium, zinc, lead, and copper base materials.

4. Determination of Silver

Silver is used in many TPB procedures as a titrant or back-titrant and also as a standard.   Hence, silver can also be determined by TPB procedures.   This is not, however, a practical approach since the titrimetric TPB methods have the same theoretical basis as halide titrations and these are superior because silver chloride is less soluble than silver TPB.   Of course, TPB methods may be of practical interest in the determination of the sum of silver and other appropriate cations.   Further, TPB titrimetric methods involving silver should be studied critically as the findings of some workers place in doubt a 1:1 stoichiometric composition for silver TPB (31,113).   However, Sant and Mukherji (131) obtained correct results in a high frequency titration of even very dilute silver salt solutions (100 ml. of 10^{-3} to $10^{-4}M$) with sodium TPB.

VIII. SOME DIVERSE APPLICATIONS OF THE TPB ION

In the following sections, some diverse applications for the TPB ion are considered.   The application of many of the procedures and methods presented in earlier sections to practical samples is briefly noted in Section VIII-1.   Some miscellaneous determinations, and enrichment and elimination procedures involving the TPB ion are treated in Sections VIII-2 and VIII-3, respectively.   The determination and detection of the TPB ion itself are considered in Section VIII-4. The use of the TPB ion in the qualitative analysis of metal ions is discussed at length in Section VIII-5. The application of TPB methods to the detection, characterization, and determination of organic compounds is considered in Section IX.

1. Use of TPB Methods in Applied Inorganic Analysis

The high selectivity of the TPB methods has prompted their introduction in the determination of potassium in many materials. The advantages of TPB methods over such classical approaches as the perchlorate, cobaltinitrite, and platinic chloride procedures have been confirmed by many workers in various practical analyses. The ease of adaptation of basic TPB procedures to the analysis of particular materials is reflected by the fact that many authors make only brief mention of materials studied without providing a special procedure or even representative results.

The gravimetric determination of potassium as potassium TPB has been applied to feldspar (160,233a), silicates generally (207d,238), glass (14,27,27a,119a,121,233a), refractories (27), carnallite (107), raw materials for cement plants (25b), coal ash (14), fertilizers, composts, and manures (18,64,193), sulfite liquor (151), water (86,239), trade effluents (239), sodium chloride (167), sea water (198), brines (27b), propellants, explosives, and gunpowder (34,89,153a,207), milk (188), wine (22,70,163), barley and malt (88), ashed heart tissue (33b), tobacco (187), reagent chemicals (112), infusion and injection solutions (38a,114), pharmaceutical grade potassium and sodium salts (110), mixtures of sodium, potassium, and magnesium chlorides (22a), mixtures of potassium salts with triethanolamine (145), potassium derivatives of amides of divalent and trivalent sulfur (16,17), and the determination of the solubility of inorganic potassium salts in formamide (27c). Both potassium and ammonium have been determined by a gravimetric TPB method in fertilizers (193,206) and wine (163,164).

The argentometric titration of a redissolved TPB precipitate (Section IV-2) has been used with eosin as indicator for the determination of potassium in fertilizer (63), water and effluents (239), silicates (85), and wine (ammonium also determined) (164). This titration conducted with chromate as indicator has been applied to potassium in glass, fertilizers, and manures (19,20), and to process liquors containing sodium and potassium chlorate (105b). The Volhard titration has been used to determine potassium in feldspar (176), and in ceramic materials (186). The argentometric back-titration of excess TPB ion permits the determination of potassium in feldspar (173) and the corresponding mercurimetric method, potassium in glass (27a) (Section IV-3).

The back-titration of excess TPB ion with a quaternary ammonium ion has been applied to the determination of potassium in fertilizers (8,37,65,183) (see Section IV-4 for the procedure), and also of potassium in blood serum, plant materials, and in waters (20a). The nonaqueous, acid–base titration (Section IV-6) has been applied to the determination of potassium in pharmaceutical infusion solutions (38a). The acidimetric titration after ignition of potassium TPB to the metaborate (Section IV-7) has been employed successfully for the determination of potassium in plant material, especially tobacco (5), and in ashed blood (15,27). The determination of potassium by acid–base titration, after mercurization (Section IV-10), has been applied to clay, clinker, and cement (25b,122), plant material, and especially tobacco (5), and water (81).

The conductiometric titration (Section V-1) has been studied in the determination of potassium in feldspar (160) and carnallite (107), and the high frequency titration, in the determination of potassium in wood ash and molasses (207b).

The determination of potassium by a potentiometric titration of the TPB ion with silver ion (Section V-2) has been applied to fly ash (87a), mineral water (81), and infusion solutions (38b); with the latter samples a back-titration with a quaternary ammonium salt was also satisfactory (38b). The polarization titration (Section V-3) has been applied to the determination of potassium in fertilizers (184).

The polarographic method involving ignition of TPB ion to metaborate (Section V-5) serves for the determination of potassium in biological materials including serum (94,95), and to reagents and in injection solutions (94). The turbidimetric TPB method has been applied to soils (170), and to serum (106,158,202,204); the procedures are summarized in Section VI-2. An ultramicro turbidimetric titration has been employed in the determination of potassium in serum (108b) (see Section VIII-2).

Ammonium, rubidium, cesium, and thallium have been determined in practical samples (see Sections VII-1 through VII-3).

2. Some Miscellaneous Determinations Involving the TPB Ion

The sum of potassium and sodium may be determined by several methods. If potassium is then determined by a TPB method, a sodium value can be obtained by subtraction. Flaschka and Amin (57) determined the sum of potassium and sodium by passage of the sample through a column of a strongly acidic cation exchange resin in the hydrogen form, and acidimetric titration of the effluent. Potassium was determined in a second aliquot by ignition of a potassium TPB precipitate to the metaborate and acidimetric titration of the dissolved residue. Where 1 mg. or less of alkali was present in the sample, these workers preferred to ignite the total sample to the metaborate and to titrate the dissolved residue acidimetrically to determine the sum of potassium and sodium. The TPB procedure for potassium was then applied to this titrated solution.

Rüdorff and Zannier (173) determined the sum of sodium and potassium by ignition to sulfates, etc., and potassium by an argentometric titration of an excess of TPB ion (Section IV-3). They applied the method to feldspar. Lange (119a) determined the sum of sodium and potassium in glass, gravimetrically, after ignition to sulfates, and then determined potassium by the gravimetric TPB method.

Gagliardi and Reimers (69) passed a solution of alkali metals through a cation exchange column in the magnesium form. Magnesium was determined in the effluent by an EDTA titration employing Eriochrome Black T as indicator, thus obtaining a value for total alkali. Potassium was determined in a second aliquot by a TPB method.

Musil and Reimers (138) placed a cation exchange column in the potassium form and passed through it a sample solution containing sodium ions. The exchanged potassium in the effluent was determined by a TPB method. Discontinuous washing of the column is recommended so that the volume of effluent is kept small. The method is subject to interference by all cations that will exchange for potassium under the conditions employed.

Chalmers and Clark (26), according to a meeting report, found that a heterometric titration of 0.1 to 1.0 mg. of potassium, employing sodium TPB as titrant, proceeds satisfactorily. Karrman and co-workers (108b) have reported a turbidimetric ultramicro titration of potassium. The potassium is precipitated with a known amount of sodium TPB, the mixture is centrifuged, and the excess TPB ion in the centrifugate is back-titrated turbidimetrically at 700 mμ with cetyltrimethylammonium bromide solution (see Section IV-4). The method has been applied to the determination of potassium in 0.2 ml. of blood serum.

Havíř and Křivánek (87b) applied a radiometric finish to the argentometric titration of redissolved potassium TPB after Rüdorff and Zannier (172) (see Section IV-2). The potassium, rubidium, or cesium TPB precipitate is dissolved in 33% aqueous acetone, silver nitrate solution labelled with Ag^{110} is added to precipitate the TPB content, and the excess silver in the filtrate is determined radiometrically.

Tufts (207a) employed the precipitation of potassium TPB and microscopic examination to estimate the size and number of potassium-containing air-borne particles. This approach had earlier been studied briefly by Vittori (207f). Belcher and co-workers (14a) ignited sodium and potassium TPB by the closed flask combustion method and determined the borate content of the combustion products. Satisfactory recovery values for boron were thus obtained. This determination was confirmed by Corner (29a).

3. Enrichment and Elimination Procedures Involving the TPB Ion

A potassium TPB precipitation has proved of value as an enrichment step prior to the flame photometric and radiometric determinations of potassium. Ammonium ion can serve to advantage as a carrier. This enrichment step was introduced in the flame photometric determination of potassium in urine by Munroe and co-workers (134). The washed potassium TPB centrifugate is treated with an excess of mercury(II) chloride and filtered. The clear filtrate is used in the flame photometric measurement. Neeb and Gebauhr (139) used the TPB enrichment of potassium in determining the potassium content of metallic sodium and of sodium salts. A mixed potassium and ammonium TPB precipitate can be fumed with nitric acid with a small amount of hydrogen peroxide present. The diluted solution is used for flame photometric measurements. Alternatively, and to advantage, the TPB precipitate can be dissolved in tetrahydrofuran and employed directly for the measurements.

Geilman and Gebauhr (76) early used K^{42}, Rb^{86}, and Cs^{134} as tracers in a basic study of the precipitation of alkali metal TPB salts.   Munroe and co-workers (134) employed K^{42} and Na^{24} in the clinical measurement of exchangeable sodium and potassium.   The potassium in serum and urine specimens can be enriched most effectively by precipitation as potassium TPB with ammonium ion as a carrier. The precipitate on mercurization yields a solution suitable for radiometric measurement of K^{42}.   Neeb and Gebauhr (139) in their development of the TPB enrichment step for flame photometric determinations of potassium (see above) employed K^{42} and radiometric measurements.

Hegemann and Pfab (90) precipitated potassium TPB by use of the free TPB acid, $HB(C_6H_5)_4$, generated by passage of a sodium TPB solution through a cation exchange column in the hydrogen form (see Section IV-8).   The washed precipitate was redissolved and titrated argentometrically, thus determining potassium.   The filtrate was employed for the flame photometric determination of the sodium content of the original sample solution.   The method was applied to glasses.   Sazonova and Leonov (179a) employed lithium TPB to separate potassium, rubidium, and cesium prior to the gravimetric determination of sodium by precipitation with lithium tetra(p-tolyl)boron.   Presumably the free TPB acid could be substituted for lithium TPB in such a procedure.

Scott and co-workers (84a,101,193a,193b,193d) employed sodium TPB in studies of the extent and kinetics of the degradation of potassium from soils and micaceous minerals.   The approaches studied included warming the mineral with an aqueous salt solution containing sodium TPB.   After degradation of potassium, the TPB ion may be destroyed by boiling with ammonium chloride or mercury(II) chloride, and the potassium content of the filtered solution may be determined by flame photometry (193d).   Other approaches to the separation and determination of the degraded potassium have been studied, including ion exchange (101,193b).   In the study of the ammonium-fixing capacity of clay minerals, sodium TPB is applicable to the prior degradation of potassium (84a,193a).

DeMumbrum (33a) treated micas with an equal weight of sodium TPB, moistened the mixture, and dried it at 110°C.   After washing with acetone in order to remove excess reagent and potassium TPB, the potassium content remaining in the mica was determined by x-ray diffraction.

Bower (22b) related the potential of a glass electrode to the sodium content of the solution in which it is immersed. The findings were applied to the determination of sodium in saline solutions; the effects of potassium were excluded by its precipitation with a calcium TPB solution.

The extraction of radioactive cesium and rubidium from an aqueous sodium TPB solution is considered in Section VII-2.

4. Determination and Detection of the TPB Ion Itself

Many of the methods for the determination of metal ions mentioned in previous sections are actually based on the determination of the TPB ion content of a precipitate. It is evident that any of these methods can be applied to the determination of the TPB ion. The same is true for those titrimetric methods in which a TPB solution is standardized. Sant and Murkherji (179) developed the following special method for the determination of the "precipitating power" of an aqueous TPB solution.

Procedure 34. Add an exactly measured amount (in excess) of $TlNO_3$ solution to a measured portion of the aqueous TPB solution. Allow to stand for 4 to 6 hr. and then filter and wash the precipitate 8 to 10 times with 10 ml. portions of water. Make the combined filtrate and washings 3 to $4N$ in HCl and titrate the excess of Tl(I) with KIO_3 solution, to the iodine chloride end point in chloroform. The $TlNO_3$ solution is standardized by the same method, employing KIO_3 as standard. Since two gram atoms of thallium are equivalent to two moles of TPB ion and to one mole of iodate ion, the calculation takes the form:

$$1 \text{ ml. of } 1M \text{ } KIO_3 = 0.68447 \text{ g. of sodium TPB.}$$

Remarks. In a series of six experiments, involving 35 to 170 mg. of sodium TPB, negative deviations between 0.1 and 0.5 mg. were obtained.

Sant and Murkherji (132) also developed a qualitative test for the TPB ion based on the intense green fluorescence under ultraviolet light of the TPB derivative of 8-quinolinol. In the acetic acid medium employed, various interferences can be excluded by addition of fluoride ion or EDTA. However, as diphenylboric acid and phenylboric acid, which are decomposition products of the TPB ion, also give fluorescent products with 8-quinolinol (150) the value of the test is severely restricted.

5. TPB Ion in the Qualitative Analysis of Inorganic Ions

Raff and Brotz (160) early demonstrated that the TPB ion is a sensitive reagent for potassium. A potassium chloride solution was repeatedly diluted 10-fold, after a test for chloride by addition of silver nitrate to a 1 ml. aliquot, and for potassium by addition of sodium TPB to a second aliquot. It was found that a clearly visible turbidity occurred in the potassium test in a solution 10 times more dilute than in the chloride test. Raff and Brotz concluded that the identification limit for potassium is 4 μg./100 ml. Their conclusion from this finding as to the solubility of potassium TPB was incorrect. In a critical study of qualitative reagents for potassium, rubidium, and cesium, Geilmann and Gebauhr (77) found that 2.5 μg of these metals in a volume of 5 ml., gave a clear turbidity even in the presence of 10 to 20 mg. of sodium or lithium. These workers recommended TPB precipitation for the qualitative separation of the heavier alkali metals from sodium and lithium.

Muraca and co-workers (136) published a thorough study of the detection of potassium in the usual semimicro scheme of qualitative analysis as potassium TPB. After removal of other groups, the resulting solution contains only sodium, lithium, potassium, ammonium, and magnesium. Of these ions, only ammonium interferes and its complete removal requires special attention. These workers found that the removal of ammonium ion is not always complete even after evaporation and ignition, especially if sulfate is present. They assumed that traces of ammonium salts remain on the cooler upper portions of the crucible. To avoid this difficulty the ignition was employed only to remove the bulk of ammonium and the last traces were then eliminated by a wet ignition employing a hypobromite oxidation.

Procedure 35. The solution remaining after separation of Group IV is treated with 0.05 ml. of a 0.5M $(NH_4)_2SO_4$ and 0.05 ml. of 0.5M ammonium oxalate and centrifuged. Discard the precipitate. Evaporate the centrifugate after addition of 1 ml. of concentrated HNO_3 and ignite. Dissolve the residue in 0.75 ml. of water and divide into three portions. Use two portions for the detection of sodium and lithium (flame spectra) and of magnesium ($MgNH_4PO_4 \cdot 6H_2O$ precipitate).

To the third portion, in a porcelain casserole, add 0.3 ml. of concentrated HNO_3, evaporate to dryness and ignite to remove ammonium salts. Cool, add 0.25 ml. of water and 0.25 ml. of $6N$ NaOH, and heat gently. Cool to nearly room temperature and then add 2 ml. of saturated bromine water and transfer the solution to a 10 ml. beaker. Wash the casserole both inside and out with distilled water. Return the test solution to the casserole and heat to boiling. Cool and add concentrated HNO_3 dropwise until the solution is distinctly brown from bromine. Boil gently until the solution is completely colorless and free of bromine, but do not allow the volume to become less than 1 ml. Transfer the solution to a small test tube, dilute to a volume of 2 ml., and add 1 drop of a sodium TPB solution. If potassium is present a precipitate forms.

Remarks. Care must be taken to expel bromine completely, otherwise a white insoluble bromination product is formed by the TPB ion which may be mistaken for potassium TPB. For a confirmation of potassium, the precipitate can be centrifuged, washed with water, and used in a flame test. The organic part gives, at first, a luminous flame; then the violet of potassium can be seen through cobalt blue glass. The requisite sodium TPB solution is prepared by dissolving 4 g. of sodium TPB and 1 g. of $AlCl_3 \cdot 6H_2O$ in 100 ml. of water, adding 1 drop of phenolphthalein solution and $6N$ NaOH until the solution color is red, filtering after several hours, and storing in a cool place.

The procedure of Muraca and co-workers was developed for use in student laboratories. It is probable that the tedious removal of ammonium employing a porcelain casserole can be greatly simplified if a platinum vessel is employed. Care must then be taken, however, to avoid the simultaneous presence of chloride and nitrate. A prior evaporation with sulfuric acid seems to be recommendable before the addition of nitric acid and the evaporation and ignition.

Paul and Gibson (153c) have reported a student procedure for the detection of potassium in the original sample solution involving the precipitation of interfering ions with sodium hydroxide and then the testing for potassium in the centrifugate by using sodium TPB. The amount of ammonia usually present in student unknowns does not precipitate under the strongly alkaline conditions employed.

Feigl and Caldas (39) applied a TPB test for potassium in silicates. The sample was fused with zinc chloride in a platinum wire loop, the bead was dissolved in water, and sodium TPB was added. An identification limit of 1 μg. was reported under these conditions. No study of interferences was reported. Stephen (201) applied a TPB test to detect potassium in the ring zone after separations had been effected according to the Weisz ring-oven method (211). The zone must be observed in transmitted light. Semiquantitative results were obtained by comparing the ring from the sample with standard sample rings and an amazingly high accuracy was obtained with 0.1 to 0.5 mg. of potassium/ml.

Amin (7), Crane (32), and Yamaguchi and co-workers (233) have explored spot tests for various metal ions involving a TPB precipitation in greater detail than other workers. Some results of Amin and Crane are compared in Table II. Amin mixes 1 drop (0.3 ml. of test solution with 1 drop of pH 5 acetate buffer and 1 drop of 3% sodium TPB solution (clarified with alumina), and observes the results after 1 min. Crane adds 1 drop of a 6% sodium TPB solution to 1 drop of the test solution (adjusted to pH 3).

TABLE II

Sensitivities of TPB Spot Tests for Inorganic Cations[a]

| Ion | Identification limit, μg. | | Dilution limit | |
	Amin	Crane	Amin	Crane
Potassium[b]	0.10	0.13	1:350,000	1:320,000
Ammonium	0.19	0.11	1:210,000	1:400,000
Rubidium	0.20	0.38	1:150,000	1:110,000
Cesium[c]	0.30		1:150,000	
Silver		0.20		1:210,000
Thallium (I)		1.5		1:28,000
Mercury (I)		1.1		1:40,000
Mercury (II)		1.4		1:30,000

[a] Data of Amin (7) and Crane (32).

[b] Crane calculated the result of Geilmann and Gebauhr (77) to correspond to a dilution limit of 1:1,600,000. Feigl and Caldas (39) gave an identification limit of 1 μg.

[c] Geilmann and Gebauhr (77) reported that 5 μg. can be detected in 5 ml. of solution.

Amin (7) obtained, essentially, the same sensitivity for the detection of potassium over a wide range of pH values and noted only a significant decrease in sensitivity at a pH lower than 1 and above 10. In contrast, Crane (32) reported that the sensitivity decreases with increasing pH and prefers to conduct the test at pH 3.   Amin found that no significant change in sensitivity occurs if 1 drop of $0.1M$ EDTA is added in the test, and hence routinely adds EDTA, thus increasing the selectivity of the test.   With this addition, 100 to 200 μg. of the following cations were reported to give no interference: Mg, Ca, Sr, Ba, Cr(III), Mn(II), Fe(III), Co(II), NI(II), Cu(II), Zn, Cd, Mg(II), Pb, Al, and Bi.   Further, these ions did not influence the sensitivity of the test for potassium.   The noninterference of mercury(II) in the presence of EDTA is interesting as Flaschka and Sadek (62) (see Section IV-13) found that mercurization of the TPB ion proceeds in the presence of EDTA; however, the huge amount of EDTA added in Amin's procedure may exert sufficient masking action.   Crane (32) found in applying the test to ammonium salts that the detection limit was *not* dependent on the type of anion present in the salt.

Amin (7) applied the test to the detection of potassium in solid samples such as rocks and especially in feldspar.   A small amount (20 mg.) of a 1:10 mixture of ground sample and sodium carbonate is taken up in a platinum loop.   A clear bead formed by heating, first gently and then strongly, in a flame is dissolved in a minimum of 1:10 hydrochloric acid.   The resulting solution is treated with 1 ml. of pH 5 acetate buffer and 1 ml. of $0.1M$ EDTA and filtered if necessary. A drop of this solution is employed in the TPB spot test.

Yamaguchi and co-workers (233) employed a cyanide masking technique and TPB precipitations to effect specific tests for silver, thallium(I), mercury(I), and mercury(II) when occurring together.

Pahlow (153) has used the formation of a TPB precipitate as an identification test and proof-of-identity test for potassium, ammonium, or organic nitrogen compounds in pharmaceutical products.

IX.   TPB SALTS OF ORGANIC COMPOUNDS

1. Preparation and Properties of TPB Salts of Organic Compounds

Precipitants for potassium have usually received application as reagents for alkaloids and for basic nitrogen compounds generally.

Hence, such use of sodium (or lithium) TPB received early study. In one of the first publications on TPB compounds, Wittig and Raff (229) reported the preparation of tetranethylammonium TPB. TPB precipitations have now been applied to the detection, isolation, characterization, determination, or theoretical study of amines generally (24a,30–32,85,86,97,99,100,104,107a–107c,113,117a,145,150b,184, 216,219,229,234,236), of quaternary ammonium compounds (2,40–32, 68,71–73,97,99,100,113,117a,123,153b,177,228,229,232,234), of alkaloids and nitrogen-containing pharmaceuticals (1,2,10a,23,24,25b,26a, 38,38b,38c,52,60,67,71–74,81a,85,97,99,100,110,113,117,130,138b,147, 153,153b,156,169,176,177,189–192,194,209,232,234,237), and of unspecified basic nitrogen compounds in wine (164). As the formation of TPB salts involves the ammonium ion, insoluble TPB salts of amines form only in significant yield from acid solution (see Equation 26).

$$R_1R_2R_3R_4N^+ + B(C_6H_5)_4{}^- \longrightarrow R_1R_2R_3R_4N\cdot B(C_6H_5)_4 \qquad (26)$$

(where R's = hyhrogen, alkyl, or aryl, etc.)

Betaine gives an insoluble TPB salt (96). If heated, some amino acids give TPB precipitates including p-aminobenzoic acid, proline, tyrosine, serine, aspartic acid, and cysteine (96). Certain amides are sufficiently basic to form even in weakly acidic medium insoluble TPB salts on standing. However, the rate of protonation is often slow, and the precipitation only occurs after prolonged standing. The yield is often low. Amides undergoing this reaction include dimethylacetamide, formamide, and dimethylformamide (236). The cyclic amide N-methylpyrrolidone-2 forms an insoluble TPB derivative, but not the corresponding 5-methylpyrrolidone-2. Monomeric N-vinylpyrrolidone-2 does not form an insoluble TPB salt; however, polyvinylpyrrolidone forms one readily with about 50% of the amide groups combining with TPB ions (236). S-benzylthiuronium compounds also form insoluble TPB salts (30,32,118). Thioacetamide oxide, formed by the action of hydrogen peroxide on thioacetamide, in the zwitter ion form, $CH_3C(SO^-){:}NH_2{}^+$, forms an insoluble TPB derivative (210).

Other types of organic ions also form insoluble TPB salts; these include tetraarylphosphonium (229), tetraarylarsonium (32,156a,221), tetraarylstibonium (221), tetraarylbismuthonium (221a), trialkylsulfonium (30,32,118), triaryltelluronium (222), trialkyloxonium

(142), diarylchloronium and diarylbromonium (140,143,144), diaryliodonium (221a), dibenziodolium (26b), and benzenediazonium (229). Bromo-dialkylsulfonium TPB, formed by the reaction of a dialkylsulfide dibromide and sodium TPB, is unstable and decomposes as given in Equation 27 (21). Amine dibromides, including pyridine and triethylamine dibromides, by an analogous reaction form the triphenylboron derivative as given in Equation 28 (21).

$$(R_2SBr)^+ + B(C_6H_5)_4^- \longrightarrow [(R_2SBr) \cdot B(C_6H_5)_4] \longrightarrow$$
$$R_2S \cdot B(C_6H_5)_3 + C_6H_5Br \quad (27)$$

$$(R_1R_2R_3NBr)^+ + B(C_6H_5)_4^- \longrightarrow [(R_1R_2R_3NBr) \cdot B(C_6H_5)_4] \longrightarrow$$
$$R_1R_2R_3N \cdot B(C_6H_5)_3 + C_6H_5Br \quad (28)$$

Polyethylene glycols and their monoesters and polyethylene adducts form insoluble TPB derivatives after conversion to a cationic (oxonium) form (148,149,150c) (see Section IX-7).

Arylisonitrile complexes of manganese and gold, $(ArNC)_6Mn^+$ and $(ArNC)_4Au^+$, form TPB salts (178). Various diphenyl-, dimesityl-, diindenyl-, dicyclopentadienyl-, etc., moieties of chromium, iron, cobalt, nickel, ruthenium, rhodium, osmium, and rhenium have been isolated and studied as TPB salts (36,43–51a,91,91a,109, 235). Substituted phosphine-containing cobalt carbonyls (98,208) and ammine rhenium carbonyls (98a) also form TPB salts.

The presence of a basic nitrogen (or other basic grouping) in an organic compound may permit the formation of a water-insoluble TPB salt (if the pH conditions employed favor formation of an onium ion). However, other structural factors must be recognized as increasing the solubility of the salt, including the presence of groups acting to solubilize the compound or to decrease the basicity of the nitrogen (or other) group. The TPB salts of hydroxyamines are more soluble in water than those of the corresponding simple amines. The presence of sugar moieties in the streptomycin structure probably accounts for its failure to form an insoluble TPB salt although many related antibiotics do so (237). Crane (30) suggested that an ionization constant greater than 10^{-11} is required for the qualitative TPB precipitation of amines at a concentration of 5 to 10 mg./5 ml. Renault (166) observed and cited examples that, if complete precipitation is required, the equivalent weight of the amine is probably of greater importance. The water solubility of some TPB derivatives of organic compounds is listed in Table III. TPB salts of organic

TABLE III

Water Solubility of Some TPB Salts of Organic Nitrogen Compounds

TPB salt[a]	Solubility of TPB salt		Solubility product of TPB salt, room temp.
	g./100 ml., room temp.	moles/liter, 25°C.	
Methylamine		36.3×10^{-4} (100)	
Dimethylamine		16.3×10^{-4} (100)	
Trimethylamine		3.9×10^{-4} (100)	
Tetramethylammonium	0.05 (234)	0.4×10^{-4} (100)	1.4×10^{-6d}
Ethylamine		28.3×10^{-4} (100)	
Propylamine		9.0×10^{-4} (100)	
n-Butylamine		11.2×10^{-4} (100)	
Pyridine		2.0×10^{-4} (100)	
Histamine[b]	0.01 (234)		6.8×10^{-12d}
Histidine	0.24 (234)		2.5×10^{-5d}
Quanidine	0.14 (234)		
Putrescine	0.03 (234)		
Cadaverine[b]	0.03 (234)		
Spermine[c]	0.02 (234)		1.1×10^{-17d}
Atropine		ca. 10^{-4} (192)	$<2.9 \times 10^{-8e}$
Serotonin	<0.001 (74)		
Tryptamine	<0.001 (74)		
Tyramine	<0.001 (74)		
Choline	0.003 (123)		
Acetylcholine	0.03 (123)		
Succinyl-bis-choline[b]			6.3×10^{-13f}

[a] Solubility data for TPB salt of the onium ion corresponding to the base listed; 1:1 molar ratio of base:TPB unless otherwise indicated.

[b] Salt formed corresponds to 1:2 molar ratio of base:TPB.

[c] Salt formed corresponds to 1:4 molar ratio of base:TPB.

[d] Calculated in (92) from data of (234).

[e] Calculated in (92) from data of (192).

[f] Calculated in (92) from data of (177).

moieties, like the corresponding salts of the alkali metals, are soluble in various polar solvents including alcohols, acetone, and acetonitrile.

Most TPB salts of organic moieties melt (with or without decomposition) at temperatures below 300°C. The melting point phenomena are considered in Section IX-8 on the identification and characterization of organic compounds. Many early workers, especially in connection with gravimetric studies, noted the poor thermal stability of the TPB salts of some organic nitrogen compounds. Wendlandt (216) and Howick and Pflaum (99,100) have reported from ther-mogravimetric study and differential thermal analysis, respectively, minimum decomposition temperatures for the TPB salts of some common amines and alkaloids.   The latter workers (100) have dis-cussed the possible oxidative pyrolytic reactions leading ultimately to boric oxide.   The important observation for practical analysis is that the minimum decomposition temperature is often far below the melting point of the salt as determined in a capillary melting tube.

The infrared spectra of the TPB salts of choline and acetylcholine in acetonitrile have been reported by Marquardt and Vogg (123). Howick and Pflaum (99,100) studied the ultraviolet absorption spectra of various amine TPB salts.   In acetonitrile the spectra of the simple amine salts are identical to the spectra of the alkali metal TPB salts (see Section II-2).   The spectra of heterocyclic amine TPB salts are the summation of the spectra of the TPB ion and of the protonated amine.   Ultraviolet absorption measurements were applied by these workers to the determination of the water solubility of the amine TPB salts (see Table III).   Chatten and co-workers (26a) studied, at length the ultraviolet and infrared spectra of some common local anesthetics of the procaine type and their TPB derivatives.   Gautier and co-workers (73a) studied the spectra of the TPB derivatives of some important alkaloids, and evolved a spectrophotometric micro determination for these alkaloids following their isolation.

Fuoss and co-workers (68), in a study of the theory of electrolytes, determined the conductance of tetra-n-butylammonium TPB at various concentrations in acetonitrile, acetonitrile–carbon tetrachlo-ride, acetonitrile–benzene, nitrobenzene, and propylene carbonate. Popov and Humphrey (156a) determined the limiting conductance of tetraphenylarsonium TPB in acetonitrile.

It is sometimes of interest, especially in isolation and character-ization studies, to isolate the organic compound from its TPB de-rivative.   A number of approaches have been investigated.   Zeidler (234) recovered histamine and related bases as their hydrochlorides, by reconstituting the TPB salt with hydrochloric acid.   The free TPB acid (and its decomposition products) can then be extracted with ether; the amine hydrochlorides are recovered by evaporating the aqueous phase.   Gayer (74) proceeded similarly to isolate bio-genetic amines from plasma, and then separated them in the aqueous phase by paper electrophoresis.

Gautier (71) noted that in some cases the free base may be recovered by treating the TPB salt with sodium hydroxide and extracting with an appropriate organic solvent. In this manner Scott and co-workers (194) dissolved an alkaloid TPB salt in either acetone or ethanol, added sodium hydroxide, heated on a steam bath for 15 min., evaporated the solvent in an air steam, extracted the residue with chloroform, washed the chloroform with water, dried, and finally concentrated. Many of the alkaloids studied were thereby recovered quantitatively, or almost so. In some cases, however, the recovery was low and it was suggested that this was caused possibly by overheating or by the use of too alkaline a medium.

This general approach has also been studied by Schultz and Goerner (191). They treat an alkaloid TPB salt with a sodium alcoholate in alcohol, especially sodium methoxide in methanol, or with sodium hydroxide and ethanol. They warmed the solution, neutralized to litmus, volatilized the alcohol on a steam bath, added sodium hydroxide solution, and extracted the free alkaloid with chloroform. On applying these processes to the isolation of strychnine, 91 to 93% recovery was obtained when sodium hydroxide was used and 83 to 86% with the sodium methylate treatment. Schultz and Goerner (191) also investigated the treatment of the solution after the sodium methoxide treatment with potassium hydroxide or potassium chloride, thus precipitating potassium TPB which could be filtered off. However, the subsequent recovery of the alkaloid was then poor. Büechl (25a) treated an acetone solution of the TPB derivative of a cyanocobalamin with an alcoholic potassium hydroxide solution and recovered the cyanocobalamin content as an oil which could be decanted and crystallized.

Schultz and Goerner (191) also studied the use of a cation exchanger. The alkaloid TPB salt, in acetone–water, is passed through the resin bed in the sodium form. The column is rinsed with acetone–water. Sodium TPB is contained in the effluent and may be precipitated as ammonium TPB and recycled (see Section III-1). The alkaloid may be eluted from the column by sodium hydroxide solution. In the isolation of strychnine by this process, a recovery as high as 97% was obtained.

It is also probable that the mercurization reaction with mercuric chloride or acetate can be applied to destroy the TPB ion and hence to permit the subsequent recovery of an organic base. However, it should be noted that some quaternary ammonium groups form insoluble mercury salts (71,72).

2. Precipitation of TPB Salts of Organic Compounds

Many of the considerations given for the precipitation of potassium TPB (Section III-2) apply to the precipitation of the TPB salts of organic compounds. In general, the precipitation should be made from aqueous solutions made acid with acetic acid, an acetate buffer, or a mineral acid. Various workers have recommended pH values ranging from 2 to 6. The work of Aklin and Dürst (2) and of Aklin (1) in the gravimetric determination of various alkaloids suggests that recovery studies at various pH values may be warranted in establishing a quantitative procedure for a particular compound. In some applications and procedures it is appropriate to effect the precipitation from warm solution (50 to 60°C.) and to allow the solution to cool prior to filtration. The literature suggests that the TPB salts of some organic moieties may precipitate slowly (in contrast to potassium TPB); hence, it may be appropriate to allow the cooled solution to stand. Some workers maintain the solution at the elevated temperature for some time, even 1 hr. or more, in order to coagulate the precipitate. Because of the decomposition of the TPB ion, this treatment is permitted only with some procedures.

In some approaches, but not in a gravimetric determination, it is allowable to add a few drops of a dilute aluminum chloride solution prior to addition of the sodium TPB solution. This addition aids in coagulating the precipitate. The TPB salts of long chain quaternary ammonium compounds often precipitate in a gelatinous form. In such cases the aluminum chloride treatment and centrifugation can be applied to advantage (71,72). If the TPB salt is relatively soluble, the precipitate should be washed most carefully. In this connection, the remarks on the washing of potassium TPB should be studied (Section III-2). If an argentometric titration is to be subsequently conducted with the redissolved precipitate, this must be washed free of halide (or the precipitation should not be effected from a hydrochloric acid medium).

In drying the TPB salts of organic compounds, it should be recognized that many have low thermal stability and may decompose significantly at temperatures far below their melting point. Where no stability information has been developed, a drying temperature below 65°C. may be appropriate. The use of a desiccant-filled vacuum desiccator is advantageous. Where expedient, the TPB salt may be redissolved (often without drying) in acetone or other appropriate solvent and recrystallized by partial evaporation and/or by addition of water. Various workers have noted that some amine TPB salts may undergo decomposition on warming in aqueous methanol or acetone; hence, warming during a recrystallization should be conducted with caution. In the drying and recrystallization steps it should be recognized that crystals may be obtained having acetone or water of crystallization.

Some additional remarks on the precipitation of TPB salts of organic compounds will be found in Section IX-3 on gravimetric determinations employing such salts.

3. Gravimetric Determination of Organic Compounds

The general conditions and precautions for the precipitation of TPB salts or organic moieties have already been considered in Section IX-2. However, some special considerations and difficulties to obtain a weighable product may be emphasized. Some workers, including Schultz and Mayer (192), have obtained voluminous precipitates with some organic nitrogen compounds that could not be coagulated by heating or standing and hence were difficult to filter. The TPB salts of some long-chain alkyl quaternary ammonium salts are said to precipitate in a gelatinous form (71). Further, Gautier and co-workers (71–73) were unable to apply a gravimetric TPB determination to such salts because they were especially unstable to warming and the precipitate appeared to contain an excess of TPB ion. Crane (31) also noted the possible presence of an excess of TPB ion in some quaternary ammonium TPB salts.

Aklin and Dürst (2) observed poor filterability for the TPB salts of some alkaloids, Ieviņš and Gudriniece (104) experienced difficulty in drying amine TPB salts to constant weight in air or *in vacuo*. They concluded that the precipitation was quantitative as no amine could be found in the filtrate, and that, hence, the losses occurred in the drying step. In some cases the recovery was only 90 to 97% of the theoretical value, and in a few cases as low as 50%. The gravimetric TPB determination of triethanolamine is difficult because of the high solubility of its TPB salt (145).

In spite of these difficulties, the gravimetric TPB method has given excellent results for the assay of many bases of pharmaceutical interest. Compounds so determined include aminopyrine (110,192), antipyrine (110), procaine hydrochloride and some related local anesthetics (26a,192), cocaine (209), atropine (156,192,209), choline (209), acetylcholine (123), succinyl-*bis*-choline (177), papaverine hydrochloride (2), pilocarpine (209), ephedrine (110), benzethonium chloride (Phemerol chloride; Hyamine 1622) (153b), strychnine nitrate (2,110), codeine and codeine phosphate (and in mixtures with phenacetin and acetylsalicylic acid) (110,192), various alkaloids (138b) morphine (1,110,138b), and a variety of opium alkaloids and their derivatives (1). The total of potassium, ammonium, and organic nitrogen bases in wine has been determined by the gravimetric TPB method (163,164). In another aliquot the total of potassium and organic bases may be determined similarly after alkalinization and volatization of ammonia. Potassium alone is determined after prior ashing of an aliquot.

4. Argentometric Titrations Involving TPB Salts of Organic Compounds

The argentometric titrations already considered in Sections IV-2 and IV-3 have been applied to the determination of a variety of organic nitrogen bases. These and other titrimetric approaches are of special interest in view of the difficulites encountered in the gravimetric TPB determination of such bases. The argentometric methods allow the use of aluminum chloride in order to coagulate the TPB precipitate.

The procedure of Rüdorff and Zannier (172) based on titration of a redissolved TPB precipitate with silver nitrate to a visual end point employing eosin as an adsorption indicator has been studied by a number of workers. Compounds so determined include atropine sulfate, antipyrine, aminopyrine, codeine phosphate, brucine, pilocarpine, hydrochloride, hexamethylenetetramine, procaine hydrochloride (189), alkylthiophenylketo bases (Thiofalicaine, etc.) (24), various antihistamines (23), and ephedrine (110).

Rüdorff and Zannier (176) described the Volhard titration of the TPB content of a redissolved TPB precipitate involving addition of an excess of silver nitrate and back-titration of this excess with ammonium thiocyanate to the iron(III)–thiocyanate end point. These workers applied the method to the determination of antipyrine, aminopyrine, atropine sulfate, pyridine nitrate, benzidine, and hexamethylenetetramine. In the case of antipyrine the titration indicated an antipyrine:TPB molar ratio of 2:1; other workers (189) had obtained a 1:1 ratio. Keller and Weiss (110) found this method to be satisfactory for the determination of ephedrine hydrochloride, and Aklin (1) obtained excellent results in the determination of morphine and other opium alkaloids.

The argentometric procedure employing chromate ion as indicator introduced by Hahn (83) has been applied to the determination of ephedrine hydrochloride by Keller and Weiss (110). These workers considered this approach more useful and generally applicable than the other argentometric methods (which they also studied).

The procedure of Rüdorff and Zannier (173) based on the determination of the excess TPB ion in an aliquot of filtrate by a Volhard titration has been employed by Ieviņš and Gudriniece (104) for the determination of aliphatic, alicyclic, and aromatic amines, benzidine, and quinoline. Keller and Weiss (110) determined ephedrine hydrochloride in this way. Poor results were obtained in the determination of atropine by this method (156).

Erdey and co-workers (37b) applied the argentometric titration methods employing Variamine Blue as indicator (see Sections IV-2, IV-3, and VII-1) to the determination of various types of nitrogen-containing compounds, either by their conversion to ammonia by Kjeldahl digestion or by use of Devarda's alloy and then precipitation of ammonium TPB.

5. Nonaqueous Acid–Base Titration of Organic TPB Compounds

The nonaqueous acid–base titration of potassium TPB has been considered in Section IV-6. This general approach has been applied to the TPB salts of amines, of the organic bases, and of quaternary ammonium compounds. Gautier and co-workers effected such a titration of long chain quaternary ammonium TPB salts (72) and of TPB salts of some organic bases of pharmaceutical interest (73). The quaternary type TPB salts are dissolved in dioxane; the TPB salts of organic bases are dissolved in anhydrous acetic acid. Both are titrated with perchloric acid in acetic acid. Methyl violet serves as indicator. As established by Pellerin (154) the TPB ion may undergo rapid decomposition in acetic acid (see Section IV-6), but the phenylboric acid produced is only weakly acidic and thus exerts no adverse effect on the titration. Gautier (71) and Renault (166) briefly reviewed the work of Gautier and co-workers.

Procedure 36. To an aliquot of the sample solution containing about 0.25 meq. of a quaternary ammonium compound or a basic nitrogen compound in water, add 5 drops of a 10% $AlCl_3$ solution. If necessary, adjust the pH to 4 to 5 by addition of 1% acetic acid. Warm the solution (50 to 60°C.), add dropwise about 1.5 times the theoretical amount of a 1% sodium TPB solution. Place the precipitating vessel in a water bath (50 to 60°C.) for about 30 min. Agitate occasionally to encourage coagulation. Cool, filter, and wash the precipitate 5 or 6 times with 5 ml. portions of 1% acetic acid. Dry the precipitate and dissolve it (on the filter) in an appropriate solvent. In the determination of quaternary ammonium compounds, dissolve in acetone and evaporate the acetone in the receiving vessel, add 10 ml. of dioxane made anhydrous by distillation from sodium. In the determination of organic bases, dissolve in 10 ml. of warm, anhydrous acetic acid (made anhydrous by addition of some acetic anhydride).

To the cooled solution add 1 or 2 drops of a 1% solution of methyl violet in anhydrous acetic acid, titrate with a 0.05N $HClO_4$ solution in acetic acid (3 ml. of 72% $HClO_4$ and 3 ml. of acetic anhydride in 250 ml. of acetic acid). Similarly titrate a solvent blank. The calculation takes the form:

$$\text{(Equiv. wt. of the organic base)} \times N_{HClO_4} \times (V - V')$$
$$= \text{mg. of organic base}$$

where V and V' are the ml. of $HClO_4$ consumed, respectively, in the titration of the sample and blank.

Remarks. The equivalent weight will of course depend on the structure of the organic compound. Thus, the aminoalkyl esters of p-aminobenzoic acid (i.e., procaine, etc.) show an equivalent weight equal to one-half of the molecular weight. Gautier and co-workers (72,73) have applied this titration to halides of the groups RMe_3N^+ and $RMe_2(C_6H_5CH_2)N^+$ (where R is long chain alkyl), to N-alkyl-pyridinium bromide, N-alkylisoquinolinium bromide, and (2-hydroxyethyl)cetyldimethylammonium bromide, and to about 31 local anesthetics, alkaloids, and other bases of pharmaceutical interest.

In general, the precision is better than 1%; however, with very dilute samples it is poorer.

Espersen (38) proceeded essentially in the manner of the above procedure (using dioxane as solvent and crystal violet as indicator) to determine the equivalent weight of the TPB salts of some nitrogen-containing pharmaceuticals; the equivalent weight with the melting point of the TPB salt permitted identification of the pharmaceutical base. Chatten and co-workers (26a) and Howick and Pflaum (99, 100) applied the procedure of Flaschka using acetone–acetic acid as solvent and crystal violet as indicator (see Section IV-6) to the assay of the TPB derivatives of some local anesthetics and amine TPB salts, respectively. The latter workers also determined the end point potentiometrically using a glass electrode as the working electrode (see Section V-2).

It is noteworthy that the nonaqueous titration approach has the advantage of relative rapidity and satisfactory accuracy on the macro and possibly the semimicro scale. Further, as the cation is titrated, not the TPB ion, the exact composition of the TPB precipitate is of little importance. The number of groups in the organic base that can be titrated is a controlling factor in the success of the method.

6. Acid–Base Titration after Mercurization of TPB Salts of Organic Compounds

As considered in Section IV-10, Flaschka and co-workers (58) developed a procedure for micro amounts of potassium based on the mercurization of the TPB ion. These workers found (60) the procedure could be applied without significant changes in details to micro amounts of the determination of organic nitrogen compounds that could be isolated as insoluble TPB salts. With amounts of sample ranging from 0.5 to 3 mg., and with most of the compounds studied, the maximum error did not exceed 0.03 mg. When applied to nitrogen bases the free base is liberated by the mercurization step. In some cases the base may be so weak as to bind one equivalent of acid (e.g., aminopyrine) and hence the molar equivalence factor $TPB:H^+$ is 1:4 rather than the usual 1:3. As the mercurization is effected in the presence of excess caustic and with heating, some esters (e.g., procaine) can undergo saponification, also leading to a factor of 1:4.

The possibility also exists that the boric acid produced might combine with the base, and then would be capable of being titrated as well.

Gautier and co-workers (71,72) noted that in their hands the method could not be applied to long chain quaternary ammonium compounds, as some form insoluble mercury salts. They also stated (71) that some basic compounds (including quaternary ammonium compounds) are partially destroyed by the alkali treatment. However, Worrell and Ebert (232) applied the method with success to cetyldimethylbenzylammonium chloride.

The mercurization approach has now been applied successfully to the determination of butylamine and various secondary and tertiary aliphatic amines (107a), of aromatic and heterocyclic nitrogen-containing compounds (107b), of procaine hydrochloride (60), codeine (117), morphine and its hydrochloride (60,110,138b) heptadone hydrochloride (60), p-hydroxyphenylmethylaminoethanol (Sympatol) tartrate (60), ephedrine (110), strychnine and its nitrate (60,110,130), aminopyrine (60,117), atropine (110,154), amphetamine sulfate (232), methamphetamine hydrochloride (232), and cetyldimethylbenzylammonium chloride (232).

7. Miscellaneous Determinations of Organic Compounds

Crane (30,31) applied the potentiometric titration given as Procedure 22 (Section V-2) to the determination of various organic compounds including methylpyridinium halides, hexamethylenetetramine, diethylamine, and glycine methyl ester. The slope of the titration curve at the end point was the greatest in the case of heterocyclic and aliphatic amines. With primary aromatic amines (e.g., aniline) the slope was not steep enough to permit detection of the end point. Of 31 compounds that gave detectable end points, 22 were determined within 2% (relative) of theory and 12 within 1%.

Kirsten and co-workers (113) made use of their potentiometric titration procedure (Section V-2) to determine various organic bases and quaternary ammonium salts. In some cases a direct titration with sodium TPB gave satisfactory results. In many cases, these workers preferred to back-titrate an excess of TPB ion in a filtrate with a quaternary ammonium salt (Oxaditon, Pharmacia). Espersen (38b) proceeded in the general manner of Kirsten and co-workers but employed another quaternary ammonium salt (pethidinium chloride) as the back-titrant. Satisfactory results were obtained in the determination of some common alkaloids and nitrogen-containing drugs.

The polarization titration (Section V-3) was applied by Schmidt (184) to the determination of organic bases. No special details or results were given; however, it was stated that exact results were obtained with various bases including quinoline. Espersen (38b) also briefly studied a dead-stop titration employing platinum electrodes and sodium TPB as titrant for the determination of nitrogen-containing drugs, but obtained no satisfactory results. Heyrovský (97) reported without full procedural details that various organic bases could be determined by argentometric titration of the redissolved TPB precipitate to a potentiometric or amperometric end point. Jansons and Ieviņš (107c) applied a direct high frequency titration with sodium TPB to the determination of various amines.

Wachsmuth (209) determined cocaine, atropine, choline, and strychnine by precipitating the TPB salt, dissolving in acetone, taking an aliquot corresponding to about 10 μg. of boron, evaporating to dryness, redissolving in 10 ml. of a 0.01% solution of 1,1'-dianthrimide in concentrated sulfuric acid, heating for 3 hr. at 100°C., cooling, and measuring the absorption at 650 mμ. Nakagawa and Isaka (138b) determined the boron content of the TPB precipitate obtained with morphine and diacetylmorphine by a colorimetric procedure employing curcumine.

The principle underlying the procedure developed by Schall (183) (Section IV-4) has been applied by Patil and Anderson (153b) to the determination of benzethonium chloride (Phemerol chloride, Hyamine 1622) and benzalkonium chloride.

Gautier and co-workers (73a) based a determination of micro amounts of various alkaloids and pharmaceutical bases on the isolation of their TPB salts, solution in acetonitrile, and spectrophotometric measurement in the ultraviolet region. The method is analogous to the spectrophotometric determination of potassium (Section VI-1).

Neu (148,149,150c) has converted polyethylene glycols and their monoesters with fatty acids, and also polyethylene oxide adducts to a cationic (oxonium) form by treatment with barium chloride or other salts. The resulting cation forms insoluble TPB derivatives. The TPB content is reproducibly associated with the molecular weight of the polymer, and by the process the determination of such polymers is possible either gravimetrically or by an acid–base titration after mercurization. In some cases it is possible to pass the polymer directly to the TPB derivative by treatment with TPB free acid (obtained by cation exchange of sodium TPB, see Section IV-8).

Three processes involving the TPB ion merely for enrichment and isolation are noteworthy. Zeidler (234) precipitated histamine and other biogenetic amines as their TPB salt, redissolved the salt in acetone, and determined the nitrogen content by a conventional micro Kjeldahl method. Schultz and Goerner (191) passed solutions of organic TPB salts through an ion exchange column thus obtaining the free base which could be determined by classical methods (see also Section IX-2). Van Pinxteren and co-workers (156) determined the atropine–hyoscyamine ratio of crude belladonna preparations by separating the TPB salts of the alkaloids, treating them with 25% hydrochloric acid and measuring the optical rotation of the resulting solution.

8. The TPB Ion in the Identification and Characterization of Organic Compounds

The formation of TPB salts is of value in the detection, identification, and characterization of various organic compounds, especially of basic nitrogen compounds. These uses are predicated on the water insolubility of such TPB salts, their definite composition, micro crystallinity, and their melting (or decomposition) usually below 300°C.

The mere precipitation of a TPB salt can serve as a detection test for alkaloids, amines, pharmaceutical bases, etc., (1,2,30,32,74,104, 169,192,194,234), and for polyethylene glycols and polyethylene oxide adducts after conversion to a cationic form (148,149). For alkaloids, TPB was found to be a more sensitive and more reliable precipitant than Mayer's reagent (1,192,194), Dragendorff's reagent (1), or other common alkaloidal reagents (169). Detection limits for various amines, alkaloids, and pharmaceutical bases have been reported (1,32,104). Crane (32) has applied the TPB precipitation as a spot test in the following form:

Procedure 37. Dissolve the test substance in dilute acetic acid or mineral acid, and if necessary, adjust the pH to about 3 with dilute NaOH solution. Place 1 drop of the resulting solution on a black

spot plate (or black, water-repellent paper). Add 1 drop of a 3 to
7% sodium TPB solution. Note the appearance of a precipitate or
of turbidity. Run a reagent blank.

Remarks. The sensitivity of the test with many amines is recorded
by Crane (32). In general if a 6% sodium TPB solution is employed,
2.5 μg. of a primary amine can be detected and 0.4 μg. of a quaternary
ammonium salt. Of course, potassium, ammonium, etc., will interfere if present.

Pahlow (153) suggested a TPB precipitation as a proof of identity
or of purity in the control of pharmaceutical preparations.

Many workers have identified or characterized basic organic nitrogen compounds by means of the melting point of their TPB salts
(13a,23,24,24a,26a,30,31,38,38c,52,74,81a,84,85,110,117a,123,138b,
145,147,194,219,228,229,234,236,237). Because such TPB salts may
undergo decomposition during recrystallization, this operation should
be accomplished with caution (from acetone or other solvent) and
without undue heating. Many workers prefer to determine the melting point of the unrecrystallized TPB salt. Wendlandt (216) and
Pflaum (100) in thermogravimetric studies and Aklin and Dürst
(2), and Aklin (1) in drying studies, established that some TPB salts
begin to decompose far below their melting point. Thus, it might be
expected that the melting point of TPB salts would be dependent on
the rate of heating. This difficulty was delineated by Wendlandt and
Dunham (219). The melting point of the TPB salts of lower amines
is markedly dependent on the rate of heating. This effect is less
pronounced with higher molecular weight amines and with several
alkaloids the melting point is increased only 7 or 8°C., when the heating rate is increased even from 2°C. to 16°C./min. (219). Thus, it
is desirable to specify the rate of heating when recording a melting
point for the TPB salt of an organic compound. (Of course, this
same phenomenon is often encountered with other alkaloidal reagents.) A number of workers have published extended lists of melting points of TPB salts (1,13a,30,31,38,52,194).

For the purpose of further characterization, the TPB salts of organic nitrogen compounds can be analyzed: their nitrogen content
may be determined (micro Kjeldahl method), their amine content
(nonaqueous acid–base titration, see Section IX-5), or their TPB
content (see Sections IX-4, IX-6, and IX-7). The ultraviolet or

infrared spectra of the TPB salts may also be of value in the differentiation of organic nitrogen compounds (26a,96,100,123).

Neu (150b) in a preliminary note has indicated the possibility of the successive formation of two derivatives of a hydroxyamine having a primary or secondary amino group.   For example, 2-aminoethanol can be isolated as its TPB salt (and its melting point determined). Then, by heating this derivative with hydrochloric acid in aqueous ethanol, 2-aminoethyl diphenylborate can be formed (cf. 150) in good yield (and its melting point can be determined).

X. SOME REAGENTS RELATED TO THE TPB ION

Potassium cyanotriphenylboron (229), cyanotri(p-tolyl)boron (223) and tetra(α-thienyl)boron (181,182) are fairly soluble in water as are the corresponding sodium salts; however, the rubidium and cesium salts are insoluble.   Hence these ions may find application in the separation of cesium from potassium and sodium.   Sodium cyanotriphenylboron (229), which is commercially available, has been studied as a precipitant for basic nitrogen compounds (84,192,216) and for the determination of alkaloids via mercurization and subsequent acid–base titration (192).   The cyanotriphenylboron salts of organic nitrogen compounds are in general more soluble than the corresponding TPB salts.   Further, in thermogravimetric studies Wendlandt found that sodium, rubidium, cesium, and thallium cyanotriphenylboron (217) and various amine cyanotriphenylboron salts (216) have no improved thermal stability over the corresponding TPB salts.

Sodium and higher alkali metal tetra(p-tolyl)boron salts are insoluble in water; hence, lithium tetra(p-tolyl)boron has been proposed as a reagent for the determination of sodium following the TPB separation of potassium, rubidium, cesium, and ammonium (179a).

Tetraphenyldiboroxide, the anhydride of diphenylboric acid, and derived aminoalkyl esters have reagent applications in the analysis of γ-pyrones, quinolinols, onium compounds, and surface-active agents.   These reagents were introduced by Neu (146) and their preparation, reactions, and analytical uses have been reviewed by him (150).   These reagents are readily prepared by the controlled hydrolysis of sodium TPB (see Equations 10 and 11, page 6) (146, 150,150a,150b).

Remarks

This chapter considers in greater detail publications known as of late 1958 (12,13). Additional papers that only became known, or that appeared, during 1959 and early 1960 were subsequently worked into the manuscript.

References

1. Aklin, O., *Dosages gravimétriques et volumetriques des alcaloïdes de l'opium et dérivés par le tétraphényl-borate de sodium*, thesis, Faculté de Pharmacie, Université de Strasbourg, 1957.
2. Aklin, O., and J. Dürst, *Pharm. Acta Helv.*, **31**, 457–476 (1956); *Chem. Abstracts*, **51**, 5359 (1957).
3. Alimarin, I. P., I. M. Gibalo, and I. A. Sirotina, *Intern. J. Appl. Radiation and Isotopes*, **2**, 117–128 (1957); *Anal. Abstr.*, **5**, item 1787 (1958); Gibalo, I. M., I. A. Sirotina, and I. P. Alimarin, *Trudy Vsesoyuz. Nauch.-Tekh. Konf. Primenen. Radioaktiv. Stabil Izotopov i Izlucheniĭ v Narod. Khoz. i Nauke, Izotopy i Izluchen. v Khim.*, **1957**, 178–185 (Pub. 1958); through *Chem. Abstracts*, **53**, 19,665 (1959).
4. Amin, A. M., *Resalet-El-Elm*, **19**, 177–182 (1953); *Risalatul-Kimia (Damascus)*, **2**, No. 6, 407–417 (1954).
5. Amin, A. M., *Chemist-Analyst*, **43**, 4–6 (1954); *Chem. Abstracts*, **48**, 5724 (1954).
6. Amin, A. M., *Chemist-Analyst*, **45**, 65–66 (1956); *Chem. Abstracts*, **50**, 16, 539 (1956).
7. Amin, A. M., *Chemist-Analyst*, **46**, 6–7 (1957); *Chem. Abstracts*, **51**, 12744 (1957).
7a. Amos, W. R., and R. F. Sympson, *Anal. Chem.*, **31**, 133–135 (1959); *Chem. Abstracts*, **53**, 5972 (1959).
8. Anonymous, *J. Assoc. Offic. Agr. Chemists*, **41**, 32–33 (1958).
9. Arnott, S., and S. C. Abrahams, *Acta Cryst.*, **11**, 449–450 (1958).
10. Auerbach, M. E., *Ind. Eng. Chem., Anal. Ed.*, **15**, 492–493 (1943); *Chem. Abstracts*, **37**, 5829 (1943).
10a. Balenović, K., N. Bregant, and Z. Štefanac, *Croat. Chem. Acta*, **29**, 45–48 (1957); *Chem. Abstracts*, **51**, 15,537–15,538 (1957).
11. Ballczo, H., and J. Sinabell, *Mikrochemie ver Mikrochim. Acta*, **34**, 404–411 (1949); *ibid.*, **35**, 178–188 (1950); *Chem. Abstracts*, **44**, 1851–1852, 8570 (1950).
12. Barnard, A. J., Jr., *Chemist-Analyst*, **44**, 104–107 (1955); *ibid.*, **45**, 110–111 (1956); Barnard, A. J., Jr., and H. Büechl, *ibid.*, **46**, 16–17 (1957); *ibid.*, **47**, 46–47 (1958).
13. Barnard, A. J., Jr., and H. Büechl, *Chemist-Analyst*, **48**, 44–45, 49 (1959).
13a. Barnard, A. J., Jr., and W. W. Wendlandt, *Revista soc. quím. Mexico*, **3**, 269–279 (1959).

14. Belcher, R., A. J. Nutten, and H. Thomas, *Anal. Chim. Acta,* 11, 120–127 (1954); *Chem. Abstracts,* 49, 6576 (1955).

14a. Belcher, R., A. M. G. MacDonald, and T. S. West, *Talanta,* 1, 408–410 (1958); *Chem. Abstracts,* 53, 5958 (1959).

15. Benzi, L. J., *Rev. brasil. cirurg.,* 34, 189–207 (1957).

16. Berg, W., and M. Goehring, *Z. anorg. u. allgem. Chem.,* 257, 273–277 (1954); *Chem. Abstracts,* 48, 8103 (1954).

17. Berg, W., M. Goehring, and H. Malz, *Z. anorg. u. allgem. Chem.,* 283, 13–17 (1956); *Chem. Abstracts,* 50, 9924 (1956).

18. Berkhout, H. W., *Chem. Weekblad,* 48, 909–910 (1952); *Chem. Abstracts,* 47, 1537 (1953).

19. Berkhout, H. W., and G. H. Jongen, *Chem. Weekblad,* 51, 607–608 (1955); *Chem. Abstracts,* 50, 3949–3950 (1956).

20. Berkhout, H. W., and G. H. Jongen, *Chemist-Analyst,* 45, 6–7 (1956); *Chem. Abstracts,* 50, 5453 (1956).

20a. Bermejo Martínez, F., and M. Goñalons Bori, *Chemist-Analyst,* 49, in press (1960).

21. Böhme, H., and E. Boll, *Z. anorg. u. allgem. Chem.,* 291, 160–163 (1957); *Chem. Abstracts,* 52, 4643 (1958).

22. Bonastre, J., *Ann. falsifications et fraudes,* 48, 347–351 (1955); *Chem. Abstracts,* 50, 1257 (1956).

22a. Booth, E., and A. Parker, Atomic Energy Research Establishment Report A/M-11, H. M. Stationary Office, London, April 1959, *Nuclear Sci. Abstracts,* 13, item 15926 (1959).

22b. Bower, C. A., *Soil Sci. Soc. Am., Proc.,* 23, 29–31 (1959); *Chem. Abstracts,* 53, 15,864–15,865 (1959).

23. Bräuniger, H., and R. Hofmann, *Pharmazie,* 10, 644–648 (1955); *Chem. Abstracts,* 50, 13,371 (1956).

24. Bräuniger, H., and K. Spangenberg, *Pharmazie,* 9, 623–629 (1954); *Chem. Abstracts,* 49, 9882 (1955).

24a. Brookes, P., R. J. Terry, and J. Walker, *J. Chem. Soc.,* 1957, 3165–3172; *Chem. Abstracts,* 51, 17,933–17,935 (1957).

25. Büechl, H., personal communication.

25a. Büechl, H. (to Heyl and Co.), Ger. Pat. 1,049,538 (July 23, 1959).

25b. Burglen, L., and P. Longuet, *Rev. matériaux construct. et trav. publ.,* C, No. 530, 257–265 (1959); *Chem. Abstracts,* 54, 6077 (1960).

25c. Buzás, L., *Magyar Kem. Lapja,* 14, 251–257 (1959); through *Chem. Abstracts,* 53, 21,430 (1959).

26. Chalmers, R. A., and S. J. Clark, paper, Midlands Section, Society for Analytical Chemistry, Birmingham, Nov. 9, 1955; summary in *Chem. Age,* 74, 21–26 (1956).

26a. Chatten, L. G., M. Pernarowski, and L. Levi, *J. Am. Pharm. Assoc., Sci. Ed.,* 48, 276–283 (1959); *Chem. Abstracts,* 53, 14,422 (1959).

26b. Clauss, K., *Chem. Ber.,* 88, 268–270 (1955); *Chem. Abstracts,* 50, 1768 (1956).

27. Cluley, H. J., *Analyst,* 80, 354–364 (1955); *Chem. Abstracts,* 49, 10,120 (1955).

27a. Cluley, H. J., *J. Soc. Glass Technol.*, **43**, 62T–72T (1958): *Chem. Abstracts*, **53**, 15,508 (1959).

27b. Collins, A. G., and J. W. Watkins, *Petroleum Engr.*, **31**, No. 12, 94, 98, 102 (1959); *Chem. Abstracts*, **54**, 1833 (1960).

27c. Colton, E., and R. E. Brooker, *J. Phys. Chem.*, **62**, 1595–1596 (1959).

28. Cooper, S. S., *Anal. Chem.*, **29**, 446–448 (1957): *Chem. Abstracts*, **51**, 7224 (1957).

29. Cooper, S. S., *Chemist-Analyst*, **46**, 62–64 (1957); *Chem. Abstracts*, **52**, 3589 (1958).

29a. Corner, M., *Analyst*, **84**, 41–46 (1959); *Chem. Abstracts*, **53**, 13,887 (1959).

30. Crane, F. E., Jr., *Anal. Chem.*, **28**, 1794–1797 (1956); *Chem. Abstracts*, **51**, 4213 (1957).

31. Crane, F. E., Jr., *Anal. Chim. Acta*, **16**, 370–377 (1957); *Chem. Abstracts*, **51**, 13,655 (1957).

32. Crane, F. E., Jr., *Anal. Chem.*, **30**, 1426–1429 (1958); *Chem. Abstracts*, **52**, 18,096 (1958).

32a. Crane, F. E., Jr., and E. A. Smith, *Chemist-Analyst*, **49**, 38–40 (1960).

33. Davies, T., and L. A. K. Staveley, *Trans. Faraday Soc.*, **53**, 19–30 (1957); *Chem. Abstracts*, **51**, 10,216 (1957).

33a. DeMumbrum, L. E., *Soil Sci. Am., Proc.*, **23**, 192–194 (1959); *Chem. Abstracts*, **53**, 19,247–19,248 (1959).

33b. Elster, K., and H. Otto, *Klin. Wochschr.*, **34**, 1139–1147 (1956); *Chem. Abstracts*, **51**, 13,135 (1957).

34. Emeury, J. M., *Mém. Poudres*, **38**, 357–370 (1956); *Chem. Abstracts*, **51**, 11,718 (1957).

35. Engelbrecht, R. M., and F. A. McCoy, *Anal. Chem.*, **28**, 1772–1773 (1956); *Chem. Abstracts*, **51**, 2461 (1957).

36. Engelmann, F., *Z. Naturforsch.*, **8b**, 775–776 (1953); *Chem. Abstracts*, **48**, 5574 (1954).

37. Epps, E. M., and J. C. Burden, *Anal. Chem.*, **30**, 1882–1883 (1958); *Chem. Abstracts*, **53**, 2935 (1959).

37a. Erdey, L., I. Buzás, and K. Vigh, *Talanta*, **1**, 377–395 (1958); *Chem. Abstracts*, **53**, 6878 (1959). cf. Erdey, L., *Chemist-Analyst*, **48**, 106–112 (1959).

37b. Erdey, L., L. Pólos, and Z. Gregorowicz, *Talanta*, **3**, 6–13 (1959); *Chem. Abstracts*, **54**, 7417 (1960).

37c. Erdey, L., K. Vigh, and L. Pólos, *Talanta*, **3**, 1–5 (1959); *Chem. Abstracts*, **54**, 7417 (1960).

38. Espersen, T., *Dansk Tidsskr. Farm.*, **32**, 99–106 (1958); *Chem. Abstracts*, **52**, 14,084–14,085 (1958).

38a. Espersen, T., *Farm. Revy*, **57**, 199–205 (1959).

38b. Espersen, T., *Dansk Tidsskr. Farm.*, **33**, 113–124 (1959); *Chem. Abstracts*, **53**, 22,735 (1959).

38c. Eugster, C. H., and P. G. Waser, *Helv. Chim. Acta*, **40**, 888–906 (1957); Eugster, C. H., F. Häfliger, R. Denss, and E. Girod, *ibid.*, **41**, 583–587 (1958); *Chem. Abstracts*, **51**, 16,407 (1957); *ibid.*, **53**, 429 (1959).

39. Feigl, F., and A. Caldas, *Mikrochim. Acta*, **1956**, 1310–1316; *Chem. Abstracts*, **50**, 8370 (1956).

40. Fernandez, J. B., L. T. Snider, and E. G. Rietz, *Anal. Chem.*, **23**, 899–900 (1951); *Chem. Abstracts*, **45**, 7469–7470 (1951).

41. Findeis, A. F., Jr., and T. De Vries, *Anal. Chem.*, **28**, 209–211 (1956); *Chem. Abstracts*, **50**, 9178 (1956).
42. Findeis, A. F., and T. De Vries, *Anal. Chem.*, **28**, 1899–1901 (1956); *Chem. Abstracts*, **51**, 4202 (1957).
42a. Finston, H. L., personal communication; unpublished work, Brookhaven National Laboratory.
43. Fischer, E. O., *Angew. Chem.*, **67**, 475–482 (1955); *Chem. Abstracts*, **49**, 15,593 (1955).
44. Fischer, E. O., and R. Böttcher, *Chem. Ber.*, **89**, 2397–2400 (1956); *Z. anorg. u. allgem. Chem.*, **291**, 305–309 (1957); *Chem. Abstracts*, **52**, 4379 (1958).
44a. Fischer, E. O., and H. Grubert, *Chem. Ber.*, **92**, 2302–2309 (1959).
45. Fischer, E. O., and W. Hafner, *Z. Naturforsch.*, **10b**, 665–668 (1955); *Chem. Abstracts*, **50**, 9199 (1956).
46. Fischer, E. O., and R. Jira, *Z. Naturforsch.*, **8b**, 1–2, 217–219, 327–328 (1953); *Chem. Abstracts*, **47**, 9202 (1953); *ibid.*, **48**, 1192–1193 (1954); *ibid.*, **47**, 11,066 (1953).
47. Fischer, E. O., G. Joos, and W. Meer, *Z. Naturforsch.*, **13b**, 456–457 (1958).
48. Fischer, E. O., and U. Piesbergen, *Z. Naturforsch.*, **11b**, 758–759 (1956); *Chem. Abstracts*, **51**, 12,579 (1957).
49. Fischer, E. O., and D. Seus, *Z. Naturforsch.*, **9b**, 386 (1954); *Chem. Ber.*, **89**, 1809–1815 (1956); *Chem. Abstracts*, **49**, 9584 (1955); *ibid.*, **51**, 12,728 (1957).
50. Fischer, E. O., D. Seus, and R. Jira, *Z. Naturforsch.*, **8b**, 692–693 (1953); *Chem. Abstracts*, **48**, 7475 (1954).
51. Fischer, E. O., and A. Wirzmüller, *Chem. Ber.*, **90**, 1725–1730 (1957); *Chem. Abstracts*, **54**, 6603 (1960).
51a. Fischer, E. O., and U. Zahn, *Chem. Ber.*, **92**, 1624–1628 (1959); *Chem. Abstracts*, **54**, 470 (1960).
52. Fischer, R., and M. S. Karawia, *Mikrochim. Acta*, **1953**, 366–374; *Chem. Abstracts*, **48**, 2322 (1954).
52a. Fix, R. C., *Beta-Decay Energetics and Nuclear Systematics*, thesis, Massachusetts Institute of Technology, Cambridge, Mass., 1956.
53. Flaschka, H., *Z. anal. Chem.*, **136**, 99–102 (1952); *Chem. Abstracts*, **46**, 9013 (1952).
54. Flaschka, H., *Chemist-Analyst*, **44**, 60–61 (1955); *Chem. Abstracts*, **49**, 14,565 (1955).
55. Flaschka, H., unpublished.
56. Flaschka, H., and H. Abdine, *Z. anal. Chem.*, **144**, 415–420 (1955); *Chem. Abstracts*, **49**, 6772 (1955).
57. Flaschka, H., and A. M. Amin, *Chemist-Analyst*, **42**, 78–80 (1953); *Chem. Abstracts*, **48**, 498 (1954).
58. Flaschka, H., A. M. Amin, and A. Holasek, *Z. anal. Chem.*, **138**, 241–244 (1953); *Chem. Abstracts*, **47**, 7366–7367 (1953).
59. Flaschka, H., A. Holasek, and A. M. Amin, *Z. anal. Chem.*, **138**, 161–167 (1953); *Chem. Abstracts*, **47**, 5842 (1953).
60. Flaschka, H., A. Holasek, and A. M. Amin, *Arzneimittel-Forsch.*, **4**, 38–40 (1954); *Chem. Abstracts*, **48**, 5442–5443 (1954).

61. Flaschka, H., and F. Sadek, *Chemist-Analyst*, **45**, 20–21 (1956); *Chem. Abstracts*, **50**, 5452–5453 (1956).
62. Flaschka, H., and F. Sadek, *Chemist-Analyst*, **47**, 30–31 (1958); *Chem. Abstracts*, **52**, 16,125 (1958).
63. Fontana, P., and B. Zanetti, *Pubbl. univ. cattolica S. Cuore, Ann. fac. agrar.*, **60**, 201–209 (1956); *Chem. Abstracts*, **52**, 7601 (1958).
64. Ford, O. W., *J. Assoc. Offic. Agr. Chemists*, **39**, 598–602 (1956); *Chem. Abstracts*, **50**, 13,352 (1956).
65. Ford, O. W., *J. Assoc. Offic. Agr. Chemists*, **41**, 533–538 (1958); *Chem. Abstracts*, **53**, 634–635 (1959).
66. Franck, U. F., *Z. Elektrochem.*, **58**, 348–354 (1954); *ibid.*, **62**, 245–250 (1958); *Chem. Abstracts*, **48**, 11,971 (1954); *ibid.*, **52**, 13,480–13,481 (1958).
67. Friedrich, W., and K. Bernhauer, *Chem. Ber.*, **89**, 2030–2044 (1956); *Chem. Abstracts*, **51**, 10,505 (1957).
68. Fuoss, R. M., J. B. Berkowitz, E. Hirsch, and S. Petrucci, *Proc. Natl. Acad. Sci. U. S.*, **44**, 27–32 (1958); *Chem. Abstracts*, **52**, 8692 (1958); F. Accasina and S. Petrucci, *Ricerca sci.*, **29**, 1633–1639 (1959); *Chem. Abstracts*, **54**, 5215 (1960); F. Accasina, S. Petrucci, and R. M. Fuoss, *J. Am. Chem. Soc.*, **81**, 1301–1305 (1959); R. M. Fuoss and E. Hirsch, *ibid.*, **82**, 1013–1017 (1960).
69. Gagliardi, E., and H. Reimers, *Z. anal. Chem.*, **160**, 1–6 (1958); *Chem. Abstracts*, **52**, 12,672 (1958).
70. Garino-Canina, E., *Ann. accad. agr. Torino*, **96** (1954–1955).
71. Gautier, J. A., "Le tétraphénylborure de sodium comme réactif de l'azote basique dans l'analyse pharmaceutique et toxicologique," in *Hommage au Doyen Rene Fabre*, Sèdes, Paris, 1956, pp. 181–188.
72. Gautier, J. A., J. Renault, and F. Pellerin, *Ann. pharm. franç.*, **13**, 725–730 (1955); *Chem. Abstracts*, **50**, 11,884–11,885 (1956).
73. Gautier, J. A., J. Renault, and F. Pellerin, *Ann. pharm. franç.*, **14**, 337–340 (1956); *Chem. Abstracts*, **51**, 1543 (1957).
73a. Gautier, J., A., J. Renault, and J. Rabiant, *Ann. pharm. franç.*, **17**, 401–408 491–497 (1959); *Chem. Abstracts*, **54**, 5016, 7068 (1960).
74. Gayer, J., *Biochem. Z.*, **328**, 39–43 (1956); *Chem. Abstracts*, **51**, 1355 (1957).
75. Geilmann, W., *Angew. Chem.*, **66**, 454 (1954).
76. Geilmann, W., and W. Gebauhr, *Z. anal. Chem.*, **139**, 161–181 (1953); *Chem. Abstracts*, **47**, 11,070 (1953).
77. Geilmann, W., and W. Gebauhr, *Z. anal. Chem.*, **142**, 241–254 (1954); *Chem. Abstracts*, **48**, 10,481 (1954).
78. Geske, D. H., *J. Phys. Chem.*, **63**, 1062–1070 (1959).
79. Gloss, G. H., *Chemist-Analyst*, **42**, 50–55 (1953); *Chem. Abstracts*, **47**, 10,398–10,399 (1953).
80. Gloss, G. H., and B. Olson, *Chemist-Analyst*, **43**, 70–71 (1954); *Chem. Abstracts*, **48**, 12,610 (1954).
81. Gübeli, O., *Mitt. Gebiete Lebensm. u. Hyg.*, **47**, 305–332 (1956); *Chem. Abstracts*, **51**, 9045 (1957).
81a. Hädicke, M., *Pharm. Zentralhalle*, **97**, 365–367 (1958); *Chem. Abstracts*, **52**, 20,881 (1958).
82. Hahn, F. L., *Ciencia* (Mexico), **14**, 249–252 (1954) (published 1955); *Chem. Abstracts*, **49**, 14,559 (1955).

83. Hahn, F. L., Z. anal. Chem., 145, 97–98 (1955); Chem. Abstracts, 49, 7442–7443 (1955).

83a. Handley, T. H., and C. L. Burros, Anal. Chem., 31, 332–334 (1959); Chem. Abstracts, 53, 9898 (1959).

84. Hannig, E., and H. Haendler, Arch. Pharm., 290, 131–136 (1957); Chem. Abstracts, 51, 12,880 (1957).

84a. Hanway, J. J., Fixation and Release of Ammonium in Soils and Certain Minerals, thesis, Iowa State College, Iowa City, 1954; J. J. Hanway, Iowa State Coll. J. Sci., 30, 374 (1956).

85. Hardegger, E., and F. Lohse, Helv. Chim. Acta, 40, 2383–2389 (1957); Cox, H. C., E. Hardegger, F. Kögl, P. Liechti, F. Lohse, and C. A. Salemink, ibid., 41, 229–234 (1958); Corrodi, H., E. Hardegger, F. Kögl, C. A. Salemink, H. Schouten, and F. Jellinek, Rec. trav. chim., 76, 109–127 (1957); Chem. Abstracts, 51, 12,058, 14,671 (1957); ibid., 52, 12,881–12,882, 17,313 (1958).

86. Havíř, J., Voda, 12, 402–403 (1956).

87. Havíř, J., Chem. Listy, 52, 1274–1278 (1958); Collection Czechoslov. Chem. Communs., 24, 1954–1959 (1959); Chem. Abstracts, 53, 5971 (1959); ibid., 54, 170 (1960).

87a. Havíř, J., Collection Czechoslov. Chem. Communs., 25, 595–597 (1960).

87b. Havíř, J., and M. Křivánek, Collection Czechoslov. Chem. Communs., 24, 3183–3185 (1959).

88. Havíř, J., and M. Trkan, Kvasny průmsyl, 2, 274 (1956).

89. Havíř, J., and J. Vřeštál, Chem. zvesti, 11, 35–39 (1957); Chem. Abstracts, 51, 7719 (1957).

90. Hegemann, F., and B. Pfab, Glastech. Ber., 28, 232–233 (1955).

91. Hein, F., P. Kleinert, and E. Kurras, Z. anorg. u. allgem. Chem., 289, 229–243 (1957); Chem. Abstracts, 51, 11,152–11,153 (1957).

91a. Herwig, W., W. Metlesics, and H. Zeiss, J. Am. Chem. Soc., 81, 6203–6207 (1959).

92. Heyl and Co., Hildesheim, Germany, brochures, 1952 and 1954.

93. Heyl and Co., French Pat. 1,043,726 (Nov. 10, 1953); British Pat. 705,719, (March 17, 1954); Chem. Abstracts, 48, 9279 (1954).

94. Heyrovský, A., Chem. Listy, 50, 69–72 (1956); Collection Czechoslov. Chem. Communs., 21, 1150–1154 (1956); Chem. Abstracts, 50, 5453 (1956).

95. Heyrovský, A., Vnitrni Lekarstri, 2, 234–239 (1956); Anal. Abstr., 4, item 2696 (1957).

96. Heyrovský, A., Chemie (Prague), 9, 100–103 (1957).

97. Heyrovský, A., Chem. Listy, 52, 40–42 (1958); Chem. Abstracts, 52, 12,649 (1958); Collection Czechoslov. Chem. Communs., 24, 170–173 (1959).

98. Hieber, W., and W. Freyer, Chem. Ber., 91, 1230–1234 (1958); ibid., 93, 462–467 (1960); Chem. Abstracts, 52, 20,146 (1958)

98a. Hieber, W., and L. Schuster, Z. anorg. u. allgem. Chem., 287, 214–222 (1956); Chem. Abstracts, 51, 7931 (1957).

99. Howick, L. C., Analytical aspects of some tetraphenylboron salts, thesis, Univ. of Iowa, 1957; Univ. Microfilms Publ. No. 23751; Chem. Abstracts, 52, 4389 (1958).

100. Howick, L. C., and R. T. Pflaum, *Anal. Chim. Acta*, 19, 342–347 (1958); *Chem. Abstracts*, 54, 1178 (1960).

101. Hunziker, R. R., *Degradation of Soils and Micaceous Minerals by the Removal of Potassium with Sodium Tetraphenylboron*, thesis, Iowa State College, 1958; *Univ. Microfilms L. C. Card* No. Mic 58-2187.

102. Ieviņš, A. F., and F. Gudriniece, *Zhur. Anal. Khim.*, 9, 270–274 (1954); *J. Anal. Chem. U.S.S.R.*, 9, 301–305 (1954); *Chem. Abstracts*, 49, 2940, 6771 (1955).

103. Ieviņš, A. F., and E. Gudriniece, *Latvijas PSR Zinātņu Akad. Vēstis*, 1954, No. 8, 131–136; through *Chem. Zentr.*, 126, 11,261 (1955).

104. Ieviņš, A. F., and E. Gudriniece, *Zhur. Anal. Khim.*, 11, 735–738 (1956); *J. Anal. Chem. U.S.S.R.*, 11, 789–792 (1956); *Chem. Abstracts*, 51, 8586, 16,210 (1957).

105. Ieviņš, A. F., J. Ozols, and E. Gudriniece, *Latvijas PSR Zinātņu Akad. Vēstis*, 1955, No. 7, 135–136; through *Chem. Abstracts*, 50, 14,307 (1956).

105a. Ieviņš, A. F., and M. Peinberga, *Latvijas PSR Zinātņu Akad. Vēstis*, 1959, No. 5, 85–90; through *Chem. Abstracts*, 54, 1174 (1960).

105b. Infield, C. H., and T. Manfredo, unpublished.

105c. International Union of Pure and Applied Chemistry, Inorganic Chemistry Section, *Nomenclature of Inorganic Chemistry*, Butterworths Scientific Publications, London, 1959.

106. Jančić, M. S., *Bull. soc. chimistes rép. populaire Bosnie et Herzégovine*, 3, 37–40 (1955); *Chem. Abstracts*, 49, 14,865 (1955).

107. Jander, G., and A. Anke, *Z. anal. Chem.*, 154, 8–17 (1957); *Chem. Abstracts*, 51, 13,645 (1957).

107a. Jansons, E., A. F. Ieviņš, and E. Gudriniece, *Uchenye Zapiski, Latv. Univ.*, 14, 9–16 (1957); through *Anal. Abstr.*, 6, item 221 (1959).

107b. Jansons, E., and A. Ieviņš, *Latvijas Valsts Univ. Ķīm. Fak. Zinātniskie Raksti*, 22, No. 6, 85–90 (1958); through *Chem. Abstracts*, 53, 12,955 (1959).

107c. Jansons, E., and A. Ieviņš, *Latvijas Valsts Univ. Ķīm. Fak. Zintāniskie Raksti*, 22, No. 6, 91–94 (1958); through *Chem. Abstracts*, 53, 12,955 (1959).

107d. Jansons, E., and A. F. Ieviņš, *Uspekhi Khim.*, 28, 980–989 (1959); through *Chem. Abstracts*, 53, 21,434 (1959).

108. Kahn, B., D. K. Smith, and C. P. Straub, *Anal. Chem.*, 29, 1210–1213 (1957); *Chem. Abstracts*, 51, 15,327 (1957).

108a. Karrman, K. J., E. Bladh, and P.-O. Gedda, *Mikrochim. Acta*, 1959, 775–778.

108b. Karrman, K. J., E. Bladh, and P.-O. Gedda, *Mikrochim. Acta*, 1959, 779–785.

109. Kauer, E., *Z. physik. Chem.*, 6, 105–117 (1956); *Chem. Abstracts*, 50, 3074 (1956).

110. Keller, W., and F. Weiss, *Pharmazie*, 12, 19–24 (1957); *Chem. Abstracts*, 51, 10,839 (1957).

111. Kemula, W., and J. Kornacki, *Roczniki Chem.* (Warsaw), 28, No. 4, 635–641 (1954); *Chem. Abstracts*, 49, 8733 (1955).

112. Kingsley, W. K., G. E. Wolf, and W. E. Wolfram, *Anal. Chem.*, 29, 939–941 (1957); *Chem. Abstracts*, 51, 12,744 (1957).

113. Kirsten, W. J., A. Berggren, and K. Nilsson, *Anal. Chem.*, **30**, 237–240 (1958); ibid., **31**, 376 (1959).
114. Klevstrand, R., *Medd. Norsk Farm. Selskap*, **17**, 190–197 (1955); *Chem. Abstracts*, **49**, 16,331 (1955).
115. Kohler, M., *Z. anal. Chem.*, **138**, 9–18 (1953); *Chem. Abstracts*, **47**, 5301 (1953).
116. Kornacki, J., *Wiadomości Chem.*, **8**, 538–544 (1954); through *Chem. Abstracts*, **49**, 11,488 (1955).
117. Kranjčević, M., and V. Broz-Kajganović, *Croat. Chem. Acta*, **30**, 47–52 (1958); *Anal. Abstracts*, **5**, item 3492 (1958).
117a. Kuhn, R., and G. Osswald, *Angew. Chem.*, **69**, 60 (1957); Kuhn, R., and G. Krüger, *Chem. Ber.*, **90**, 764–777 (1957); *Chem. Abstracts*, **51**, 12,061, 14,677 (1957).
118. Kuhn, R., and H. Trischmann, *Ann.*, **611**, 117–121 (1958); *Chem. Abstracts*, **52**, 14,523–14,524 (1958).
119. Lane, E. S., *Analyst*, **82**, 406–415 (1957); *Chem. Abstracts*, **51**, 14,466 (1957).
119a. Lange, J., *Sprechsaal*, **92**, 305–310 (1959); *Chem. Abstracts*, **53**, 18,417 (1959).
120. Lappert, M. F., *Chem. Revs.*, **56**, 959–1064 (1956); *Chem. Abstracts*, **51**, 2536 (1957).
121. Levina, N. D., and L. I. Panteleeva, *Zavodskaya Lab.*, **23**, 285–287 (1957); *Chem. Abstracts*, **52**, 679 (1958).
122. Lieber, W., *Zement-Kalk-Gips*, **10**, 61–62 (1957); *Chem. Abstracts*, **51**, 10,304 (1957).
123. Marquardt, P., and G. Vogg, *Hoppe-Seyler's Z. physiol. Chem.*, **291**, 143–147 (1952); *Chem. Abstracts*, **48**, 12,855 (1954).
124. Mével, N., and B. LaCruche, *Mikrochim. Acta*, **1958**, 241–247; *Chem. Abstracts*, **53**, 8936 (1959).
125. Montequi, R., A. Doadrio, and M. Fernández Santiso, *Inform. quím. anal.* (Madrid), **11**, 1–7 (1957); *Chem. Abstracts*, **51**, 10,298 (1957).
126. Montequi, R., A. Doadrio, and C. Serrano, *Anales real soc. españ. fís. y quím.* (Madrid), **52B**, 597–600 (1956); *Publs. inst. quím. "Alonso Barba"* (Madrid), **10**, 183–188 (1956); *Chem. Abstracts*, **51**, 11,906 (1957).
127. Montequi, R., A. Doadrio, and C. Serrano, *Anales real soc. españ. fís. y quím.* (Madrid), **53B**, 447–452 (1957).
128. Montequi, R., A. Doadrio, and C. Serrano, *Inform. quím. anal.* (Madrid), **11**, 8–12 (1957); *Chem. Abstracts*, **51**, 10,312 (1957).
129. Montequi, A., A. Doadrio, and C. Serrano, *Anales real soc. españ. fís. y quím.* (Madrid), **54B**, 29–34 (1958); *Chem. Abstracts*, **52**, 11,663 (1958).
130. Montequi, M. R., and Santiso, *J. méd. Bordeaux*, **134**, 650–655 (1957); *Chem. Abstracts*, **52**, 15,748 (1958).
131. Mukherji, A. K., and B. R. Sant, *Anal. Chem.*, **31**, 608–609 (1959); *Chem. Abstracts*, **53**, 13,884 (1959).
132. Mukherji, A. K., and B. R. Sant, *Mikrochim. Acta*, **1959**, 370–371; *Anal. Abstr.*, **6**, item 4846 (1959).
133. Mukoyama, T., *Kagaku no Ryôiki*, **10**, 103–111 (February 1956); *Chem. Abstracts*, **51**, 17,611 (1957).

134. Munroe, D. S., H. Renschler, and G. M. Wilson, *J. Physiol.* (*London*), **128**, 68P (1955); *Phys. in Med. Biol.*, **2**, 239–254 (1958); *Chem. Abstracts*, **52**, 18,616–18,617 (1959).

135. Muraca, R. F., *Chemist-Analyst*, **43**, 69–70 (1954); *Chem. Abstracts*, **48**, 12,612 (1954).

136. Muraca, R. F., H. E. Collier, J. P. Bonsack, and E. S. Jacobs, *Chemist-Analyst*, **43**, 102–103 (1954); *Chem. Abstracts*, **49**, 774–775 (1954).

137. Muraire, M., *Chim. anal.*, **39**, 184–188 (1957); Chem. Abstracts, **51**, 11,921 (1957).

138. Musil, A., and H. Reimers, *Z. anal. Chem.*, **152**, 154–158 (1956); *Chem. Abstracts*, **51**, 3360 (1957).

138a. Mýl, J., J. Krapil, and O. Leman, *Chem. průmysl*, **9**, 77 (1959); *Chem. Abstracts*, **53**, 17,030 (1959).

138b. Nakagawa, Y., and H. Isaka, *Eisei Shikenjo Hôkoku*, **76**, 69–73 (1958); *Chem. Abstracts*, **53**, 16,465 (1959).

139. Neeb, K. H., and W. Gebauhr, *Z. anal. Chem.*, **162**, 167–174 (1958); *Chem. Abstracts*, **53**, 126 (1959).

140. Nesmayanov, A. N., N. V. Kruglova, R. B. Materikova, and T. P. Tolstaya, *Zhur. Obshcheĭ Khim.*, **26**, 2211–2218 (1956); *Chem. Abstracts*, **51**, 4974–4975 (1957).

141. Nesmeyanov, A. N., and V. A. Sazonova, *Izvest. Akad. Nauk S.S.S.R.*, *Otdel. Khim. Nauk*, **1955**, 187; *Bull. Acad. Sci., U.S.S.R., Div. Chem. Sci.*, **1955**, 167; *Chem. Abstracts*, **50**, 1646 (1956).

142. Nesmeyanov, A. N., V. A. Sazonova, G. S. Liberman, and L. I. Emel'yanova, *Izvest. Akad. Nauk S.S.S.R.*, *Otdel. Khim. Nauk*, **1955**, 48–53; *Bull. Acad. Sci., U.S.S.R., Div. Chem. Sci.*, **1955**, 41–45; *Chem. Abstracts*, **50**, 1644 (1956).

143. Nesmeyanov, A. N., and T. P. Tolstaya, *Doklady Akad. Nauk S.S.S.R.*, **105**, 94–95 (1955); *Chem. Abstracts*, **50**, 11266 (1956).

144. Nesmeyanov, A. N., T. P. Tolstaya, and L. S. Isaeva, *Doklady Akad. Nauk S.S.S.R.*, **104**, 872–875 (1955); *Chem. Abstracts*, **50**, 11,266 (1956).

145. Neu, R., *Z. anal. Chem.*, **143**, 254–257 (1954); *Chem. Abstracts*, **49**, 2949 (1955).

146. Neu, R., *Chem. Ber.*, **87**, 802–805 (1954); *Chem. Abstracts*, **49**, 9538 (1955).

147. Neu, R., *Arzneimittel-Forsch.*, **4**, 601–606 (1954); *ibid.*, **6**, 94–99 (1956); *Chem. Abstracts*, **49**, 2679 (1955); *ibid.*, **50**, 14,183 (1956).

148. Neu, R., *Fette, Seifen, Anstrichmittel*, **59**, 823–826 (1957); *Chem. Abstracts*, **53**, 17,752 (1959).

149. Neu, R., *Seifen-Öle-Fette-Wachse*, **84**, 167–170 (1958).

150. Neu, R., *Chemist-Analyst*, **47**, 106–109 (1958); *Chem. Abstracts*, **53**, 6883 (1959).

150a. Neu, R., *Arch. Pharm.*, **292**, 437–442 (1959).

150b. Neu, R., *Naturwissenschaften*, **46**, 262–263 (1959); *Chem. Abstracts*, **54**, 1519 (1960).

150c. Neu, R., *Arzneimittel-Forsch.*, **9**, 585–587 (1959).

151. Neumann, F., *Das Papier*, **7**, 388–391 (1953); *Chem. Abstracts*, **48**, 362 (1954).

152. Nutten, A. J., *Ind. Chemist*, **30**, 29–31, 57–59 (1954).
153. Pahlow, M., *Deut. Apoth.-Ztg. ver. Süddeut. Apoth.-Ztg.*, **93**, 541–542 (1953); *Chem. Abstracts*, **47**, 12,763 (1953).
153a. Parpaillon, M., *Mém. poudres*, **39**, 417–428 (1957); *Chem. Abstracts*, **52**, 21,107 (1958).
153b. Patel, D. M., and R. A. Anderson, *Drug Standards*, **26**, 189–193 (1958).
153c. Paul, A. D., and A. J. Gibson, Jr., *J. Chem. Educ.*, **36**, 380–381 (1959); *Chem. Abstracts*, **54**, 1173 (1960).
154. Pellerin, F. M., *Ann. pharm. franç.*, **14**, 193–196 (1956); *Chem. Abstracts*, **50**, 16,039 (1956).
155. Pflaum, R. T., and L. C. Howick, *Anal. Chem.*, **28**, 1542–1544 (1956); *Chem. Abstracts*, **51**, 942 (1957).
156. Pinxteren, J. A. C. van, M. E. Verloop, and D. Westerink, *Pharm. Weekblad*, **91**, 873–883 (1956); *Chem. Abstracts*, **51**, 6953 (1957).
156a. Popov, A. I., and R. E. Humphrey, *J. Am. Chem. Soc.*, **81**, 2043–2047 (1959); *Chem. Abstracts*, **53**, 16,689 (1959).
157. Power, M. H., personal communication.
158. Power, M. H., and C. Ryan, *Clin. Chem.*, **2**, 230–231 (1956).
159. Prodinger, W., *Organische Fällungsmittel in der quantitativen Analyse*, Ferdinand Enke Verlag, Stuttgart, Germany, 3rd ed., 1954, pp. 15–19, 223–225; 4th ed., 1957, pp. 15–26.
160. Raff, P., and W. Brotz, *Z. anal. Chem.*, **133**, 241–248 (1951); *Chem. Abstracts*, **46**, 59 (1952).
161. Razuvaev, G. A., and T. G. Brilkina, *Doklady Akad. Nauk S.S.S.R.*, **85**, 815–818 (1952); *ibid.*, **91**, 861–864 (1953); *Uchnye Zapiski Gor'kovsk. Gosudarst. Univ. im. N. I. Lobachevskogo, Ser. Kim.*, **1958**, No. 32, 169–173; *Chem. Abstracts*, **47**, 3744 (1953); *ibid.*, **48**, 3180 (1954); *ibid.*, 9855 (1960).
162. Razuvaev, G. A., and T. G. Brilkina, *Zhur. Obshcheĭ Khim.*, **24**, 1415–1421 (1954); *J. Gen. Chem. U.S.S.R.*, **24**, 1397–1402 (1954); *Chem. Abstracts*, **49**, 15,591 (1955); *ibid.*, **50**, 5443 (1956).
163. Reichard, O., *Z. anal. Chem.*, **140**, 188–197 (1953); *Chem. Abstracts*, **48**, 2317 (1954).
164. Reichard, O., *Wein u. Rebe*, **1954**, No. 32, 668.
165. Reimers, H., *Chemiker-Ztg.*, **81**, 357–359 (1957); *Chem. Abstracts*, **51**, 16,179 (1957).
166. Renault, J., "Le tétraphénylborure de sodium comme réactif analytique," in *Mises au point chimie analytique pure et appliquée et d'analyse bromatologique*, J. A. Gautier, Ed., 6th series, 1958, pp. 109–125.
167. Riva, B., *Ann. chim.* (Rome), **48**, 50–55 (1958); *Chem. Abstracts*, **52**, 9861–9862 (1958).
168. Rochow, E. G., D. T. Hurd, and R. N. Lewis, *The Chemistry of Organometallic Compounds*, Wiley, New York, 1957.
169. Rosenthaler, L., and F. Lüdy-Tenger, *Pharm. Acta Helv.*, **32**, 35–46 (1957); *Chem. Abstracts*, **51**, 10,003 (1957).
170. Rubia Pacheco, J. de la, and F. Blasco López-Rubio, *Inform. quím. anal.* (*Madrid*), **9**, 1–9, 21 (1955); *Chem. Abstracts*, **49**, 10,796 (1955).
171. Rubia Pacheco, J. de la, and F. Blasco López-Rubio, *Chemist-Analyst*, **44**, 58–60 (1955); *Chem. Abstracts*, **49**, 14,565 (1955).

172. Rüdorff, W., and H. Zannier, *Z. anal. Chem.*, **137**, 1–5 (1952); *Chem. Abstracts*, **47**, 68–69 (1953).

173. Rüdorff, W., and H. Zannier, *Z. anal. Chem.*, **140**, 1–5 (1953); *Chem. Abstracts*, **48**, 1198 (1954).

174. Rüdorff, W., and H. Zannier, *Z. anal. Chem.*, **140**, 241–244 (1953); *Chem. Abstracts*, **48**, 2513 (1954).

175. Rüdorff, W., and H. Zannier, *Z. Naturforsch.*, **8b**, 611–612 (1953); *Chem. Abstracts*, **48**, 4293 (1954).

176. Rüdorff, W., and H. Zannier, *Angew. Chem.*, **66**, 638–639 (1954); *Chem. Abstracts*, **49**, 775 (1955).

177. Rutkowski, R., *Arzneimittel-Forsch.*, **3**, 537–539 (1953); *Chem. Abstracts*, **48**, 5442 (1954).

178. Sacco, A., *Gazz. chim. ital.*, **86**, 201–206 (1956); *Rec. trav. chim.*, **75**, 646–647 (1956); Sacco, A., and M. Freni, *Gazz. chim. ital.*, **86**, 195–198 (1956); Sacco, A., and L. Naldini, *Rend. ist. lombardo sci.* Part I, **91**, 286–290 (1957); *Chem. Abstracts*, **50**, 16,512–16,513, 16,520–16,522 (1956); *ibid.*, **52**, 11,501 (1958).

178a. Sadek, F. S., and C. N. Reilley, *Anal. Chem.*, **24**, 494–498 (1959); *Chem. Abstracts*, **53**, 12,921 (1959).

179. Sant, B. R., and A. K. Mukherji, *Talanta*, **2**, 154–155 (1959); *Chem. Abstracts*, **53**, 14,844 (1959).

179a. Sazonova, V. A., and V. N. Leonov, *Zhur. Anal. Khim.*, **14**, 483–484 (1959); *Chem. Abstracts*, **54**, 9608–9609 (1960).

180. Sazonova, V. A., and I. I. Nazarova, *Zhur. Obshcheĭ Khim.*, **26**, 3440–3445 (1956); *J. Gen. Chem. U.S.S.R.*, **26**, 3829–3833 (1956); *Chem. Abstracts*, **51**, 9514 (1957); *ibid.*, **52**, 14,558 (1958).

181. Sazonova, V. A., and E. P. Serebryakov, U.S.S.R., Pat. 106,396, (Aug. 25, 1957); *Chem. Abstracts*, **52**, 2667 (1958).

182. Sazonova, V. A., E. P. Serebryakov, and L. S. Kovaleva, *Doklady Akad. Nauk S.S.S.R.*, **113**, 1295–1298 (1957); *Chem. Abstracts*, **52**, 354 (1958).

183. Schall, E. D., *Anal. Chem.*, **29**, 1044–1046 (1957); *Chem. Abstracts*, **51**, 13,645 (1957).

184. Schmidt, H. J., *Z. anal. Chem.*, **157**, 321–338 (1957); *Chem. Abstracts*, **52**, 968 (1958).

185. Schmidt, H. J., personal communication.

186. Schmied, W., and L. Stegmüller, *Ber. deut. keram. Ges.*, **34**, 135–141 (1957).

187. Schneyder, J., *Fachliche Mitt. Oesterr. Tabakregie*, **1957**, 25–29; *Chem. Abstracts*, **51**, 18,490–18,491 (1957).

188. Schober, I. R., and A. Fricker, *Z. Lebensm.-Untersuch. u. -Forsch.*, **95**, 107–108 (1952); *ibid.*, **97**, 177–182 (1953); *Chem. Abstracts*, **46**, 11,479 (1952); *ibid.*, **48**, 298 (1954).

189. Schultz, O. E., and H. Goerner, *Deut. Apoth. Ztg. ver. Süddeut. Apoth.-Ztg.*, **93**, 585 (1953); *Chem. Abstracts*, **47**, 12,763–12,764 (1953).

190. Schultz, O. E., and H. Goerner, *Arch. Pharm.*, **288**, 520–525 (1955); *Chem. Abstracts*, **50**, 12,404 (1956).

191. Schultz, O. E., and H. Goerner, *Arch. Pharm.*, **291**, 386–391 (1958); *Chem. Abstracts*, **53**, 3600–3601 (1959).

192. Schultz, O. E., and G. Mayer, *Deut. Apoth.-Ztg. ver. Süddeut. Apoth.-Ztg.*, **92**, 358–359 (1952); *Chem. Abstracts*, **46**, 11,580 (1952).

193. Schwaibold, J., and M. Kohler, *Landwirtschaftliches Jahrbuch für Bayern,* **30,** Heft 1/2, 55–62 (1953).
193a. Scott, A. D., A. P. Edwards, and J. M. Brenner, *Nature,* **185,** 792 (1960).
193b. Scott, A. D., R. R. Hunziker, and J. J. Hanway, *Soil Sci. Soc. Am., Proc.,* in press (1960).
193c. Scott, A. D., R. R. Hunziker, and M. G. Reed, *Chemist-Analyst,* **48,** 11–12 (1959); *Chem. Abstracts,* **53,** 19,525 (1959).
193d. Scott, A. D., and M. G. Reed, *Soil Sci. Soc. Am., Proc.,* in press (1960); A. D. Scott *et al.,* unpublished.
194. Scott, W. E., H. M. Doukas, and P. S. Schaffer, *J. Am. Pharm. Assoc., Sci. Ed.,* **45,** 568–570 (1956); *Chem. Abstracts,* **50,** 16,044 (1956).
195. Sirotina, I. A., and I. P. Alimarin, *Zhur. Anal. Khim.,* **12,** 367–371 (1957); *J. Anal. Chem. U.S.S.R.,* **12,** 381–385 (1957); *Chem. Abstracts,* **52,** 1849–1850, 12,672–12,673 (1958).
196. Solari, J., *Inds. aliment et. agr. (Paris),* **73,** 25–27 (1956); *Anal. Abstr.,* **3,** item 2898 (1956); *Chim. anal.,* **38,** 91–93 (1956); *Chem. Abstracts,* **50,** 17,285 (1956).
197. Spier, H. W., *Biochem. Z.,* **322,** 467–470 (1952); *Chem. Abstracts,* **46,** 11,028 (1952).
198. Sporek, K. F., *Analyst,* **81,** 540–543 (1956); *Chem. Abstracts,* **51,** 1770 (1957).
199. Sporek, K. F., personal communication.
200. Sporek, K. F.; and A. F. Williams, *Analyst,* **80,** 347–354 (1955); *Chem. Abstracts,* **49,** 10,120 (1955).
201. Stephen, W. L., *Mikrochim. Acta,* **1956,** 1540–1543; *Chem. Abstracts,* **50,** 14,434 (1956).
202. Sunderman, F. W., Jr., and F. W. Sunderman, *Am. J. Clin. Path.,* **29,** 95–103 (1958); Sunderman, F. W., *et al., ibid.,* **30,** 269–283 (1958); *Chem. Abstracts,* **52,** 10,273 (1958).
203. Sykes, A., *Ind. Chemist,* **31,** 245–247, 305–307 (1955); *ibid.,* **32,** 164–166, 223–225 (1956).
204. Teeri, A. E., and P. G. Sesin, *Tech. Bull. Registry Med. Technologists,* **27,** 280–283 (1957); *Am. J. Clin. Path.,* **29,** 86–89 (1958); *Chem. Abstracts,* **52,** 8262 (1958).
205. Teijgeler, C. A., *Chem. en Pharm. Tech. (Dordrecht),* **13,** 48, 57–58, 75–76, 90–92 (1957); *Chem. Abstracts,* **52,** 1838 (1958).
206. Tendille, C., *Ann. inst. natl. recherche agron. Sér. A. Ann. agron.,* **6,** 1055–1058 (1955); *Chim. anal.,* **38,** 371 (1956); *Chem. Abstracts,* **54,** 5340 (1960).
207. Tranchant, J., and L. Marvillet, *Mém. poudres,* **38,** 337–341 (1956); *Chem. Abstracts,* **51,** 11,172 (1957).
207a. Tufts, B. J., *Anal. Chem.,* **31,** 242–243 (1959); *Chem. Abstracts,* **53,** 11,724 (1959).
207b. Veĭs, A., and A. Ieviņš, *Latvijas Vals's Univ. Kīm. Fak. Zinātniskie Raksti,* **22,** No. 6, 95–99 (1958); through *Chem. Abstracts,* **53,** 12,921 (1959); *Anal. Abstr.,* **7,** item 369 (1960).
207c. Veĭs, A. R., and A. F. Ieviņš, *Zhur. Anal. Khim.,* **14,** 143–144 (1959); *Anal. Abstr.,* **6,** item 3911 (1959).

207d. Venturini, A., *Boll. lab. chim. provinciali* (*Bologna*), **9,** 425–429 (1958); through *Chem. Abstracts,* **53,** 15,864 (1959).

207e. Vicaire, P., *Soc. sci. nat. et phys. Maroc., Compt. rend. séances mensuelles,* **24,** 185–187 (1958); *Chem. Abstracts,* **54,** 2088–2089 (1960).

207f. Vittori, O., *Tech. Notes, Cloud Physics Lab.* (*University of Chicago*), No. 5, 18–19 (Dec. 15, 1956).

208. Vohler, O., *Chem. Ber.,* **91,** 1235–1238 (1958); *Chem. Abstracts,* **52,** 20,147 (1958).

209. Wachsmuth, H., and E. Mertens, *J. pharm. Belg.,* **13,** 58–62 (1958); *Chem. Abstracts,* **52,** 14,080 (1958).

210. Walter, W., *Angew. Chem.,* **70,** 404 (1958).

211. Weisz, H., *Mikrochim. Acta,* **1954,** 140–147, 376–387, 460, 785–794; *Chem. Abstracts,* **48,** 4259, 9272, 9256 (1954); *ibid.,* **49,** 3718 (1955).

212. Wendlandt, W. W., *Anal. Chem.,* **28,** 1001–1002 (1956); *Chem. Abstracts,* **50,** 11,159 (1956).

213. Wendlandt, W. W., *Anal. Chim. Acta,* **16,** 216–220 (1957); *Chem. Abstracts,* **51,** 11,922 (1957).

214. Wendlandt, W. W., *Chemist-Analyst,* **46,** 38–39 (1957); *Chem. Abstracts,* **51,** 12,755 (1957).

215. Wendlandt, W. W., *Chemist-Analyst,* **46,** 8 (1957); *Chem. Abstracts,* **51,** 12,745 (1957).

216. Wendlandt, W. W., *Chemist-Analyst,* **47,** 6–7 (1958); *Chem. Abstracts,* **52,** 12,787–12,788 (1958).

217. Wendlandt, W. W., *Chemist-Analyst,* **47,** 38–39 (1958); *Chem. Abstracts,* **52,** 2005 (1958).

218. Wendlandt, W. W., personal communication.

219. Wendlandt, W. W., and R. Dunham, *Anal. Chim. Acta,* **19,** 505–507 (1958); *Chem. Abstracts,* **53,** 21,000 (1959).

220. Wittig, G., *Angew. Chem.,* **62A,** 231–236 (1950); *Chem. Abstracts,* **44,** 8810 (1950).

221. Wittig, G., and K. Clauss, *Ann.,* **577,** 26–39 (1952); *Chem. Abstracts,* **47,** 3260–3261 (1953).

221a. Wittig, G., and K. Clauss, *Ann.,* **578,** 136–146 (1952); *Chem. Abstracts,* **47,** 12,282–12,283 (1953).

222. Wittig, G., and H. Fritz, *Ann.,* **577,** 39–46 (1952); *Chem. Abstracts* **47,** 3261–3262 (1953).

223. Wittig, G., and W. Herwig, *Chem. Ber.,* **88,** 962–976 (1955); *Chem. Abstracts,* **50,** 13,731–13,732 (1956).

224. Wittig, G., and G. Keicher, *Naturwissenschaften,* **34,** 216 (1947); *Chem. Abstracts,* **43,** 5758 (1949).

225. Wittig, G., G. Keicher, A. Rückert, and P. Raff, *Ann.,* **563,** 110–126 (1949); *Chem. Abstracts,* **43,** 7448–7449 (1949).

226. Wittig, G., and H. Ludwig, *Ann.,* **589,** 55–76 (1954); *Chem. Abstracts,* **49,** 12,435–12,437 (1955).

227. Wittig, G., F. J. Meyer, and G. Lange, *Ann.,* **571,** 167–201 (1951); *Chem. Abstracts,* **45,** 5556–5557 (1951).

228. Wittig, G., and R. Polster, *Ann.*, **599**, 1–12, 13–22 (1956); *Chem. Abstracts*, **51**, 248–250 (1957).

229. Wittig, G., and P. Raff, *Ann.*, **573**, 195–209 (1951); *Chem. Abstracts*, **46**, 6607–6608 (1952).

230. Wittig, G., and P. Raff, U. S. Pat. 2,853,525 (Sept. 23, 1958), to Heyl & Co.; Chem. Abstracts, **53**, 4211 (1959).

231. Wittig, G., and K. Torssell, *Acta Chem. Scand.*, **7**, 1293–1301 (1953); *Chem. Abstracts*, **49**, 7511 (1955).

232. Worrell, L., and W. R. Ebert, *Drug Standards*, **24**, 153–157 (1956).

233. Yamaguchi, R., K. Osawa, and M. Yamaguchi, *Hoshi Yakka Daigaku Kiyô*, **7**, 10–13, 14–17 (1958); *Chem. Abstracts*, **52**, 15,339 (1958).

233a. Yankov, H. F., *Chemist-Analyst*, **48**, 38–39 (1959); *Chem. Abstracts*, **53**, 20,724–20,725 (1959).

234. Zeidler, L., *Hoppe-Seyler's Z. physiol. Chem.*, **291**, 177–178 (1952); *Chem. Abstracts*, **48**, 12,616–12,617 (1954).

235. Zeiss, H. H., and W. Herwig, *J. Am. Chem. Soc.*, **78**, 5959 (1956); *Ann.*, **606**, 209–215 (1957); *Chem. Abstracts*, **51**, 4982 (1957).

236. Zief, M., *J. Org. Chem.*, **24**, 1338–1339 (1959).

237. Zief, M., Woodside, R., and E. Huber, *Antibiotics & Chemotherapy*, **7**, 604–605 (1957); Chem. Abstracts, **52**, 9268 (1958).

238. Zymny, E., *Glas-Email-Keramo-Tech.*, **6**, 236–237 (1955); *Chem. Abstracts*, **49**, 12,183 (1955).

239. Zymny, E., *Prakt. Chem.*, **6**, 327–329 (1955); *Chem. Abstracts*, **50**, 12,375 (1956).

Recent Advances in Gas Chromatography Detectors

ROBERT B. SELIGMAN AND FORREST L. GAGER, JR., *Philip Morris, Inc., Richmond, Virginia*

I. INTRODUCTION

The applications of gas chromatography to analytical problems have increased phenomenally since James and Martin published their paper on the gas chromatographic separation of fatty acids (32). Numerous papers on theory and on applied usage have been presented at international symposia. Many arrangements of apparatus and many new detectors have been described in journals throughout the world.

The aim of this review is to evaluate some of the established methods and some of the more recent advances in vapor detection.

Gas chromatography, as a separatory technique, is dependent upon detecting devices. Only by means of a detector can the chromatographer tell if, when, and how well the components of a mixture are separated. Only through the application of a reliable detector can materials be analyzed quantitatively. We refer the reader to the original papers of James and Martin, to the books written by Phillips and by Keulemans, and to the proceedings of international symposia for presentations concerned generally with gas chromatography and specifically with detectors (6,12,32,35,48). At the London Symposium, James and Boer reviewed the properties of numerous types of detectors (4,31).

The Committee on Gas Chromatography has outlined specific points which must be considered in the selection of any detector (11). These factors include sensitivity, linearity of response, necessity of calibration, response time and volume of detector, reproducibility, temperature range, and applicability to types of vapors. An important feature of sensitivity considerations is the reporting of normal base line stabilities, both short and long term (noise and drift). The Committee has recommended that sensitivities be reported in terms of vapor concentrations. For theoretical considerations of detectors, this is particularly important; however, the method suggested by Dimbat, Porter, and Stross is more practical for comparing instruments (13). This latter method is based upon the response recorded during a chromatographic analysis. This response determines the sensitivity of the entire chromatographic apparatus and provides an attractive standard for comparing different pieces of apparatus, especially those that are commercially obtainable. Their calculation is:

$$S = A \cdot C_1 \cdot C_2 \cdot C_3 / W$$

where S = sensitivity in cm.^{3} mv./mg.; A = peak area in cm.^{2}; C_1 = reciprocal chart speed of recorder in min./cm.; C_2 = recorder scale in mv./cm.; C_3 = flow rate of carrier gas corrected to cell conditions in cm.^{3}/min.; and W = weight of component in mg.

Whenever possible, either the concentration method or the Dimbat method of reporting sensitivities will be used in this review. Otherwise, absolute amounts detectable will be recorded.

II. ADVANCES AND INNOVATIONS IN ESTABLISHED DETECTORS

1. Martin Density Balance

The gas density balance has been used extensively by Martin and James (42) and by others, especially in England. Recently, more sensitive detectors have been devised, but the density balance retains certain advantages. Perhaps the least appreciated of these is its use in determining molecular weights of compounds from data measured with two different carrier gases and a known standard (38). Molecular weights of unknown materials are, of course, particularly applicable to qualitative analyses. If the molecular weights of the components of the mixture are known, however, calibrations are not necessary for the individual compounds. The density balance has this distinct advantage over other detectors. When quantitative analyses are desired for mixtures whose qualitative composition is known, no synthetic mixture need be run for standardization.

The presence of vapors more dense than the carrier gas causes a pressure across, and therefore a flow of gas through, the anemometer portion of the gas density balance. This flow of pure carrier gas is measured by a heat source with auxiliary thermocouples. Because the sample vapors never touch the detecting element, there can be no decomposition, and compounds can be recovered unchanged.

Quantitatively, the density balance is sensitive (capable of detecting 1 molecule in 10,000 of nitrogen) and has excellent stability. It can be used over a wide temperature range and with all vapors whose densities are different from that of the chosen carrier gas.

The cost is relatively high and the construction of the balance itself is rather difficult. Martin drilled an intricate maze of passages from a metal block. Munday and Primavesi (45) have reported a skeleton model constructed from tubing. This was simpler to build and was more readily checked for leaks. They reported, however, a lower sensitivity than that obtained with the solid model. The decrease was explained as being due to the geometry of their detector. The positioning of the thermocouples is critical in relation to sensitivity.

Since the detector depends on the density of gases, the temperature must be very closely controlled. This has been achieved by using a vapor jacket as an integral part of the detector assembly.

2. Thermal Conductivity Cells

Thermal conductivity detectors (katharometers) have been used extensively and quite satisfactorily in gas chromatography (1,12,15, 31,35,48,51). Hot-wire and thermistor katharometers have been reported by many investigators. In the United States, manufacturers have utilized both types for commercial gas chromatography units. In England and Europe, where helium is expensive and in limited supply, manufacturers have frequently used other detectors (hydrogen flame and the density balance).

Platinum and tungsten wires in straight and coiled configurations have been used as the filaments. In the conductivity detector, the filaments are arranged as resistances in a Wheatstone bridge circuit. When carrier gas is passed over both the reference and the sample elements, a balanced circuit exists. When other vapors pass over the hot filament in the sample cell, the resistance changes and the imbalance is recorded potentiometrically. The detectors are rugged, reliable, and easily used by nontechnical personnel. When helium or hydrogen is used as the carrier gas, the detectors are sensitive over a wide temperature range.

Thermistor units have been popular also. At moderate temperatures, sensitivities greater than those obtained with hot wires are realized. The sensitivity falls off, however, with increased temperature. The use of higher resistance elements (the thermistors have a negative resistance coefficient) for specified temperature ranges has been fruitful. Thermistor detectors are especially sensitive to temperature changes and require fine temperature control. The construction of the Wheatstone bridge circuit requires a carefully matched pair of thermistors for the sample and reference variable resistances. Theoretically, two variable resistors placed in series in the sample gas stream and two in the reference gas would give an extremely sensitive detector. In practice, however, it is almost impossible to obtain four thermistors whose temperature–resistance characteristics are identical over a wide temperature range. Thus, experience in our laboratories has shown that the use of four thermistors in the bridge is impractical.

Signal amplification can be used with katharometers, especially with the thermistor types which give high signal-to-noise ratios. Such a system has been used (2) to detect impurities in organic solvents in the parts-per-million range. Factors involving the selection and operation of thermistors as detector elements have been reported in the literature (2,7,8). Although the noise level of thermistors is low, drift and general instability is somewhat higher than with hot wire filaments. "Aging" the thermistors does, however, aid in improving their performance; the aging should be carried out before the matching of pairs of thermistors (7). The use of hydrogen as the carrier gas with thermistors should be avoided because reduction of the metallic oxide resistors can take place (20). Glass-coated elements can be used to prevent this reduction, but the response time of the coated thermistor is increased.

Katharometers lack linear response and must be calibrated not only for different vapors but also for each set of conditions as well (5,36,52). These detectors are sensitive to changes in pressure, flow, and temperature. Therefore, conditions must be carefully controlled for reproducible results. In the case of thermistors, the current must also be precisely controlled as the sensitivity changes markedly with small changes in current. This current control is more important at the lowest temperature range for a particular thermistor cell, where the sensitivity is at a maximum, but it is less critical as the sensitivity decreases with increased temperatures. Possible reactions (such as hydrocarbon cracking) at the heated element have to be considered because the detector element is of necessity hotter than the cell wall. As the temperature of operation is increased, the possibility of changes at the hot surface becomes especially important.

Several methods have been described whereby the sensitivities of thermal conductivity detectors have been increased. Greene (23) passed the vapors from the column through two hot tubes, one containing copper oxide and the other iron, to yield carbon dioxide and hydrogen. The carbon dioxide was removed, and the hydrogen was measured by a thermal conductivity cell which was at room temperature. Norem has reported a similar device which is available commercially (46). Martin and Smart previously had used a combustion method, but detected the resultant carbon dioxide spectrophotometrically (43).

Recently, Zlatkis and Ridgway (65) placed a nickel cracking catalyst after the column but before the detector. When hydrogen was the carrier gas, methane and water were formed. The water was adsorbed and the methane measured in the cell. Once again, the cell was operated at room temperature, thereby retaining the maximum sensitivity of a thermistor detector. These two methods have limited applicability. They are effective only for certain classes of compounds and they must be calibrated not only for the percentage conversions but also for the stoichiometric relationships involving the number of carbon atoms in each eluted compound.

The sensitivity of a katharometer can also be increased by reducing the pressure at the outlet of the chromatography column. Thus, the concentration of the organic vapor in the carrier gas is higher (relative to operation at atmospheric or slightly higher pressures) and the signal is increased up to 50-fold (20).

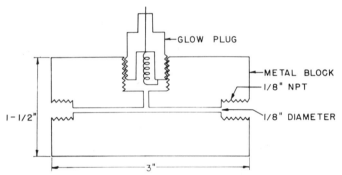

Fig. 1. Glow plug thermal conductivity cell cross section. (Courtesy of Jackson Laboratory, E. I. du Pont de Nemours and Co. Reprinted from *Anal. Chem.*, **30**, 1163 (1958), and from *Gas Chromatography*, Academic Press, New York, 1958, p. 132.)

A novel thermal conductivity detector has been reported by Felton (19). Model airplane "glow plugs" have been mounted in a steel block as shown in Figs. 1 and 2. These plugs are inexpensive, rugged, and can be used at very high temperatures. The filaments are probably the most readily replaced or installed of any yet reported. They are merely screwed into the block, one wire attached, and the circuit completed through the block itself. The unit has been tested at 550°C.

Another inexpensive, rugged, and simple katharometer was described recently by Stuve (60). A small, tungsten-filament, light bulb with the glass envelope removed was mounted in a metal block. The detector was used with the combustion method to give

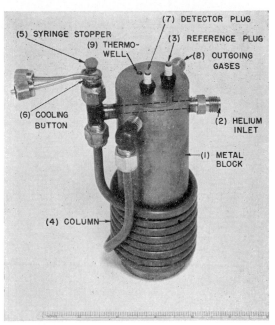

Fig. 2. High temperature glow plug apparatus. (Courtesy of Jackson Laboratory, E. I. du Pont de Nemours and Co. Reprinted from *Gas Chromatography*, Academic Press, New York, 1958, p. 132.)

"ample sensitivity." Although not extremely sensitive ($S = 97$ cm.^{3} mv./mg.), the detector was reported to be very stable. No noise was detected and the drift was recorded as less than 1% of full scale (5 mv. recorder) in two hours. The unit did not require extensive thermostatic control and was not affected by changes in carrier gas flow. The construction of the entire detector block was simple and economical.

These rugged units, developed by Felton and Stuve, should be especially attractive for student demonstrations or instrumentation training in academic laboratories.

3. Flame Measuring Devices

A. MICROFLAME DETECTOR

Three detectors which measure properties of flames have been reported. All destroy the compound detected and all are limited in

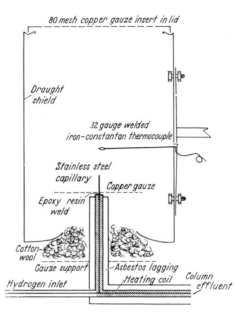

Fig. 3. Wirth's hydrogen flame detector. (Reprinted from *Vapor Phase Chromatography*, Academic Press, New York, Butterworths, London, 1957, p. 157.)

applicability to combustible compounds. They are, however, sensitive and can be operated over a wide range of temperatures.

The flame detector, originated by Scott (54) is a very simple, low-cost, measuring device. The eluted sample is burned and the temperature of the flame is measured by a thermocouple. The detector is sensitive (0.1 μg. of benzene per ml. of carrier gas), can be used at very high temperatures, and gives a linear response. It, therefore, is especially good for quantitative analyses.

Scott originally used hydrogen as the carrier gas. With hydrogen, however, the base-line changed slightly as each peak was eluted. This change has been attributed to flow rate fluctuations. Both Scott (54) and Wirth (63) have reported modifications which stabilize the base-line. Scott introduced either hydrogen or nitrogen as his carrier gas; Wirth made two changes in the design of the microflame detector. His detector is shown in Fig. 3. He added hydrogen to the nitrogen carrier gas after the stream passed from the column but just before combustion took place. Wirth also replaced the glass combustion jet with a metal hypodermic tip. He claimed this type of jet produced a superior base-line compared to Scott's glass-tipped model, which drifted with time because of an increase in temperature.

Henderson and Knox (29) have used either nitrogen or carbon dioxide as the carrier gas. They added hydrogen to the column effluent before combustion in a manner similar to that used by Wirth. In studies related to the response of the flame detector they found, as did Scott, that a linear relationship existed between the heats of combustion and sensitivities for various compounds. They have recommended this device for detecting substances with high molecular weights and high heats of combustion.

The combustion detector destroys the sample, which limits its use for qualitative analyses. A by-pass system may be used, however, which will allow only a fraction of the effluent vapors to be destroyed by passage through the detector. The remaining vapors can be recovered. Certain compounds which are not combustible, such as water and halogenated hydrocarbons, give little or no response. Thus, even though the detector is sensitive, the applicability of the flame device is limited as to the types of vapors that can be detected.

B. EMISSIVITY DETECTOR

Another detector, in which the response is based on the measurement of a second property of a flame, is the emissivity detector developed by Grant (22). In this unit, coal gas is mixed with the effluent vapors from the chromatography column, and the combined gases are burned. Standard flame photometer components measure the emitted light. A reflector, a condensing lens, and a photo cell are mounted as shown in Fig. 4. The sensitivity of the detector varies with the chemical nature of the compounds being detected. It is generally as sensitive as a thermal conductivity cell using nitrogen as carrier gas ($S = 25$ cm.^{3}mv./mg. for benzene).

The variable response may be used effectively, however, as a qualitative tool. The response by emissivity for n- and cyclo-paraffins is considerably lower than for aromatic compounds. Grant cited two chromatographic patterns which compared the emissivity and katharometer detectors. The peaks for the aromatic hydrocarbons, benzene and toluene, were comparable in size for the two detectors. The peaks for cyclohexane and n-octane, however, were much smaller with the emissivity detector than with the katharometer (Fig. 5).

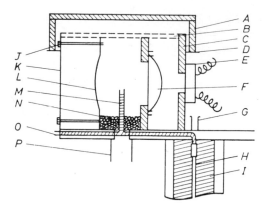

Fig. 4. Emissivity detector. A. drought-proof Sindanyo top, B. double layer of 40 mesh copper gauze, C. Sindanyo front for photocell mounting, D. metal stops for draught-proof top, E. selenium photocell, F. glass condensing lens, G. column inlet, H. column, I. column heating jacket, J. supports for reflector, K. aluminum housing, L. metal reflector, M. stainless steel jet, N. 2 cm. deep layer of porcelain beads, O. coal gas inlet, P. air inlet from blower. (Reprinted from *Gas Chromatography*, Butterworths, London, 1958, preprints p. D26.)

He calculated a table of response factors (emissivity response divided by katharometer response) for a variety of compounds. The relative responses showed that the emissivity detector had an advantage for aromatic compounds, and since the detector can be used at high temperatures, it is especially useful for aromatic and fused ring compounds.

The detector is simple and rugged, and the volume between column and jet is small, insuring a rapid response. For quantitative analyses, a linear relationship exists between response and weight of sample (peak heights were measured). In common with other flame detectors, draughts must be avoided, and well controlled gas flows are necessary to maintain base-line stability.

C. FLAME IONIZATION DETECTOR

Flame ionization has been measured in combustion studies for some time (17,59). The flame ionization detector (26,44) for gas chromatography measures a third property of flames—ionization. The vapors are burned in a manner similar to that developed by Scott (54); ionization takes place within the flame, and the conductance

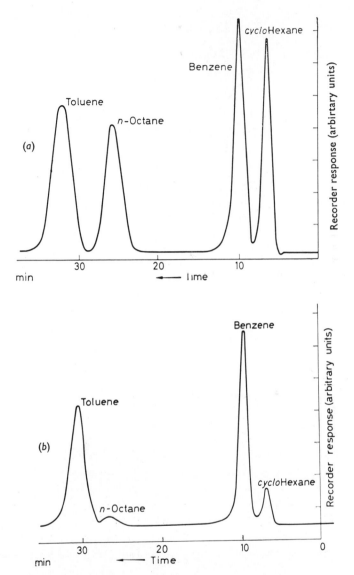

Fig. 5. Comparison of detector responses toward hydrocarbons.   a. katharometer, b. emissivity detector.   (Reprinted from *Gas Chromatography*, Butterworths, London, 1958, preprints p. D31.)

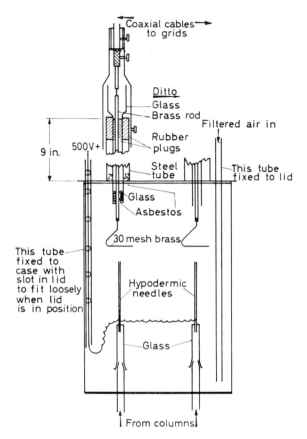

Fig. 6. Dual-jet flame ionization detector. (Reprinted from *Gas Chromatography*, Butterworths, London, 1958, preprints p. I78.)

between two electrodes is determined. Harley placed platinum electrodes in the flame (26). In another model, described by Mc-William (44), the metal jet itself was the positive electrode; the negative pole was positioned 1 cm. away and within the flame. This detector was simple, sensitive (S = 800 cm.[3] mv./mg. for benzene), and gave a high signal-to-noise ratio. It also showed linearity of response, low background, excellent stability, and insensitivity to flow and temperature variations. It was also insensitive to vibration, but dust-free air was required for the burner. The adjustment of the upper electrode was critical and had to be positioned for optimum sensitivity while retaining linearity of response.

McWilliam has attained a sensitivity of 1×10^9 cm.^{3}mv./mg. with a dual-jet detector cell (Fig. 6) and an impedance conversion measuring circuit. He reported a stable base-line which was insensitive to changes in the nitrogen–hydrogen ratio, to flow rate, to vibration, to ambient temperature, and to variations in the flow of air to the jet. The small volume after the column makes this detector particularly effective for use with high efficiency capillary columns. A glass wool and carbon air filter removed all dust from the air stream. He reported that increasing the nitrogen–hydrogen ratio gives greater sensitivities; in practice, however, this is limited by the possible extinction of the flame.

Noncombustible compounds, of course, are not detectable. Therefore, the detector is insensitive to carbon dioxide and this gas can be used to replace nitrogen as the carrier gas. The choice of column phases becomes very important with this extremely sensitive detector. The level of vapor detection probably surpasses the normal vapor pressures of stationary liquids. A dummy column or a carrier gas saturator connected to the reference jet should balance out this effect.

4. Radiation Counters

Radiological detectors, although restricted in use because they measure only radioactive materials, are becoming increasingly important for gas chromatography. Detectors of this type have not been extensively reported in the literature. Tracing and labeling techniques, coupled with gas chromatographic separations, have a great potential in analytical chemistry. Improved counters will be of invaluable assistance as this potential is realized.

Kokes, Tobin, and Emmett (37) have studied catalytic reactions by cracking hydrocarbons labeled with C^{14} and by analyzing the products chromatographically. Thermal conductivity and radiation detectors recorded the distribution of radioactivity in the total mass. Evans and Willard (18) reported a similar technique with labeled halogen compounds. Both groups passed the radioactive vapors over the windows of Geiger counters. This procedure, naturally, limits the sensitivity when weak emitters are separated.

Recently, an improved flow-proportioned counter has been developed by Wolfgang (64), which allows full-flow detection rather than detection involving flow past a counter window (Fig. 7). This permits the measurement of weak beta-radiation from tritium and C^{14}. These low intensity emitters are not readily detected even with thin-window counters. Methane was added to the effluent vapors from the usual chromatography detector, since both helium and nitrogen are poor counter gases. The gas mixture is then passed through the counter. Mass and activity distributions can be recorded

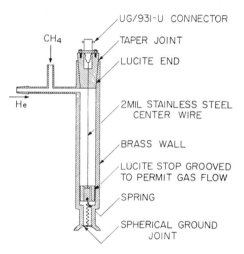

Fig. 7. Full-flow counter for gas chromatography. (Reprinted from *Anal. Chem.*, **30,** 905 (1958).)

concurrently, using conventional and counter detectors in series. Specific activities can thereby be determined directly. The counter can be operated at 200°C., and the sensitivity inherent in radioactivity counting surpasses that of the thermistor thermal conductivity cell used for the mass analysis. As little as 10^{-9} curie can be easily detected. Although this sensitivity is reported as being very good, the authors added that very low specific activities cannot be detected. The authors (64) state that this is because the unlabeled mass overloads the chromatographic column. Increasing the diameter of the column should overcome this difficulty, provided the detectors are not sensitive to the increased flow rates which are necessary to achieve the desired separations.   The possible poisoning of the counter must be considered when it is used as a detector.

5. Dielectric Constant Detectors

Griffith, James, and Phillips (24) have described a sensitive detector utilizing dielectric constant measurements.   The response time, however, was large because the vapors were detected while adsorbed and equilibration was necessary.   Turner (61) eliminated the adsorbent and devised a detector which gives a rapid linear response and which is simple, robust, and sensitive.   The unit, as described, was designed for preparative chromatography, but the author states that, reduced in size, the detector could be used for analytical columns.

The cell contains silver-plated electrodes in a brass block.   The change in capacity of the resultant condenser, accompanying a change in the dielectric constant of the vapors, is converted electronically to a change in potential.   The sensitivity of the detector varies with the nature of the vapors coming from the column (2 to 8 μg./cm.^{3} of N_2 for acetone and ether, respectively).   Functional groups in the structure of the molecule are necessary for detection of organic compounds.   This limits the applicability and, therefore, the versatility of the detector.   It is, however, relatively insensitive to carrier gas flow rate and pressure changes as well as to changes in temperature. Since these parameters are more variable in preparative work than in analytical determinations, the detector is particularly well suited to large scale apparatus.

III. IONIZATION DETECTORS

1. Glow Discharge Detector

The first publication concerning a glow discharge detector appeared in 1956 when Harley and Pretorius (27) described their very simple device.   Use was made of the fact that the voltage existing across a normal gaseous discharge is a function of the type of gas used.   This voltage changes by several volts when minute amounts of an impurity are introduced into that gas.   By exploiting this principle with the detector shown in Fig. 8, as little as 10^{-12} moles of a substance was detected.

The detector consisted of a small platinum disk cathode and a tungsten wire anode forming one arm of a Wheatstone bridge which was supplied with 900 v. from a d.c. source. The bridge was balanced with carrier gas flowing through the detector at a pressure low enough to produce a normal glow discharge between the electrodes. Compounds eluted from the column caused a voltage change across the detector which was measured by a recording potentiometer.

In September 1957, R. C. Pitkethly presented the results of more elaborate studies on these low pressure electric discharge detectors. This was given before the Analytical Division of the American Chemical Society in New York City and was later published (49).

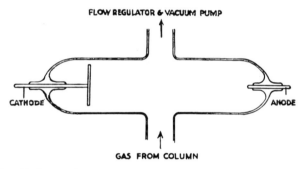

Fig. 8. Glow-discharge detector. (Reprinted from *Nature*, **178**, 1244 (1956).)

He recommended the use of modified neon lamps (Philips SBC 200/260 v.) with longitudinal gas flow for the detector tubes. Figure 9 shows this apparatus in more detail. The electrodes were made of iron; one a circular disk 10 mm. in diameter, and the other a strip, 2 mm. wide bent to form a ring of equal diameter. The two electrodes were spaced 1 to 1.5 cm. apart. Two such lamps were used in this system as seen in Fig. 9.

The voltage–current–pressure characteristics of these modified neon tube detectors were studied and the optimum conditions selected to give the lowest sensitivity to current and pressure variations. As can be seen from Fig. 10, these settings are 1 to 1.5 ma. of current and 3 to 5 mm. of pressure. Subsequent work in our own laboratory with glow discharge detectors of a different design showed the need of determining these characteristic voltage–current–pressure curves for each new detector if optimum operating conditions were to be obtained.

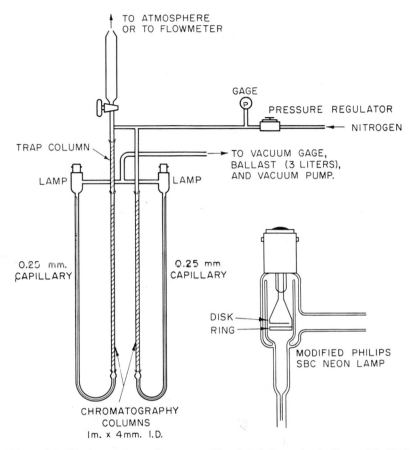

Fig. 9. Modified neon lamp detector. (Reprinted from *Anal. Chem.*, **30**, 1310 (1958).)

Pitkethly's results confirmed the extreme sensitivity available from these glow-discharge tubes, for he could detect hydrocarbon gases in nitrogen at concentrations of 1 in 10^9.

This high sensitivity presents some difficulties in sampling. Sample charges normally used for gas chromatography are much too concentrated for this type of detector. Such high concentrations of vapor in the column's effluent gas stream will extinguish the glow in the tube, causing discontinuity in the recorded pattern. Subsequently, when the vapor concentration in the tube falls to a detectable level, the glow

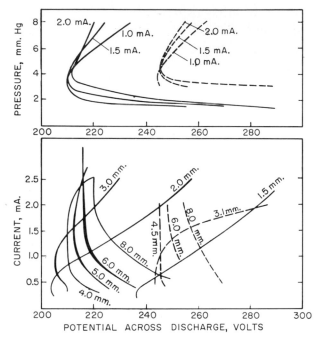

Fig. 10. Voltage–current–pressure characteristics of modified neon lamp detector
(Reprinted from *Anal. Chem.*, **30,** 1311 (1958).)

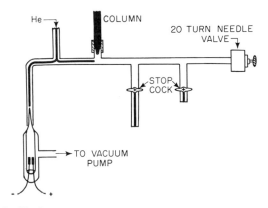

Fig. 11. Sample dilution apparatus.   (Printed with the permission of the American Chemical Society.)

will be spontaneously resumed. In our hands, these discontinuities were accompanied by peak trailing which we felt was due to slow desorption of vapors from the surface of the electrodes. This extinguishing phenomenon, caused by high vapor concentrations, can produce considerable frustration when working with completely unknown samples.

Pitkethly diluted his samples in two ways: through use of a nonvolatile solvent, cetane; and through use of a chamber filled with carrier gas. The nonvolatile solvent proved unsuccessful because the cetane vapors penetrated the column, upsetting the balance completely. Dilution with the carrier gas was more practical.

Another approach aimed at circumventing this problem of extremely small sample charges has been reported recently (56). A sample dilution system (Fig. 11) was utilized. The column's effluent stream entered a manifold system as indicated. A capillary tube, 20 cm. in length, connected one end of the manifold to a metered source of helium. The helium flow was regulated at approximately the same rate as the carrier gas. This extra helium flowed through an open-ended tube into which a capillary probe was installed. This probe led directly into the gauge which was maintained at the reduced operating pressure, from 3 to 5 mm. of mercury. Extending in the other direction from the column's exit was a series of capillaries of known lengths, each provided with a stopcock. For additional versatility, a 20 turn needle valve was also included in this part of the system. Manipulation of the stopcocks or the valve allowed all, or a fixed portion of, the vapors to pass through the dilution stream and into the detector gauge.

This dilution method has the advantage of varying the amount of column effluent which passes through the discharge tube, allowing mixtures having components present in both very high and very low concentrations to be run simultaneously. In addition, that portion of the column's effluent gas diverted from the detector is now available for subsequent analysis.

The few minor difficulties of sample dilution and sample overloading should not detract from the usefulness of these glow discharge detectors. They are extremely sensitive, they are rugged, and they can be applied to gas chromatography with new stationary phases on which the advantages of very low vapor concentrations can be exploited.

2. Low-Pressure Discharge Device

A preliminary communication appeared in 1957 (53) describing a sensitive ionization gauge detector based on the ionization potentials of vapors. Use is made of the fact that most volatile organic compounds ionize between 8 and 14 v., while helium, the carrier gas, has a much greater ionization potential (24.5 v.). This gauge and the adjustable metal leak are shown in Fig. 12. A very small fraction of

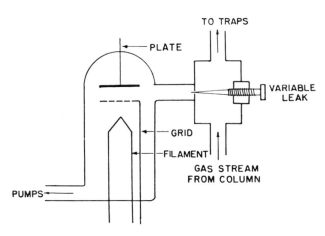

Fig. 12. Ionization gage detector. (Reprinted from *Nature*, **179**, 541 (1957).)

the column's effluent gas stream passed through the leak into an RCA 1949 ionization gauge with the glass envelope modified to permit the gas to flow between the gauge components. The potential difference was adjusted to 18 v., a value not sufficient to ionize the carrier gas, helium; consequently, there was no plate current when helium alone was flowing through the detector. When a substance of lower ionization potential passed into the gauge, ions were formed and this ion current from the plate was amplified and recorded on a Speedomax recorder.

Typical operating conditions were given as follows: pressure in the envelope, 0.2 mm. Hg; filament emission, 5 ma.; grid potential, +18 v.; plate potential, −27 v. Sensitivities in the range of 10^{-12} moles were claimed by the authors when only 0.5% of the column's effluent gas stream passed into the gauge.

One worker (28) has reported that several difficulties must be overcome before this ionization gauge can become a practical detector. The extremely small ion current from the plate requires special equipment for amplification. In addition, the tungsten filament ionization gauges are short-lived. Replacing the tungsten filament with irradiated thorium increased the life of the gauge but introduced a problem in surface absorption which resulted in filament poisoning, detector instability, and trailing chromatographic peaks.

This type of detector and its auxiliary equipment is quite expensive, yet it is surprising it has not been exploited more thoroughly. The extremely fascinating feature of varying the grid potential seems most attractive. In this lies the possibility of inherent qualitative differentiation when using this ionization gauge as a detector. In principle, it approaches the very new field of low ionization potential mass spectroscopy. Samples eluted from the gas chromatography column could be passed through the gauge which is set with successively increasing grid potentials. Thus, only those materials whose ionization potentials are exceeded at each of the settings will be detected. A study of compound type versus ionization potential will aid in these qualitative investigations.

3. Beta-Ray Ionization Detector

Beta-ray ionization has been applied to gas chromatography detectors by Dutch and American Shell personnel (4,10). A source of beta radiation bombards the vapors coming from the column, ionization takes place, and the current flow between two electrodes is measured. The two groups have described different devices based on this ionization principle. Deal (10) used a single ionization chamber (for the sample) and matched the ionization current electrically for zero balancing. A differential cell, developed by Boer (4), employs a common central electrode and independent Sr^{90} beta-emitter sources for sample and reference gases. Figures 13 and 14 illustrate his model.

Boer's detector is sensitive ($S = 600$ cm.^{3} mv./mg.), requires little calibration, can be used at high temperatures, and is not affected by changes in flow rate. The cell itself is simple, but the auxiliary equipment is more elaborate and costly than for most other detectors. The beta-ray source (Sr^{90}) must be properly shielded and handled for

safety.   Although the cell is well shielded when in use, adequate precautions plus trained personnel are required when constructing or
repairing the detector.

Boer has reported that sensitivity to variations in temperature and
pressure are parameters which affect the ionization current.   He has

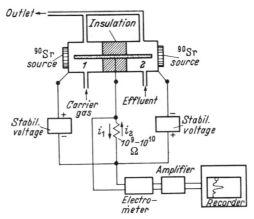

Fig. 13. Schematic diagram of beta-ray ionization detector. (Reprinted from
Vapor Phase Chromatography, Butterworths, London, 1957, p. 174.)

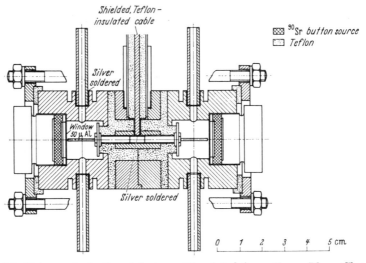

Fig. 14. Beta-ray ionization detector. (Reprinted from *Vapor Phase Chromatography*, Butterworths, London, 1957, p. 179.)

minimized these variables by using a common outlet tube for his differential cell. The ionization cross section, Q, is also involved and is different for individual compounds. He calculated a factor based on the Q values for the compound and for the carrier gas:

Factor = (Q component − Q carrier gas)/mol. wt. of component

In quantitative analyses the peak area of each component is divided by its factor. The percentage by weight of each component can then be calculated. Excellent agreement between calculated and actual weight percentage compositions were reported for a hydrocarbon mixture.

4. "Argon" Detector

In 1958, J. E. Lovelock (40) described a very sensitive detector whose operation is based on the unique ionization properties of noble gases, in this instance, argon. As little as 10^{-12} moles of most organic substances was analyzed by use of this detector which was relatively insensitive to changes in temperature, pressure, and gas flow rate.

The principles behind the detector's operation were first established by Jesse and Sadauskis (33). They found that the rare gases produced ions and an equal concentration of long lived metastable atoms when exposed to ionization radiation. In the presence of small traces of organic vapors the metastable rare gas atoms transferred their energy of excitation by collision. If the ionization potential of these vapors was less than the excitation potential of the rare gas atom, the transfer of energy on collision led to the ionization of the added vapors. Since the ionization potentials of most organic molecules are lower than the excitation potential of argon, these vapors are ionized on collision with the metastable atoms of this noble gas.

An ionization chamber easily measures the steady level of ionization in an irradiated gas and any increased ionization due to the addition of another gas or vapor. It follows, therefore, that a detector can be based on the combined use of a rare gas as a carrier gas and an ionization chamber containing a source of ionizing radiation. In practice, commercially available argon is preferred because its metastable atom has a low excitation potential which is not transferred upon collision with impurities present in the gas cylinder. This is not true of commercially available helium.

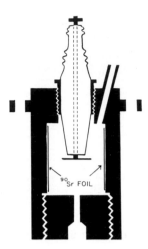

Fig. 15. Argon detector. (Courtesy of J. E. Lovelock, Medical Research Council, London.)

In the first publication (40), a sealed source of Sr^{90} was used as the ionization chamber. (This type of equipment is commercially available for use with industrial thickness gauges.) A 10 mc. Sr^{90} source of beta radiation was preferred since the noise level was inversely related to the mean number of ionizing particles entering the chamber in unit time. This factor was 100 times greater from the Sr^{90} source than from a radium alpha-particle source. The author claimed no external radiation hazard in that only 10 mr./hr. of radiation was available at the surface of the apparatus. Figure 15 illustrates the latest design of this detector as supplied by Dr. Lovelock.

The ionization current of approximately 10^{-8} amperes was conveyed to a recorder through a modified d.c. current amplifier (55,62). The high resistance of the amplifier (2×10^9 ohms) developed a steady voltage across it. An equal and opposite voltage was applied to the input of the amplifier so that a zero reading was obtained when pure argon was flowing; when the mobile gas was mixed with organic vapors positive deflections resulted.

Based on earlier work (33), it was predicted that ionization would increase with increasing concentrations of organic vapors. The response of the detector was found to follow this prediction when the applied potential was less than 300 v. At this potential, however, the relationship between ionization and organic vapor concentration was linear only over a small, limited range. At a higher potential, 500 v., the detector's response became linear over a much wider range of concentration, and sensitivity increased. At much higher potentials the sensitivity increased still further but the response with concentration became nonlinear once more. At voltages over 1000, sparks appeared in the detector chamber as foreign gases were introduced into the argon stream. Thus, applied potentials must be selected to produce maximum sensitivity without causing detector instability.

When the response of this detector to different molecular species was determined, it was found that most organic molecules with ionization potentials below 11.6 ev. (the excitation potential of metastable argon) had closely similar molar sensitivities. However, those compounds whose ionization potentials lie above 11.6 ev. do not respond in this detector This includes such molecules as N_2, CO_2, O_2, CH_4, and H_2O.

In general, this detector was very sensitive (detected 2.5×10^{-12} moles), required no thermostatting, was insensitive to changes in gas flow rate (between 5 and 100 ml./min.), exhibited linearity of response, operated at temperatures up to 200°C., and demonstrated no "poisoning" or "memory" effects at gross loadings of sample. This is an important feature which is not exhibited by many of the other ionization devices. As with other ionization devices, the ionization of any organic vapor molecule passing through the detector is followed by its destruction. In this particular device, the proportion of destroyed molecules is only 1 in 10^9 when operating under normal conditions.

A second publication by Lovelock (41) described alternate methods of exciting rare gas atoms. These included spark discharge operating at atmospheric pressure; radio-frequency discharge; silent discharge at low pressure; and corona discharge at atmospheric pressure. As few as 10^{-13} moles of most organic vapors can be detected by using the spark device.

5. Radio-Frequency Glow Detector

Almost simultaneous with Lovelock's description of means for exciting rare gas atoms (41), Karmen and Bowman (34) developed a glow detector which was based on the properties of an electric discharge in helium caused by the application of radio-frequency voltage at atmospheric pressure. The change in direct current resulting from the rectifying properties of the gas discharge was measured as a means of detecting small changes in the composition of the gas.

The authors found that ignition of a stable glow discharge in flowing helium could be accomplished at atmospheric pressure, eliminating the need for operating at controlled reduced pressures. The direct current produced by this discharge was little affected by fluctuations in temperature, pressure, and gas flow rate. This direct current was applied directly to the input terminals of a standard 1 mv. recorder without additional amplification. When a hydrocarbon passed through the discharge, the d.c. output decreased, and the decrease was proportional to the concentration of the hydrocarbon in the helium stream.

The radio-frequency power was supplied by a stabilized conventional low power radio transmitter operating in the 5 to 10 Mc. region. Direct current across the discharge could be increased to several hundred microamperes before "breakdown" occurred. This breakdown was characterized by higher current and incandescence of the tube element. The maximum amount of current that could be produced in the tubes without breakdown generally increased with an increase in frequency. The operating current was usually chosen at the upper range, but just before breakdown. Even so, no difficulty with shortened tube life was experienced.

It is claimed that this type of detector is simple to construct, and has been adapted to two types of conventional chromatographs, resulting in increased resolving power due to the use of micro samples. Operating at temperatures near 200°C. (to separate fatty acid esters), the authors estimate this radio-frequency glow detector can detect one molecule of the methyl ester in 10^9 molecules of helium.

IV. SECONDARY DETECTORS

All of the detectors described above have a single common fault; none can identify the individual organic vapors as they emerge from the chromatographic column. Many will argue that this is an unimportant factor. It is unimportant for routine analysis or trace analysis of known mixtures, but for analysis of complex mixtures of completely unknown materials, this is not true. Some will question the use of a secondary detector, saying that chemical pretreatment, and the use of several carefully selected stationary phases will *almost* guarantee the identity of the unknown constituent. Experience, however, has taught us that the only way to remove the "almost" is through the use of a secondary detector.

As predicted by Patton (47) in his early publication on this subject, the mass spectrometer is ideally suited as a secondary detector. This instrument requires only micrograms of material from which unequivocal identifications are obtained. Samples can be either vapors or liquids, and with the recent advances made in high temperature mass spectrometry, solids of mass 1500 can be investigated.

The usefulness of these supplementary techniques, gas chromatography and mass spectrometry, is shown in publications dealing with complex mixtures (3,9,11,15,16,21,25,39,57,58). The combined instrument reported by Gohlke further demonstrates the advantages of these two techniques (25). Although this combination had been tried before (58,30), it was not made practical until the advent of the time-of-flight mass spectrometer. The major objection to this type of apparatus is the high initial cost and the restricted use of an instrument as versatile as a mass spectrometer. One other problem is the very high sensitivity of this instrument. Chromatographic fractions must be isolated in an extremely pure state to use this secondary detector to its fullest advantage because traces of air, water, or very volatile solvents can obscure the pattern of the unknown material being identified.

The ultraviolet spectrophotometer is another useful secondary detector. Its use is restricted to compounds having ultraviolet absorbance, but it has the advantage of not being hindered by traces of solvent or nonabsorbing impurities. In some instances its sensitivity approaches that of the mass spectrometer, and it is more readily adapted to very high boiling liquids and to solids. It is not as specific as the mass spectrometer, but recent work in vapor phase ultraviolet spectrophotometry has increased the potential specificity of this instrument.

The infrared spectrophotometer is another instrument suitable as a secondary detector. Its relative insensitivity, compared to these other instruments, is being steadily decreased. Micro techniques using KBr pellets, beam condensing systems, and micro gas cells make detection and identification of fractions of micrograms possible. This concentration requirement is easily in the range of most gas chromatographic fractions. Here again, functional group analysis and specific compound identification result.

Other types of secondary detectors could be mentioned. They are not as elegant (nor as expensive) as the ones described but they serve a useful purpose. Indicators, chromogenic spray reagents, and paper strip chromatograms fall into this category. For example, the use of paper chromatographic techniques showed definitely that nornicotine decomposed on our gas chromatographic apparatus (preheated at 250°C., column at 200°C.). Ultraviolet spectrophotometry failed as a secondary detector in this instance because of its lack of specificity.

We cannot overemphasize the use of a secondary detector when separating unknown complex mixtures. Only through their use can unequivocal identifications become assured.

V. CONCLUSION

The most outstanding recent advances in gas chromatography detectors have been the high sensitivity ionization devices. Extremely small samples are detectable, and maximum efficiency columns have been made practical. The first commercial instrument which utilized an ionization detector was displayed at the Amsterdam Symposium in 1958 (50). Lovelock's "Argon" detector was included and the instrument showed excellent stability over a wide temperature range. The over-all construction of the instrument was simplified because of the detector's relative insensitivity to changes in temperature, pressure, and flow rate. McWilliam's flame-ionization detector and Karmen's radio-frequency gauge have similar advantages and should prove to be equally useful. All three of these detectors have been applied to capillary columns and are now available commercially. They are stable and more easily adapted to routine application than the discharge tubes which require vacuum systems and whose electrodes are more easily poisoned.

The hydrogen flame detector and modifications of it give reliable analyses at reasonable cost. The sensitivities, although lower than those of the ionization gauges, are excellent and their linear response is particularly well suited to quantitative analyses. The presence of an open flame, the limited applicability to combustible compounds, and the sample destruction are disadvantages which will restrict the general use of these detectors.

Thermal conductivity cells have been replaced by more sensitive detectors in many applications. These katharometers are, however, generally applicable to the detection of all types of compounds, especially if hydrogen or helium is the carrier gas. These detectors are attractive for student training and for preparative-scale units where limited sensitivity is not detrimental, but where reliability is essential.

The very specialized use of radiological detectors in gas chromatography is becoming an important one. As more and more labeled compounds become available, the applications of gas chromatographic techniques to tracer experiments will increase. The flow counter developed by Wolfgang is especially well adapted to the micro analyses necessary in biological and medicinal chemistry.

The intense interest in gas chromatography as an analytical technique leads to developments which contribute to rapid design obsolescence. Many sensitive instruments are available which will operate over a wide temperature range. A selective use of these instruments allows the analyst to attack his problem with increasingly efficient, rapid, and accurate analyses.

References

1. Ambrose, D., and R. P. Collerson, *J. Sci. Inst.*, **32**, 323 (1955).
2. Bennett, C. E., S. Dal Nogare, L. W. Safranski, and C. D. Lewis, *Anal. Chem.*, **30**, 898 (1958).
3. Beynon, J. H., *Mikrochim. Acta*, **1956**, 417.
4. Boer, H., A Comparison of Detection Methods for Gas Chromatography Including Detection by Beta-ray Ionization, in D. H. Desty, ed., *Vapour Phase Chromatography*, Academic Press, New York, Butterworths Scientific Publications, London, 1957, p. 169.
5. Browning, L. C., and J. O. Watts, *Anal. Chem.*, **29**, 24 (1957).
6. Coates, V. C., H. J. Noebels, and I. S. Fagerson, eds., *Gas Chromatography*, Academic Press, New York, 1958.
7. Cowan, C. B., and P. J. Sterling, The Selection and Operation of Thermistors for Katharometers, in V. J. Coates, H. J. Noebels, and I. S. Fagerson, eds., *Gas Chromatography*, Academic Press, New York, 1958, p. 165.
8. Davis, A. D., and G. A. Howard, *Chem. and Ind.; Brit. Inds. Fair Rev.*, **1956**, R25.

9. Day, E. A., D. A. Forss, and S. Patton, *J. Dairy Sci.*, **40,** 932 (1957).
10. Deal, C. H., J. W. Otvos, V. N. Smith, and P. S. Zucco, *Anal. Chem.*, **28,** 1958 (1956).
11. Desty, D. H., *Nature*, **179,** 242 (1957).
12. Desty, D. H., ed., *Vapour Phase Chromatography*, Academic Press, New York, Butterworths Scientific Publications, London, 1957.
13. Dimbat, M., P. E. Porter, and F. H. Stross, *Anal. Chem.*, **28,** 290 (1956).
14. Dimick, K. P., and J. Corse, Volatile Flavor of Strawberries. Minor Constituent Analysis by Gas Chromatography and Mass Spectrometry, presented at meeting of American Chemical Society, Miami, Florida, April 1957.
15. Donner, W., T. Johns, and W. S. Galloway, Use of a Mass Spectrometer as a Gas Chromatography Detector, presented at meeting of the American Society for Testing Materials, Committee E-14 on Mass Spectrometry, New York, May 1957.
16. Drew, C. M., J. R. McNesby, S. R. Smith, and A. S. Gordon, *Anal. Chem.*, **28,** 979 (1956).
17. Duclos, D. P., and W. M. Grounds, *Rev. Sci. Inst.*, **27,** 111 (1956).
18. Evans, J. B., and J. E. Willard, *J. Am. Chem. Soc.*, **78,** 2908 (1956).
19. Felton, H. R., and A. A. Buehler, *Anal. Chem.*, **30,** 1163 (1958); Felton, H. R., A Novel High Temperature Gas Chromatography Unit, in V. J. Coates, H. J. Noebels, and I. S. Fagerson, eds., *Gas Chromatography*, Academic Press, New York, 1958, p. 131.
20. Forss, D. A., personal communication.
21. Galloway, W. S., and T. Johns, Investigations of the Combined Use of Mass Spectroscopy and Gas Chromatography, presented at the Pittsburgh Conference on Analytical Chemistry and Applied Spectroscopy, Pittsburgh, Pennsylvania, March 1957.
22. Grant, D. W., An Emissivity Detector for Gas Chromatography, in D. H. Desty, ed., *Gas Chromatography*, Butterworths Scientific Publications, London, 1958, preprints p. D25.
23. Greene, G. E., *Nature*, **180,** 295 (1957).
24. Griffith, J., D. James, and C. Phillips, *Analyst*, **77,** 897 (1952).
25. Gohlke, R. S., The Use of Time of Flight Mass Spectrometry and Vapor Phase Chromatography in the Identification of Unknown Mixtures, presented at meeting of the American Chemical Society, New York, September 1957.
26. Harley, J., W. Nel, and V. Pretorius, *Nature*, **181,** 177 (1958).
27. Harley, J., and V. Pretorius, *Nature*, **178,** 1244 (1956).
28. Harrow, L. S., personal communication.
29. Henderson, J. I., and J. H. Knox, *J. Chem. Soc.*, **1956,** 2299.
30. Holmes, J. C., and F. A. Morrell, *Appl. Spectroscopy*, **11,** 86 (1957).
31. James, A. T., Detection of Vapors in Flowing Gas Streams, in D. H. Desty, ed., *Vapour Phase Chromatography*, Academic Press, New York, Butterworths Scientific Publications, London, 1957, p. 127.
32. James, A. T., and A. J. P. Martin, *Biochem. J.*, **50,** 679 (1952); **52,** 238 (1952); *Analyst*, **77,** 915 (1952).
33. Jesse, W. P., and J. Sadauskis, *Phys. Rev.*, **100,** 1755 (1955).
34. Karmen, A., and R. L. Bowman, *Ann. N. Y. Acad. Sci.*, **72,** 714 (1959).

35. Keulemans, A. I. M., *Gas Chromatography*, Reinhold, New York, 1957.
36. Keulemans, A. I. M., A. Kwantes, and G. W. A. Rijnders, *Anal. Chem. Acta*, **16**, 29 (1957).
37. Kokes, R. J., H. Tobin, Jr., and P. Emmett, *J. Am. Chem. Soc.*, **77**, 5860 (1955).
38. Liberti, A., L. Conti, and V. Crescenti, *Nature*, **178**, 1067 (1956).
39. Levy, E. J., D. M. G. Lawrey, L. P. Herk, Jr., and W. H. Stahl, The Application of Isolative Vapor Phase Chromatography and Mass Spectrometry to Problems in Odor Research, presented at meeting of the American Society for Testing Materials, Committee E-14 on Mass Spectrometry, Cincinnati, Ohio, May 1956.
40. Lovelock, J. E., *J. Chromatography*, **1**, 35 (1958).
41. Lovelock, J. E., *Nature*, **181**, 1460 (1958).
42. Martin, A. J. P., and A. T. James, *Biochem. J.*, **63**, 138 (1956).
43. Martin, A. E., and J. Smart, *Nature*, **175**, 422 (1955).
44. McWilliam, I. G., and R. A. Dewar, Flame Ionization Detector for Gas Chromatography, in D. H. Desty, ed., *Gas Chromatography*, Butterworths Scientific Publications, London, 1958, preprints p. I74.
45. Munday, C. W., and G. R. Primavesi, Properties of the Martin Gas Density Balance and Possible Modifications Thereof, in D. H. Desty, ed., *Vapour Phase Chromatography*, Academic Press, New York, Butterworths Scientific Publications, London, 1957, p. 146.
46. Norem, S. D., A Combustion Device for Use in Conjunction with Chromatographic Columns, in V. J. Coates, H. J. Noebels, and I. S. Fagerson, eds., *Gas Chromatography*, Academic Press, New York, 1958, p. 191.
47. Patton, H. W., J. S. Lewis, and W. I. Kaye, *Anal. Chem.*, **27**, 170 (1955).
48. Phillips, C. G. S., *Gas Chromatography*, Academic Press, New York, 1956.
49. Pitkethly, R. C., *Anal. Chem.*, **30**, 1309 (1958).
50. Pye Argon Chromatograph, W. S. Pye and Co., Ltd., Cambridge, England.
51. Ray, N. H., *J. Appl. Chem.*, **4**, 21 (1954).
52. Rosie, D. M., and R. L. Grob, *Anal. Chem.*, **29**, 1263 (1957).
53. Ryce, S. A., and W. A. Bryce, *Nature*, **179**, 541 (1957).
54. Scott, R. P. W., *Nature*, **176**, 793 (1955); Scott, R. P. W., A New Detector for Vapour Phase Partition Chromatography, in D. H. Desty, ed., *Vapour Phase Chromatography*, Academic Press, New York, Butterworths Scientific Publications, London, 1957, p. 131.
55. Scroggie, M. G., *Wireless World*, **58**, 14 (1952).
56. Seligman, R. B., Novel Applications of Gas Chromatography in Tobacco Research, presented at Southeast Regional American Chemical Society Meeting, Raleigh, North Carolina, November 15, 1957.
57. Seligman, R. B., F. E. Resnik, A. E. O'Keeffe, J. C. Holmes, F. A. Morrell, D. P. Murrill, and F. L. Gager, Jr., *Tobacco Science*, **1**, 124 (1957).
58. Seligman, R. B., F. E. Resnik, A. E. O'Keeffe, J. C. Holmes, F. A. Morrell, and D. P. Murrill, New Techniques of Smoke Analysis. I. Vapor Phase Chromatography, presented at Ninth Annual Tobacco Chemists' Conference, Raleigh, North Carolina, October 1955.
59. Shuler, K. E., and J. Weber, *J. Chem. Phys.*, **22**, 491 (1954).

60. Stuve, W., A Simple Katharometer for Use with the Combustion Method, in
D. H. Desty, ed., *Gas Chromatography*, Butterworths Scientific Publications,
1958, preprints p. A1.
61. Turner, D. W., *Nature*, **181**, 1265 (1958).
62. Wellman, W. L., and J. E. Lovelock, *J. Inst. Heating and Ventilation Eng.*, **22**,
421 (1955).
63. Wirth, M. M., The Hydrogen Microflame Detector Using Nitrogen as a Carrier Gas, in D. H. Desty, ed., *Vapour Phase Chromatography*, Academic Press,
New York, Butterworths Scientific Publications, London, 1957, p. 154.
64. Wolfgang, R., and F. S. Rowland, *Anal. Chem.*, **30**, 903 (1958).
65. Zlatkis, A., and J. A. Ridgway, *Nature*, **182**, 130 (1958).

Trends in the Determination of Fluorine

C. A. HORTON, *Oak Ridge National Laboratory,*
Oak Ridge, Tennessee

I. SCOPE

The determination of fluoride has been of interest ever since Berzelius first developed methods for the determination of this element in 1816. The first real commercial use of fluorine compounds other than in aluminum production, however, began only about 1930 with the introduction of the chloro–fluoro refrigerants. With the development of atomic reactors and bombs, interest in commercial development of both inorganic and organic fluorine compounds and consequently analytical needs took another advance. Today, with small amounts of fluoride being important in water treatment for the control of dental caries, in air pollution studies, and with interest in fluorine containing insecticides, pharmaceuticals, dyes, plastics, greases, and other products, and usage in the petroleum, electroplating, and aluminum industries, a definite requirement for varied and suitable analytical methods exists.

During each of the past several years, over a hundred modified or new methods for the determination of fluoride have appeared annually in the literature. In spite of this activity, few of the methods are as yet completely satisfactory for the analysis of all the types of samples encountered.

This chapter can only discuss in detail the development in methods for the determination of fluoride during the period since 1953. Since elemental fluorine is now commercially available, a section on the determination of elemental fluorine and on analyses for impurities in this gas are also included.

For the benefit of those who have not previously determined fluoride in samples, a brief résumé of prior methods is presented with a list of sources of earlier reviews of analytical methods.

An attempt is made to point out the difficulties and shortcomings of both the prior and recent methods for the determination of fluoride, and to challenge analytical chemists toward development of more satisfactory methods and techniques. No attempt is made to cover the determination of fluorine in organic fluorine compounds.

II. LITERATURE AND REVIEWS ON DETERMINATION OF FLUORINE

Progress in analytical methods for the determination of fluoride in inorganic and organic compounds up until 1953 has been covered in a monograph by Elving, Willard, and this author (55). Horton (96) summarizes the earlier material and includes some of the information contained herein. The same volume contains recommended procedures for the separation and determination of this element. Other earlier good reviews, encyclopedic volumes and bibliographies (32,57,108,137,153,174) also should be consulted for varied viewpoints on this topic.

III. RÉSUMÉ OF METHODS TO 1953

1. General Processes Involved in Determination

The determination of elemental fluorine, the most electronegative element, is considered separately in Section VII.

Methods for the determination of ionic fluoride ion depend on the formation of either insoluble metal fluorides or fluorosilicates or of stable, soluble metal fluo, borofluo, or silicofluoride complexes. Since other anions often exhibit similar behavior with the same metals, methods for separation of fluoride from other elements are usually crucial for success in determinations. The amount of fluoride in the sample analyzed determines the choice of gravimetric, volumetric, colorimetric, fluorometric, or other methods for chemical determination in descending order. A second consideration is the effect of other elements in the original sample or after varied preliminary treatments and separations on the character of the precipitate, the visual or instrumental endpoint chemical indicator or physical property response, the chromophoric metal concentration indicator, or the metal fluorescent agent, respectively. Except for the gravimetric methods, all other methods for fluoride determination are somewhat indirect. That is, the first excess, or final excess of metal ion which does not precipitate or form a stable fluoride complex, is detected in one way or another.

2. Preparation of Samples for Separation of Fluoride

Many samples to be analyzed, consist largely of organic matter, such as animal tissues, vegetables, fruits, leaves, needles, soils, etc. In such samples, only the inorganic fluorides adsorbed or contained therein are generally of interest. In the few cases where the content of organic fluoride compounds is important, other decomposition techniques are utilized. For both of the common methods for separating fluoride from other elements involving volatilization (Section III-3), it is generally necessary to get rid of most, or all, of the organic matter. The common method is to ash the sample in a muffle furnace in the presence of a metal salt which forms a nonvolatile, insoluble fluoride, stable at the ashing temperature. Calcium or magnesium oxides are generally used to stabilize the fluoride, and the mixture that is ashed must be alkaline. Samples are often ashed, after drying at about 110°C., at approximately 600°C. Other fixative agents and temperatures are occasionally recommended.

During the ashing process, or prior to it, the fluoride in certain types of samples, such as plants, is converted to a form that is not amenable to separation by the Willard-Winter technique (Section III-3). As yet, the other volatilization separative technique has not been tested on ashed samples of a naturally organic origin. Such samples, and also certain silicates and other types mentioned later, must be fused with an alkaline flux before separation by volatilization, or other methods, is undertaken.

Other groups of samples, such as air, water, or aqueous solutions, must be concentrated to a small volume, or dried to a solid before separating the fluoride from interfering ions by the technique (Section III-3).

Fluorine in organic compounds, generally, must be converted to inorganic fluoride prior to analysis. Methods for such conversion are discussed briefly in another chapter (182) and in prior reviews on this topic (55,129).

3. Separation of Fluoride by Volatilization

Since 1933, fluoride has been separated from other elements generally by volatilization as hexafluosilicic acid, from perchloric or sulfuric acid. As developed by Willard and Winter (226), and studied extensively, the technique is usually applicable for all substances soluble in, or decomposed by, perchloric or sulfuric acids. Recovery is moderately slow to very slow, however, for samples containing appreciable to large amounts of aluminum, zirconium, boron, or gelatinous silica. The solution temperature is maintained at 135°C., during volatilization with a steam carrier gas, to avoid excess acid in the distillate. Improved still designs with spray traps have permitted use of sulfuric or phosphoric acid for distillations at temperatures up to 165°C., allowing complete recovery of fluoride from samples rich in aluminum, boron, and zirconium, with only traces of sulfate or phosphate carried into the distillate. Evolution of the other hydrogen halides is prevented by adding a silver salt to the solution that is being distilled. Traces of chlorine or oxidants in the distillate, which often oxidize organic indicators or chelates used for final estimation, are usually reduced with hydroxylamine hydrochloride.

The older volatilization method involved evolution of silicon tetrafluoride from concentrated sulfuric acid.

4. Gravimetric Determination

The first method for the gravimetric determination of fluoride involved precipitation of calcium fluoride. This remains as one of the two forms used, even today, for gravimetric determination. The precipitate is generally very gelatinous, filters with difficulty, adsorbs other ions, and may become colloidal. Treadwell and Hall (210) give one of the most suitable procedures.

Lead chlorofluoride is precipitated in the gravimetric method most generally used for large amounts of fluoride in inorganic or organic fluorine compounds. About 2×10^{-7} moles (4μg./l.) of fluoride remains in solution when PbClF is precipitated from a solution $0.1M$ in chloride. Unfortunately the composition of the precipitate varies appreciably from the stoichiometric ratio, depending on the exact technique utilized, so that results can never be better than ±0.5%. A volumetric method also depends on formation of this insoluble salt. Belcher and MacDonald (19) and some texts (5,93,

228) give satisfactory procedures depending on precipitation of lead chlorofluoride.

The precipitation of triphenyltin fluoride (55) has the advantage of a very favorable factor, and the precipitate filters and washes easily. As originally tested, the method had the disadvantage that the precipitant, triphenyltin chloride, is not very soluble itself, and has been commercially unavailable.

Other forms of insoluble salts used in gravimetric methods include lanthanum, bismuth, barium, and thorium fluorides, and for silicious complexes, various alkali metal fluosilicates. Since these techniques have received only cursory study and suffer from the same difficulties as the other gravimetric procedures mentioned, details are omitted here (55).

5. Volumetric Determination

The volumetric methods for fluoride fall into several separate categories discussed below.

A. PRECIPITATION OR COMPLEXATION DIRECT METHODS

a. Zirconium Titrant. Although zirconium forms the most stable complex of the metals with fluoride ion, the fact that varied soluble and insoluble complexes may form has deterred its use as a titrant. Nevertheless, the same strong complexing power has enabled use of a zirconium titrant for samples containing aluminum, boron, or other metals which form fairly stable complexes with fluoride. Alizarin or purpurin, or their sulfonates, generally serve as the endpoint indicators for titrations.

b. Aluminum Titrant. The formation of insoluble sodium fluoaluminate is the basis for titrations using neutral aluminum chloride as the titrant. The titration is generally carried out in a hot solution containing sodium chloride with methyl red or Eriochromcyanine R as indicator. Conductometric and fluorometric detection of the endpoint has also been utilized.

c. Iron(III) Titrant. Formation of insoluble sodium iron(III) hexafluoride, Na_3FeF_6, is the basis of methods wherein iron(III) is the titrant. Precipitation is best in a solution saturated with sodium chloride. Thiocyanate is used as a visual indicator, or a potentiometric endpoint detection may be utilized.

d. Rare Earth Metal Titrants. Until recently only cerium(III) and yttrium have served for titrants in the rare earth group of elements. Cerous nitrate titrant has generally been used with methyl red or ampho magenta visual indicators or by potentiometric or conductometric endpoint detection, using the picrate, acetate, or trichloroacetate in the last case. Yttrium nitrate is used for titration of large amounts of fluoride in neutral solution with methyl red as the indicator.

e. Thorium Titrants. The most frequently used titrant for both microgram and milligram quantities of fluoride is thorium nitrate. The reaction depends on the formation of insoluble thorium fluoride. Titration is generally performed in a solution of closely controlled pH, which has varied from pH 2.7 to 3.5 for various investigators. As a visual endpoint indicator, Alizarin Red S has served more analysts to best satisfaction, although Chrome Azurol S has had considerable use. This author prefers Purpurin Sulfonate, Alizarin Red S, Eriochromcyanine R, 2,3-Dicyanoquinizarin, or Chrome Azurol S, in that order, as the best of several hundred indicators investigated (224). At first, titrations were performed using a 50% ethanolic solution, but aqueous solutions are as satisfactory, or more so, with the bicolor indicators mentioned above. Fluorometric, conductometric, and amperometric endpoint detections have been used for this titrant to a lesser extent than visual indicators. The endpoint color change from yellow to pink is difficult for some analysts to recognize, and the endpoint shade varies widely between various observers. For fluorometric titration a 40 or 50% ethanolic medium is recommended (225).

The early tendency in using this titrant was to control only the initial acidity by addition of a fixed concentration of hydrochloric acid to a neutral sample. More recently, a buffer, generally monochloroacetate, has been used. Although salts and ionic strength have an effect on the titer, results for definite conditions are reproducible.

If oxidants are in the sample to be titrated, they are reduced with hydroxylamine hydrochloride before titration to avoid effect on visual indicators.

f. Other Titrants. Excess lead, after the endpoint in lead chlorofluoride precipitation, can be detected amperometrically. Similar conductometric, turbidimetric, and potentiometric techniques have been published where calcium fluoride is precipitated.

g. Interferences in Precipitation or Complexation—Direct Titration Methods. In most of the cases discussed above (a–f), several cations and anions seriously interfere. The cations may interfere by competing with the titrant for fluoride ions present or by competing for the chromophoric endpoint indicator. Such cations usually include aluminum, beryllium, cerium(III), iron, other rare earth metal ions, thorium, titanium, and zirconium. The anions also interfere by forming either insoluble salts or very stable complexes with the metals used as titrants. These often include arsenate, oxalate, phosphate, and sulfate ions, especially.

B. PRECIPITATION—INDIRECT METHODS

Silver Titrant. The chloride present in precipitated lead chlorofluoride, or the excess of chloride in the filtrate from precipitation of this salt when a known amount of chloride is previously present, may be estimated by modifications of the standard Volhard method. Although the effect of some ions is less with this volumetric modification of the lead chlorofluoride gravimetric technique, it generally gives no better results. Fairly satisfactory volumetric procedures that use this principle are published elsewhere (5,125,218,228).

Permanganate Titrant. When calcium fluoride is precipitated with a standard excess of calcium ion, the excess calcium can then be precipitated as calcium oxalate. Either the oxalate in the second precipitate or the excess of standard oxalate added for the precipitation can be estimated by the usual permanganate titration. This, then, is a doubly indirect volumetric method for the determination of fluoride.

C. NEUTRALIZATION METHODS

Fluosilicate Reactions. Numerous volumetric methods for determination of fluoride and silicofluoride are based on the hydrolysis of the latter ion. The reaction can proceed in either two steps or as a combined reaction:

$$H_2SiF_6 + 2KOH \longrightarrow K_2SiF_6 + 2H_2O \qquad (1)$$

$$K_2SiF_6 + 4KOH \longrightarrow 6KF + SiO_2 + 2H_2O \qquad (2)$$

Since fluoride is often separated by volatilization as hexafluosilicic acid, it is somewhat surprising, on first glance, that reactions (1) and

(2) have not been used widely for the volumetric determination of fluoride. The reason that it has not, is that volumetric methods using thorium are generally more sensitive and precise, and that other acids may accompany the fluosilicic into the distillate.

Hydrofluoric Acid Reactions.   The moderately weak hydrofluoric acid may be titrated directly with sodium hydroxide using phenolphthalein as a visual indicator or electrometrically with gold and calomel electrodes in the presence of quinhydrone.   Naturally, any other strong acid interferes in such a determination.

6. Colorimetric Determination

For the determination of small amounts of fluoride, the colorimetric procedures are most popular.   These depend on the bleaching of the color of metal chromophoric combinations due to stronger complexing of the metal ion by fluoride.   Most often a zirconium–Alizarin Red S mixture is used, since this metal forms a strong fluoride complex even in fairly acidic solution and the adverse effect of other anions can often be compensated for.   By adding a sample to a sulfuric acid solution containing 0.15 mole Alizarin Red S per 1.0 mole of zirconium, and on measuring the color after aging for an hour either visually or at 520 to 525 mμ, differences of ±0.05 p.p.m. of fluoride at the 1 p.p.m. level can be measured.   Procedures were available prior to 1953 for the direct estimation of fluoride using this reagent system and also for distillates from the Willard–Winter separation (55).

Other colorimetric methods also depend on stronger complexing of the particular metal by fluoride ion.   Among these are the systems: iron(III)–thiocyanate, acetylacetonate, salicylate, and 5-sulfosalicylate (55); aluminum–aurintricarboxylate (55), hemotoxylin complex (166), and Eriochromcyanine R complex (55); thorium–Alizarin Red S, Chrome Azurol S, and Thoron (94) complexes; and titanium–peroxy complex.   Additional colorimetric methods depend on the silicon content of fluosilicate ions, and are based on the formation of colored, reduced molybdosilicate species or the effect of fluoride on other molybdenum phosphates or arsenates (55).

7. Fluorometric Methods

Fluoride decreases the fluorescence of certain metal complexes and causes fluorescence of other chelates when it forms complexes with the metal concerned. Procedures based on the aluminum–morin-, quercetin-, 8-quinolinol-, or maclurin complexes, thorium–morin- or quercetin fluorescences, and of the fluorescence of salicylic acid liberated from its titanium or iron(III) complex have been developed for qualitative or quantitative use. Generally, the use of fluorescence increases sensitivity as compared to most of the colorimetric absorption indicator methods.

8. Other Methods for Determination

A. CHEMICAL METHODS

Nephelometric and turbidimetric methods have been used to detect the equivalence point in titrations of fluoride with calcium or thorium (55,95).

The inhibitory effect of fluoride on enzyme action has been applied to the determination of low amounts of fluoride. For example, the hydrolyzing action of hog liver esterase (stabilized with glycerol) on ethyl butyrate is inhibited by traces of fluoride. The time and temperature of the process must be controlled in this technique.

The extent of etching of glass, measured by changes in wettability or contact angle of an air bubble, has also been used to estimate fluoride in the form of hydrogen fluoride.

B. SPECTROGRAPHIC METHODS

The emission spectrographic detection or determination of fluoride generally requires estimation of the intensity of molecular band heads of the alkaline earth metal fluorides. The band head at 5291 A. due to a CaF emitter detects down to 2.5 μg. of fluoride using a d.c. arc.

The singly ionized fluorine line at 6856 or 6902 A. provides a sensitivity limit of 200 μg. of fluoride using an a.c. spark; greater sensitivity, about 0.1 p.p.m., can be obtained using a hollow cathode discharge tube.

The silicon line of silicon tetrafluoride can be measured spectrographically as an indirect measure of fluorine content.

C. PHYSICAL METHODS

Varied organic fluorine compounds may be determined in admixture with other organics by infrared techniques. Rough estimations of inorganic fluorides can be obtained from intensity measurements of x-ray diffraction lines.   Volatile inorganic, or thermally decomposed organic fluorides can be estimated from the intensity of the mass signals of fragments or ions in mass spectrometers.

IV. ADVANCES AFTER 1952

One aim of this chapter is to review recent trends in methods for the determination of fluoride.   The advances after 1952 are included here in some detail, although, of necessity, some overlap with material in Section III occurs for clarity.

1. Preparation of Samples for Separation

Since 1950 it has been found that vegetation samples, when ashed with the usual fixatives, sometimes leave a residue from which it is difficult to volatilize all the fluoride as hexafluosilicic acid.   Thus, common practice is to fuse the ash residue, containing calcium oxide or another fixative, with sodium hydroxide at 600°C. (84,170,173) or with sodium peroxide (133a).   In fact, preliminary studies (84, 133a) indicate that it is possible to fuse the sample directly with sodium peroxide without preliminary ashing.   Fusion techniques are also often advantageous in the pyrolytic separation of fluoride.

Evaporations of alkaline fluoride solutions have usually been carried out in borosilicate ware, and such vessels are suggested in association with standard methods (2,5).   In spite of discussions of prior work citing losses during evaporation (55), some recent papers recommend evaporation in borosilicate ware.   Other recent papers (61,85,165, 197), however, tend to confirm losses, especially when large amounts of fluoride are present.   The effect usually is not strictly an actual "loss."   It is, in effect, a diminution of the effective fluoride, indicated as present in the subsequent estimation step of the method for determination.   The factors involved are adsorption of fluoride on the walls of the borosilicate ware, leaching of silicate from the glass and formation of fluosilicate, leaching or reaction of boron in the glass with formation of fluoborate, and combination of the fluoborate as an unreactive constituent on the surface of the glass.

Due to these continued reports of losses, even if restricted to small proportions of the fluoride, the author recommends evaporation in platinum dishes or, if these are unavailable, in quartz or low-boron vessels.

2. Separation of Fluoride by Volatilization

A. EVOLUTION AS HEXAFLUOSILICIC ACID

Only a few minor advances have taken place in the separation of fluoride by volatilization of hexafluosilicic acid using the Willard–Winter technique. Several special still designs have been devised to reduce the amount of nonvolatile acid carried over with the fluoride in the water vapor carrier gas (21,24,34,55,132,209). A micro size still (194), using a nitrogen sweep and a small amount of added water to minimize the volume of distillate, has also been designed. Over 97% of 5 μg. of fluoride was recovered in 10 ml. of distillate using this apparatus. As an aid in eliminating attention by analysts during the volatilization, electronic devices (55,58), refluxing liquid stills (60), or combinations thereof (24,103,116) have been developed. Sulfuric acid azeotropes also have been used in a jacket for temperature control and for concurrent supply of water vapor to the reaction flask (82). Use of these techniques has encouraged the use of sulfuric or phosphoric acid at temperatures as high as 165°C. for volatilization (80,189). The increased temperature allows complete, relatively rapid, recovery of fluoride from samples which contain aluminum, zirconium, or other ions which retard volatilization from perchloric acid at 135°C.

The varied still head designs may not completely prevent some small carry-over of the nonvolatile acid. Addition of a soluble silver salt to the distillate precipitates any phosphate or chloride, while fluoride remains in solution. Sulfate has been precipitated with a soluble barium salt (213), however, barium fluoride is not very soluble. Ion exchange methods may also be used to separate the fluoride from phosphate or sulfate carried over into the distillate (Section IV-3).

B. DIFFUSION AS HYDROGEN FLUORIDE

Less than about 20 μg. of fluoride in a sample volume of 1 ml. or less has recently been separated by vapor diffusion of hydrogen fluoride (193). A polyethylene apparatus is used and a diffusion period of about 20 hr. at 50°C. is required for complete transfer.

This method tolerates a 250-fold excess of aluminum or phosphate ions.

C. PYROLYTIC SEPARATIONS

Pyrolytic separations were announced publicly about 1950. The Warf, Cline, and Tevebaugh (55,221) method depends on hydrolytic decomposition of halides at about 1000°C. in the presence of superheated steam. Alkali and alkaline earth metal fluorides require the presence of a reaction accelerator such as uranium(IV, VI) oxide, U_3O_8. The fluorides of groups III, IV, VI, and the actinide group do not require an accelerator for fast quantitative evolution of the fluoride. All the halides in the sample are evolved and they are usually absorbed in dilute caustic. The reaction is best carried out in a platinum reactor (55,122a,151,221), but a nickel apparatus (52,77, 202) is almost as satisfactory in many cases, and quartz or Vycor reactors have been used at 760°C. for alumina–silica catalyst samples (73) or with a copper liner at higher temperatures (75). Besides uranium oxide, titanium dioxide has been used as an accelerator for cryolite samples (172), and aluminum oxide for zirconium or uranium-bearing samples (52).

The Powell and Menis modifications of the pyrolytic separation uses moist oxygen and a silica reactor tube (164). As in the previous procedure, no accelerator or flux is generally required for fluorides of metals in groups III, IV, VI, and the actinide or rare earth groups. For alkali metals, uranium oxide is a suitable accelerator at 1000°C.; tungsten oxide at 800°C. Refractories, such as certain glasses, phosphates, and clays, also require a flux. Sodium tungstate is used as a flux with tungsten oxide as the accelerator. The moisture saturated oxygen is passed through the apparatus at the fast rate of 2 to 3 l./min., and the gases are absorbed in dilute caustic after condensation in a short, quartz, air-cooled condenser tube to avoid wall adsorption and promote decomposition of any intermediate species containing fluoride. In addition to fluoride, sulfate, nitrate, and the halides are all collected in the condensate from the pyrolysis. These ions may interfere, if present, in the final estimation procedure unless removed or a method insensitive to the extraneous ions present is used. Work continues at this laboratory on other fluxes and accelerators at varied reaction temperatures. The method is applicable to solid organic fluorine compounds, such as perfluoroethylene. A similar moist oxygen pyrolysis has been used for decomposition of other organic fluorine compounds (55) and to determine their carbon content (66).

This general pyrolysis technique seems most applicable to the types of samples which are most unfavorable for separations by the Willard–Winter technique.

3. Separation by Other Methods

Ion exchange has begun to serve as a method for the isolation of fluoride during the past several years. Cation resins have been used to remove metal ions which may compete with the metal and/or indicator used for volumetric, colorimetric, or fluorometric determination of fluoride (7,14,48,53,54,92,110,144,199,222,227). Metals which exist as anions must be treated for conversion to the cation form to facilitate their removal by such cation resins. Another technique (229,230) utilizes the thorium salt of a cation resin to strongly adsorb fluoride and the other anions that thorium attracts.

Anion resins allow separation of the fluoride from other anions, such as sulfate or phosphate, which often interfere in the final determination of fluoride. Generally, fluoride is the easiest and among the first ions eluted from the anion resin column (6,112,115,116,122a,148, 149). By eluting with small volumes of elutriant some concentration of fluoride is feasible. Sulfate and phosphate elute much later.

Newman (146) converts many of the metals to anions by formation of ethylenedinitrilotetraacetate complexes, adsorbs these on a strong base anion exchanger, and then elutes fluoride using ammonium chloride elutriant at pH 9.2.

The adsorption of negatively charged metal fluoride complexes on the anion resin must be considered when such resins are to be used. Such ions include SiF_6^{2-}, ZrF_6^{2-}, AlF_6^{3-}, ZrF_6^{2-}, all of which generally will not elute at the same time as the simple uncomplexed fluoride ion.

Magnesium oxide, some calcium salts, and alumina (179,212) adsorb fluoride from neutral, neutral, or acidic solutions, respectively. The use of the first two solid neutral adsorbants allow concentration of fluoride prior to subsequent volatilization by the Willard–Winter technique (Sections III-3 and IV-2). The last, alumina, has been used mainly to remove fluoride in order to decrease its corrosive effect in acidic solutions. The solid alumina with adsorbed fluoride does not readily liberate fluoride by volatilization using the Willard–Winter technique.

Paper chromatography also has served for the separation and detection of fluoride. For example, the radioactive phosphoric acid liberated by hydrofluoric acid from a spot of radioactive zirconium phosphate on paper was diffused away by a trichloroacetic acid–isopropanol–water mixture and then was counted (37). In a second method, phosphate and fluoride were separated on a paper strip using a mixture of methanol plus ammonium hydroxide (231). Anions also have been separated using a butanol–water–methanol solvent mixture on paper strips (207). An acetone–water–acetic acid elutriant, separates fluoride from other ions on a calcium chloride impregnated paper (86), however, either phosphate or oxalate ions tend to interfere. Hydroxamine derivatives of fluoacetate, formate, acetate, etc., are separated (25) on paper using a mixture of ammonia, pyridine, ethanol, and water.

Various fluorinated and chloro–fluoro organic liquids and gases have been separated by gas chromatography (59,160,162,169,200).

Solvent extraction of tetraphenylstibonium fluoride, $(C_6H_5)_4SbF$, into carbon tetrachloride allows separation of fluoride, accompanied by a portion of the other halide ions, from cations which do not complex fluoride strongly (143). Unfortunately the extraction coefficient, $E_a^\circ = 16.5$, requires three or more extraction steps for complete separation of fluoride into the organic phase. Also, perchlorate forms an insoluble, salt-consuming reagent. Thus, this particular separation scheme has no special advantage.

4. Gravimetric Determinations

In a recent paper, lanthanum fluoride is described to be precipitated by use of a known excess of standard lanthanum solution from a solution of about pH 2. The excess lanthanum in the filtrate, or centrifugate, is precipitated with cupferron from a neutral solution and is weighed as the oxide (109,163).

Precipitation as triphenyltin fluoride has been improved (12) by shaking the aqueous test solution at pH 4 to 8 with the reagent in chloroform for 30 min. Using this idea, from 10 μg. to 50 mg. of fluoride was determined in the presence of phosphate, borate, aluminum, and iron. The precipitate is weighed after drying at 110°C. and has a very favorable gravimetric factor.

A method in which lithium fluoride is precipitated (37a) has also been published recently.

5. Volumetric Determinations

A. PRECIPITATION OR COMPLEXATION DIRECT METHODS

Recent trends are toward a continuation of titrations with thorium nitrate and more use of aluminum chloride titrants. Some additional papers have appeared which also use other titrants.

Zirconium Titrant. The zirconium titration of fluoride using Alizarin Red S indicator, in a very dilute acidic solution, has been extended down to the range of 10 to 100 μg. of fluoride in 40 ml. of water (124).

Aluminum Titrant. A pH meter has been used for endpoint detection in the titration of a solution saturated with salt at pH 7 and containing 40% acetone or 50% ethanol with an aluminum ion titrant (39). Quinhydrone also has been used to produce a potential change at the endpoint (205). Eriochromecyanine R proves to be a good indicator for visual titrations of neutral, salt-saturated solutions with aluminum titrant at about 80°C. (17,20,71).

A complex of aluminum with Superchrome Garnet Y is used as a titrant for solutions buffered at pH 4.6 with amperometric endpoint detection at -0.37 v. vs. a S.C.E. (55). Several metallic ions and chloride seriously interfere (223). One paper (154) indicates that the endpoint does not occur at the stoichiometric composition, Na_3AlF_6.

Iron(III) Titrant. Thiocyanate continues in use as a visual endpoint indicator for titrations using ferric chloride as titrant, in a solution of pH 5 to 6, containing salt and ethanol (196).

Salicylate indicator has been used in a pH 3.1 acetate solution (141). Excess iron may also be detected amperometrically in 50% ethanolic, salt-saturated, almost neutral solutions (105). An amperometric titration in the presence of ethanol has been recently reported (90).

Rare Earth Metal Titrants. Murexide has recently served as the indicator for the titration of pH 5 to 6, 50% methanol solutions, with cerium(III) (33,34). A conductometric (51,113) or high-frequency titration with lanthanum acetate titrant, however, seems preferred to the cerium titrant procedures.

Thorium Titrant. Since analysts often have considerable difficulty with visual detection of the endpoint in the titration of fluoride with thorium titrants, spectrophotometric titrations are coming into use (138a,146). With Alizarin Red S indicator, wavelengths of 520 (133,138a), 525 (122a), or 540 mμ (46) have been chosen. A flow-type titration cell for the spectrophotometer may be used (55, 122a). Continuous spectrophotometric titration devices adaptable for fluoride analyses are also available (220). Small line voltage differences do not produce serious errors in such spectrophotometric titrations (134). Present data (46), indicate that instrumental endpoints are no more precise than careful, visual endpoints (87), and may have a slight negative bias. Among the other instrumental endpoint detection methods used recently are high-frequency oscillometry using an initial pH of 5.9 (78), conductometry in an unbuffered pH 3.0 solution (52), potentiometry in the presence of sulfanilic acid at pH 6.7 using a platinum and S.C.E. electrode couple (168), and amperometrically in 0.1M potassium nitrate plus gelatin at pH 1 to 7 at -1.4 v. using a mercury drop (44) or in pH 2.8 monochloroacetate solution containing potassium bromide and sulfate with ferric indicator ion and rotating palladium electrode at 0.2 v. (88).

The precision of visual titration with thorium using a pH 2.7 buffer is $\pm 2.4\%$ relative (standard deviation); the mean accuracy is 99.2% (195). An over-all variation of $\pm 9\%$ has been obtained for ashing, distillation, and titration of plant samples (84).

Other Titrants. For titration with lead nitrate, forming lead chlorofluoride, the iron ion couple has been used as indicator ion in a pH 3.5, acetate buffered solution for potentiometric endpoint detection (42).

Calcium chloride has been used for the turbidimetric endpoint titration of 10^{-2} to $10^{-1}M$ fluoride in pH 1 to 7 solution (31), and with a bismuth–bismuth fluoride electrode, sensitive to fluoride concentration, at pH 8 in a solution containing some acetone (23) for milligram amounts of fluoride.

B. PRECIPITATION INDIRECT METHODS

Disodium Ethylenedinitrilotetraacetate Titrant. Lead chlorofluoride is dissolved in dilute nitric acid, treated with tartrate, ammonia, and cyanide, and titrated using Eriochrome Black T indicator. Alternately, the excess lead in the supernate can be titrated (217).

After precipitation of calcium fluoride with a known excess of standard calcium ion solution, the excess may be similarly titrated with disodium (ethylenedinitrilo) tetracetate (17,18,89).

Potassium Ferrocyanide Titrant. The excess calcium remaining after precipitation of calcium fluoride has been titrated in 50% ethanolic solution saturated with ammonium chloride using ferricyanide as the redox indicator ion (206).

Potassium Iodide Titrant. The excess acid iodate remaining after formation of fluosilicate as described on p. 158 can be back-titrated with potassium Eriochrome Black T indicator with a precision of 2% in the 0.2 to 2.0 mg. fluoride range (122x). The excess lead after lead chlorofluoride precipitation has been similarly titrated with use of Pyrocatechol Violet indicator (216).

After precipitation of calcium fluoride with excess standard calcium solution the excess has been titrated with the same reagent using Eriochrome Black T indicator (17,18,89). It is claimed that sulfate, phosphate, or arsenate does not interfere.

C. NEUTRALIZATION METHODS

Fluosilicate Reactions. A sample containing 0.35 to 2.5 mg. of fluoride in about 22 ml. of solution is treated with a fresh silica "solution," 16 ml. of ethanol, and neutralized to the mixed methyl red–bromocresol green endpoint with standard sodium hydroxide (carbonate-free). Then, 10 ml. of $0.01N$ potassium hydrogen iodate and 3 g. of potassium chloride are added and the mixture is stirred for 2 hr. at about 0°C. While cool, the excess acidity is back-titrated with standard sodium hydroxide (47). This method depends on the reactions:

$$6F^- + SiO_2 + 4KH(IO_3)_2 + 2KCl \longrightarrow$$

$$K_2SiF_6 + 4K(IO_3)_2^- + 2H_2O + 2Cl^- \quad (3)$$

$$KH(IO_3)_2 + NaOH \longrightarrow NaK(IO_3)_2 + H_2O \quad (4)$$

It is somewhat surprising that no precipitation of potassium fluosilicate was noted under the operational conditions used. The results require a correction which is a function of the initial volume.

The reverse reaction, equation 2, has been used for distillates from the Willard–Winter separation (204). The combined reaction of equations (1) and (2) has also been used in a conductometric method using a solution containing ethanol (70).

The fluosilicate content of commercial hydrofluoric acid is usually determined also by the reaction in equation (2) (145).

Hydrofluoric Acid Reactions. After removal of other stronger acids by ion exchange techniques, the moderately weak hydrofluoric acid in a solution can be titrated to the phenolphthalein or a potentiometric endpoint with standard base (188). A slight sulfate correction was required. Similar titrations are applicable after pyrolysis separations if other volatile halides are absent from the sample, or after cation separation by ion exchange (199).

D. TITRANT COMPARISONS

One study (70) indicates 1 to 10 mg. of fluoride per 100 ml. can be titrated with equal precision by visual thorium titration using Alizarin Red S indicator, aluminum titration using Eriochromecyanine R indicator, or by conductometric titration with aluminum ion titrant.

6. Colorimetric Determination

No appreciably novel advances have been published up to 1959 in the way of colorimetric methods since the early 1950 period. A number of the old, and some new chromophoric agents for metals which complex fluoride have been investigated. Some of these provide a greater sensitivity, allow greater pH variation, or decrease the deleterious effect of other ions. Table I lists the newer systems investigated, with a brief summary of the pH conditions, the equilibrium time required, the wavelength used, and other operational conditions. Table II lists the tolerable limits for various foreign ions on some of the colorimetric procedures.

A few comparative studies of various colorimetric methods have been published during recent years. The divergence of opinion as to the best colorimetric procedure has led to the inclusion of three different ones as alternate standard methods by the A.P.H.A. (2). A Japanese study (68) prefers a zirconium–Alizarin Red S chromophoric system used in a mixed hydrochloric-sulfuric acid medium to two iron(III) methods for the 0 to 5 p.p.m. range. Another, some-

TABLE I

Conditions of Newer Colorimetric Fluoride Methods

Metal used	Chromophore	pH	Equilibrium time, min.	mμ	Conditions	Reference
Al^{3+}	Aluminon	4.6	45	524		92
	Eriochromecyanin R	4.5	15+	535	Heated 60°	126
	Chrome Azurol S					11,128
	Hematoxylin	4.6	60 to 240	550	H_2O_2 added	166
			15	570	H_2O_2 added	72,99
	Morin				80% Ethanol	16
Be^{2+}	Chrome Azurol S	6		575	Pyridine–HCl buffer	13
	Quinalizarin					214
Fe^{3+}	Ferron	2 or 2.6 to 3.8		620	2 cm. cell	121,147
	5-Phenylsalicylic acid	2		575	Ethanol, 40%	130,147
	Salicylic acid	3.1		530	Chloroacetate buffer	15
	Salicylic acid	2.7		550		
				515		147
	Salicylic acid	low		vis.	HNO_3, Ethanol	49
	Resoacetophenone	2 to 3		465	10% Acetone	147
	Thiocyanate	4.5			complex extract in AmOH	
		2.9			measured	203
	Tiferron	2		640		147
	Sulfosalicylic acid	2		515		147
	Kojic acid	2		490		147

		pH	Time	λ	Remarks	Ref.
Mo	Silicomolybdenum blue	1.5 final	10	700	Indirect	43
Th⁴⁺	Thoron[a]	~2	15 to 180	545	Reduce oxidants	56,80,94
	Morin	2		410	Some Ethanol	62
	Chrome Azurol S	4	60	605	1 or 5 cm. cell Buffer + stabilizer	171
	Chrome Azurol S	~3	10	595	Chloroacetate buffer	121
	Amaranth	~7		521	Lake on paper	120
	Chromotrope 2B		60	515		122b
	Alizarin	2.85		515	ClOAc buffer	68,150
	Alizarin Red S	2.8	60 to 120	525	ClOAc buffer differential color	123
	Alizarin Red S		60	525	10 cm. cell, 2 cm. cell	29
	Alizarin Red S			525	1 cm. cell, ClOAc buffer	175
	Alizarin Red S	2.9		530	Nonlinear, linear	79,83
	Alizarin Red S			525	0.002N HCl, NH₂OH·HCl, 2 cm. cell	29
Ti⁴⁺	Quinalizarin disulfonate	3.9	~1440	550	±0.01 pH, NH₄OAc buffer	146
	Ascorbic acid	4.2		360	Phthalate buffer, HSO₃	180
	Chromotropic acid	2.85	Under 15		ClOAc buffer	8
	Peroxide	low			Str. H₂SO₄	117,122
	Peroxide	0.1		420	Indirect, H₂SO₄, SiO₂	67
Zr⁴⁺	Alizarin Red S	low	10	510	HCl	215
	Alizarin Red S		60	525	5 cm. cell	36
	Alizarin Red S			420 and 520		41

Table continued

TABLE I (*continued*)

Metal used	Chromophore	pH	Equilibrium time, min.	mμ	Conditions	Reference
	Alizarin Red S	low	60	520	HCl, H_2SO_4	45
	Alizarin Red S			vis.	Perm. stds.	63,64,65
	Alizarin Red S	0.8 to 1.2		530	HCl, H_2SO_4	72
	Alizarin Red S			550		91
	Alizarin Red S			500	HCl, H_2SO_4	114
	Alizarin Red S		60	525	HCl, H_2SO_4	138,185
	Alizarin Red S		60	vis.	HCl	186
	Alizarin Red S		20	vis.	HCl	208
	p-Dimethylaminoazophenyl-arsenate	low			Extract dye	167
	p-Dimethylaminoazophenyl-arsenate	low	60	500	Filter solution	106
	Eriochromecyanin R		Under 240	550	Aerosol + hydroquinone	1
	Eriochromecyanin R	low	any	528	Const. Temp., HCl	135
	Eriochromecyanin R	low	≥60	568	5 cm. cell, HCl	4
	Eriochromecyanin R	low	10	528	HCl	144
	Eriochromecyanin R	low	60	568	1 cm. cell, 0.3M HCl	
	Pyrocatechol Violet	1		525		111
	Purpurin sulfonate	0.2	30 to 180	520		219
	2,3,7-Trihydroxy-9-Phenylfluorone	low		540	10% Cyclohexanol	176
	SPADNS	low	None	570	HCl	21,22

a = 1-(*o*-arsenophenylazo)-2-naphthol-3,6-disulfonic acid.

TABLE II
Interference Effect on Colorimetric Fluoride Procedures

Alk. $CaCO_3$	Al^{3+}	Fe^{3+}	Mn^{4+}	Mg^{2+}	Ca^{2+}	Cl^-	NO_3^-	SO_4^{2-}	PO_4^{3-}	Cl_2	Miscellaneous	Reference
325	0.2	5		200	400	1,800		400	1.0	0.10		138
400	0.25	2	0.05			2,000		300	5	0.01		2
200	0.5	5	5	200	200	200	900	600	1	0.01	1,000 Na^+ 100 Si	118
		20			500	2,000	2,000				10 Th	91
	0.9	1	0.15							0.01	1,000 UO_2^{2+} 25 Fe^{2+}	81
2,000	5	20				5,000		2,000	10			232

Maximum μg./ml. for Effect of 0.1 μg./ml. F^- or Less

what earlier study prefers an aluminum–hematoxylin system over the zirconium–Alizarin Red S, iron(III)–thiocyanate, or titanium–peroxide methods that were tested. A comparison of varied titanium chromophoric systems (8) indicated chromotropic acid at pH 3 was most satisfactory. A similar comparison of iron(III) systems (147) indicated Resoacetophenone at pH 2 to 3 in a 10% ethanol medium is more satisfactory than the commonly used thiocyanate complex. A further comparison recommended the iron(III)–sulfosalicylic method over titanium–chromotropic acid, or iron–Tiferron systems (184). Another study (69) indicated reagent instability for the aluminum–hematoxylin system at pH 4.6 plus a nonlinear calibration curve. The same paper recommends an iron-(III)–sulfosalicylic acid system for over 10 μg. of fluoride.

A further indirect colorimetric method (227) depends on measuring the amount of thorium–Alizarin Red S liberated into a solution, from paper impregnated with the complex as a polymer, at 520 mμ, by 1 to 15 p.p.m. of fluoride. The same paper confirmed earlier infrared studies (95) which indicated that a chelate-type complex exists between the dye and the thorium ion. Early workers believed that the color change was due to formation of an adsorption lake.

Another group of colorimetric methods, very recently available (61a,61b,89a), utilize the color of chloranilic acid measured at 530 mμ for 2 to 100 p.p.m. of fluoride, or 330 mμ for 0.5 to 3 p.p.m. The dye is liberated from the lanthanum or thorium salt in a buffered aqueous solution containing methyl cellosolve due to the formation of the more stable metal fluorides. Except for phosphates, most of the common anions do not interfere with these two methods.

Uranium(VI) fluoride in gases has been determined by the rate of green color development of a column of solid salicylic acid (79). From 0.1 to over 5 mg./l. can be estimated by passing the gas sample through the column at a known rate.

A qualitative to semiquantitative colorimetric test for 0.1 μg. to 0.3 mg. of fluoride per ml. depends on the rose color formed with a spot of potassium ferrocyanide plus iron(III) chloride on paper (76). Another qualitative method (156) triturates the sample, which may contain an alkaline earth metal fluoride, with potassium bisulfate and ferric chloride. Decolorization of the normal intense color after addition of thiocyanate shows that fluoride is present.

Continuous colorimetric flow-type analyzers have been developed for water control purposes (220).

Color reactions for elemental fluorine are discussed in Section VII.

7. Other Methods for Determination

A modification of an earlier fluorometric method (225) uses the aluminum–Morin complex in a pH 4.4 buffered, 10% ethanol medium for determination of 1 p.p.m. ± 0.02 p.p.m. fluoride in 0.25 ml. of water (30). Another method uses the decrease in fluorescence of the aluminum–Eriochrome Red B or Superchrome Garnet Y complexes for the determination of amounts less than 25 μg. of fluoride to ± 0.2 μg. (165). The change in fluorescence of magnesium oxinate (38) or other similar complexes impregnated in paper may be used for estimation of fluoride in the air. Hydrofluoric acid also decreases the fluorescence of magnesium oxinate in amyl alcohol (178), but water and other acids interfere.

The catalytic effect of fluoride on electron interchange of the cerium(III, IV) system with radioactive cerium and measurement of the activity of extracted cerium(IV), has been developed as a method (3). Likewise, catalysis of the cerium(IV) bisulfate reaction with iodide to form a blue complex measured at a fixed reaction time, at constant temperature, has been applied for determination of 0.3 to 0.9 p.p.m. fluoride (119).

The decrease in diffusion current of aluminum dye complexes has been used for the polarographic determination of fluoride: Solochrome Violet RS or Pontachrome Violet SW in pH 4.6 acetate medium at −0.5 v. for 0.1 to 40 μg. (26,127); Eriochrome Violet BA for up to 2 mg. (142).

The increased current that passes between an aluminum (10) or zirconium (136) electrode and a platinum electrode has also been applied to the determination of fluoride. In a weak acid solution, such as $0.2M$ acetic, formic, or weaker benzoic or nitric acids, fluoride (and to a lesser extent chloride or bromide using aluminum) allows partial dissolution of the oxide coating on the metal, increasing the effective potential difference and the current passed. For a constant medium, stirring rate, temperature, and area of metal exposed, the maximum current observed is directly proportional to the halide present. The same system could be applied to an endpoint detection in a volumetric determination. Ovsepyan and Tarayan (155) have used the current of the system for estimating aluminum in a salt saturated, pH 3 to 7, solution by titration with fluoride Published (164) and unpublished work (97) indicates that the reverse titration is possible down to a level of about 1 μg. of fluoride per ml. using thorium nitrate as titrant. The same aluminum–platinum electrode system is used for continuous analyses.

For air samples, the air is scrubbed by a flow of $1M$ acetic acid containing a detergent and then passes by the electrodes and the current is recorded (98). The present apparatus records concentrations between 0.1 to 10 μg. of fluoride per l. of air.

A semiquantitative detection scheme uses autoradiography (counting is also possible) of a paper with a spot of zirconium radioactive phosphate (P^{32}) treated with a drop of test solution and chromatographed with a mixture of trichloroacetic acid, isopropanol, and water (37,159).

A radiometric, precipitation titration with samarium containing radioactive europium measures the development of activity in the supernate after the completion of precipitation (152).

The change in freezing point of uranium(VI) fluoride has been used to estimate the presence of small quantities of hydrogen fluoride or Freons in this substance (35). Almost any other extraneous component interferes in such a technique.

Mass spectra of halogen fluorides (101) can be used for identification and estimation purposes.

Both infrared and mass spectra have been used in a study of the pyrolysis products of perfluoroethane (139), and infrared has been used to study the fluorination products of CF_2ClCF_2Cl (131).

The molecular weight effect on the pressure difference through an orifice has been used for continuous analysis of uranium(VI) fluoride in gas mixtures (157).

Nuclear magnetic resonance spectra of fluosilanes (181) are of use for identification of these compounds in future mixtures.

A spectrographic method for 0.3 to 6% fluorine in enamels, measures the CaF band head at 529.1 mμ (198). A Japanese study (102) uses flame emission excitation for the calcium fluoride band in a method for solutions.

Positive ion-emission current between a heated electrode pair can be used to estimate dichlorodifluoromethane in amounts as small as 0.1 p.p.m. in dust-free air (183).

V. DIFFICULTIES OF PAST AND PRESENT METHODS

This section is written as an attempt to point out the shortcomings of the various procedures involved in determinations of fluoride. Since the most complicated cases with which more troubles are apt to be encountered are analyses of the traces often found in plants, vegetation, and animal tissues or fluids, the discussion below is restricted to these types. A somewhat broader group of sample types are considered in the other sections. Analyses for the fluorine content of organic fluorine-containing compounds are another and different subject.

1. Preparation of Samples for Separation of Fluoride

Until the past few years fluoride has been exclusively separated from interferences by volatilization of hexafluosilicic acid, usually from perchloric acid solution. For safety in this step, most, or all, of the organic matter in a sample must be removed or destroyed, also concentrating the fluoride in the inorganic residue. This organic removal by ashing in the presence of a fixative has presented several difficulties. As yet, there is only one excellent study of retention of fluoride during the ashing, limited to one fixative and type of sample (194). In the study, the recovery of radioactive fluorine-18 was determined for the ashing of blood serum with magnesium oxide. For 5 ml. of serum with 5 μg. of total fluoride, 75 mg. of oxide was required for retention. Previous studies of ashing fixatives and ashing temperatures indicated losses or incomplete recovery for soils heated for short periods at 900°C., or for longer periods at 500°C., with calcium hydroxide as the fluoride fixative agent; with blood ashed at 450°C. for 1 hr. with calcium hydroxide fixative; with soils or carbohydrates ashed with calcium hydroxide; grasses or minerals with magnesium acetate at 500°C.; soils with magnesium peroxide or nitrate; eggs with aluminum nitrate (55). Difficulty in obtaining a homogeneous mixture of sample and fixative has been noted for some mixtures: oats or corn with calcium oxide; organic acid containing samples with aluminum nitrate.

Megregian's review (137) recommends ashing of organic type samples with calcium oxide. The retarding effect of aluminum ion on hexafluosilicic acid evolution suggests that aluminum fixatives should not be used where this separation process is to be used.

Part of the difficulty encountered in the use of fixatives, is that they contain traces of fluoride. For example, use of magnesium acetate was abandoned in one study since it could not be purified down to a negligible fluoride content (4). A good comparative study, at several ashing temperatures for purified fluoride-free fixatives with varied types of samples using radioactive fluorine tracer, seems in order.

Two main types of samples have been subjected to a fusion step prior to separation by hexafluosilicic acid volatilization.

One class is the complex minerals and glasses which contain fluoborates, beryllates, silicates, and sometimes fluoaluminates or fluophosphates, which are insoluble in aqueous sulfuric or perchloric acids near the boiling point. For such samples, where hexafluosilicic acid volatilization is contemplated, silica removal is usually required to prevent formation of stable silicon oxyfluoride. Most of these compounds can now be decomposed with concurrent evolution of their fluoride content by the fusion pyrolysis separation described in Section IV-2c.

The second class is plant samples in which, during ashing with a fixative to remove the organic matter, fluoride content may become partially inaccessible for the hexafluosilicic acid volatilization separation. Fusion with an alkali metal hydroxide in a nickel vessel at about 670°C. (84,170,173), or with a peroxide in a steel bomb (84,133a), converts the fluoride to a soluble form for separation by the Willard–Winter technique. Recently the organic removal by oxidation and conversion to a soluble fluoride has been accomplished simultaneously in a Parr bomb peroxide decomposition. Direct fusion-pyrolysis separation and decomposition has not beeen attempted for this type of sample.

2. Separation of Fluoride

A. VOLATILIZATION BY WILLARD–WINTER TECHNIQUE

The main difficulties of volatilization of fluoride from acidic solution, mainly as hexafluosilicic acid, are retardation of evolution by complexing ions and acid carry-over into the distillate. The retardation effect decreases at higher solution temperatures while the acid carry-over often increases concurrently. The acid carry-over can be reduced by special design of the still head to hold back acid droplets, coupled with reduction of solution bumping, which often occurs when ions are added to precipitate the chloride. Since present high ionic strength titrations and some colorimetric estimation techniques can tolerate high chloride content, the use of silver ion to prevent volatilization of hydrochloric acid can now often be omitted. The recent innovation of nitrogen as an additional carrier gas (194) reduces the volume of distillate requisite for complete volatilization. It this is partially bubbled through the solution, the stirring produced would help to decrease bumping by any precipitate present, while also aiding volatilization of fluoride. The use of such a carrier gas deserves further study in macro to semimicro- as well as in micro type stills. The good results of the steam or oxygen pyrolysis separations are very dependent on rapid gas flow. The traces of other anions in the distillates could be rather easily removed by an anion-exchange resin column. The resins could be safely used in this circumstance, since metals which might form differently adsorbed fluoride complexes are, except for silicon, absent in the distillates. The recent phosphate removal from distillates by precipitation with silver ion appears successful but the possible occlusion of some of the fluoride requires further study. Similarly, sulfate has been precipitated with barium but here coprecipitation of fluoride might be expected.

3. Relative Stability of Various Fluoride Complexes

Although the importance of considering the difference in stability, or extent of dissociation, of the varied metal fluoride complexes and low-solubility compounds and the existence of more than one complex for many metals has been stressed previously (55), not enough attention is paid to the formation equilibrium constants and solubility products of the various fluorides. Although considerable work has been done on the stability and solubility products of some of the metal fluoride compounds and complexes, there is considerable discordance in the data, partly due to the use of ionic strengths of a moderately high level. Data on two important complexes, the fluoborate and fluosilicate types, are especially meager. In all such studies the hydrogen ion concentration and the competitive complexing of oxygen, hydroxyl, or other anion groups needs consideration. For our purposes a general order of stability is sufficient. All available values are cited by Bjerrum and others (28,211). The order of decreasing stability for the soluble complexes are listed in Table III. The order of decreasing solubility products, corresponding to more soluble or

TABLE III
Relative Stability of Metal Fluorides

Decreasing order of stability of soluble fluoride complexes

Zr > Th > Pu(IV) > Ti(IV) > Sc = Al > Be > Fe(III) = Ga > U(VI) as UO_2^{++}

ion = Cr(III) > Gd(III) > In = Sb(III) = Ce(III) > La(III) > U(IV) >

V(IV) as VO^{2+} > Mg > Ca > Hg(II), Pb(II), > Fe(II), Ni, Ca, Cu(II), Zn, Cd,

Hg(I), Ag, Au, Pt

Values for the following elements known to form fluoride complexes are unavailable

Si(IV), Nb(V), Ta(V), Hf(IV), Bi(III), B as BO_3^{3-}, Se(IV), Sn(IV), Mn(III)

Decreasing order of solubility constants of sparingly soluble fluorides

$ThF_4 \cdot 4H_2O$, $ThF_4 \cdot xH_2O$, Na_3AlF_6, AlF_3, CaF_2, SrF_2, MgF_2, PbF_2, BaF_2, LiF

Unavailable readily are data for

LaF_3, YF_3, triphenyltin fluoride, BiF_3, and K_2SiF_6

less highly complexed salts for the insoluble compounds are listed like-wise. Methods for calculating the species probably predominant in any given system are available. In all cases the time factor is important, especially where fluoride in the presence of acid speeds corrosion, or when formation of a noncolored product is concerned (e.g., 201).

The relatively high stability fluoride complexes are of most advantage for use with chromophoric agents for estimation of lesser amounts of fluoride. Correspondingly, the less stable complexes may be desirable for determination of larger quantities of fluoride.

The formation of fluoro complexes, usually varying in stability with the valence of the metal concerned, leads to changes in redox potentials of the couples and changes in the adsorption characteristics of ion-exchange resins or changes in their transferance through ion-selective membranes. Addition of the stronger complexing metals, such as aluminum or zirconium, to acidic fluoride solutions decreases, or practically obliviates, the deleterious corrosion properties of the free fluoride of such media.

4. Difficulties of Volumetric and Colorimetric Methods

Many of the volumetric and practically all the colorimetric, methods for the final estimation of fluoride suffer from difficulties which similar methods for determination of other elements do not have to the same extent.

a. Competition for the chromophore or indicator by other metals in the solution. For example, Alizarin or its sulfonate, commonly used as a chromophoric indicator with zirconium or thorium, also forms colored complexes with many other metals.

b. Competition for the fluoride by other metals which form stable or somewhat stable fluoride complexes. This effect is minimized by using the most stable metal ions as a basis for the estimation.

c. Competition for the metal used in the estimation by other anions. The worst offenders generally are phosphate, arsenate, sulfate, oxalate and sulfite.

d. Oxidation, reduction, or other destructive reaction of the chromophore or indicator. For the organic dye and chelating substances, chlorine, hypochlorite, chromate, cerate, etc., often use up all this reagent. Stannous tin or other strong reductants also may interfere. The effect of oxidants is decreased or eliminated by treating the solution with a mild reductant, such as hydroxylamine, thiosulfite, etc.

For colorimetry, use of zirconium chelates in a strongly acidic solution minimizes the interference of other anions. Cationic impurities may be sufficiently low, as in water, or are removed in a separation process before the final estimation.

In the titrimetric and some of the colorimetric methods, separation from competing cations and anions is almost always required prior to the estimation steps of the methods. Among the serious interferences are those due to sulfate and phosphate. The present recourse is that of separation prior to the estimation process. An additional factor is the visual detection of the somewhat subtle color changes noted with many of the indicators in the titrimetric and colorimetric methods. The recent use of photometric titration and further use of filter or prism photometers in the colorimetric methods tend to minimize this difficulty in fluoride determinations. In addition, the use of alternate physical methods for endpoint detection helps reduce, in some instances at least, the deleterious effect of some colored cations, other cations forming colored or fluorescent indicator complexes and oxidants which normally tend to adversely affect such chromophoric indicators. The instrumental endpoint detection schemes, however, have some other disadvantages, which are discussed in Section VI-5.

5. Difficulties of Physical and Instrumental Methods

Among the techniques used for endpoint detection in the titrimetric methods, other than color change, are: amperometry, potentiometry, conductometry, high-frequency phenomena, and radioactivity measurements. In general, the amperometric detection of excess titrant depends on the absence of any appreciable amount of ions reduced at, or below the potential used in the procedures, as well as the absence of other anions reacting with the titrant. The potentiometric techniques, depending on potential change of a metal couple, require absence of other couples influencing potential measurement; those depending on hydrogen ion concentration measurement depend on the absence of buffers, strong acids, or strong bases in the solution. Conductometric techniques generally require an initial solution of fairly low conductance and are favored by use of a similar type titrant. The high-frequency techniques are less restricted in conductance requirements but have sometimes shown spurious changes in response, besides the one desired. The radiometric methods require some sort of intermittent phase separation before counting.

Other physical methods have certain difficulties. The mass spectrometric methods are invalidated by changes in abundance of the varied fluorine-containing mass fragments with matrix changes and instrumental variables, as well as a tendency for retention of previous samples in the apparatus. The infrared methods are often restricted to organic fluorine compounds. For the infrared active inorganics HF, SiF_6, UF_6, ClF_3, MoF_6, trouble with window corrosion and the necessity of anhydrous handling in corrosion-resistant apparatus usually restrict applications to some of the simpler mixtures. Nuclear magnetic resonance spectra have not, as yet, been applied to fluorine analyses, but they may be adversely influenced as in mass spectrometric techniques. The x-ray techniques are generally not sufficiently precise for quantitative results. Ultraviolet and visible spectrophotometry methods are adversely influenced by other absorbing species in the sample and cannot be recommended.

Spectrographic techniques are generally based on the intensity of alkaline earth metal fluoride bands and require complete interaction of the metal and fluoride prior or during excitation and may suffer from matrix effects.

Cryoscopic, molecular weight, gas density, sonic, and other physical methods are generally restricted to supposedly pure fluorine compounds or binary mixtures.

VI. CHALLENGES FOR FUTURE INVESTIGATION

The author suggests here some possible approaches for future developments concerned with analytical work that involves fluorides. It is hoped that other investigators will undertake the original thinking and experimental work required for demonstrating the usefulness, or lack thereof, for these ideas.   The author, himself, is now involved in other interesting analytical development work.   Thus, the efforts of others are invited in this field.

1. Direct Methods Avoiding Separations

It is apparent from the previous discussion that all the present quantitative methods depend on:

a.   Precipitation of an insoluble fluoride which is weighed, or the excess metal ion is estimated by gravimetric, volumetric, or colorimetric methods.   Previous sections indicate the difficulties involved in precipitation of inorganic fluorides and the numerous other anions which also form insoluble salts with the same metal ions.   No future is seen for discovery of more selectively precipitated inorganic fluoride salts.   The other agent used for gravimetry, triphenyltin ion, suggests that investigation of other organometallic compounds might lead to the discovery of a still more desirable precipitant.

b.   Formation of an insoluble precipitate or stable soluble complex with a metal;   the excess uncomplexed metal is detected.   In all cases, so far investigated, many other anions also behave like fluoride to a greater or lesser extent.   For example, phosphate ion, which is almost identical crystallographically and in chemical reactions, forms precipitates and complexes with the same metals as does fluoride.   In fact, in titrating mixtures of the two with thorium, the result is proportional to their sum.   On the other hand, in colorimetric methods using zirconium in fairly acidic solution the competition for metal is somewhat less, but still serious.   One hope, in such cases, is to find a metal or organic agent which will serve as a masking agent for the anions other than fluoride. Another hope is to investigate the effect of other anions on metals which form strong fluoride complexes or organic substances which may give fluoride chelates or adducts which have as yet not been investigated thoroughly. One such system is discussed below.

Very recently the formation of a new colored complex containing fluoride has been reported (18a), which has been applied to the detection of fluoride and more recently (18b) to the determination of fluorine in organic compounds. The investigators find that the red   colored   cerium(III)-1,2-dihydroxyanthraquinonyl-3-methyl-amine-N,N-diacetic acid complex is changed to a lilac–blue double complex, by the addition of fluoride in the complex (measured at 610 mμ). The uncomplexed dye is yellow at the recommended acetate-buffered pH of 4.3. The common inorganic anions, except for phosphate, do not interfere when present in 100-fold excess. Strong complexers such as oxalate, citrate, tartrate, and ethylenedinitrilotetraacetate inhibit the color reaction. Many heavy metals also prevent formation of the bluish double complex, although mercury(II), manganese(II), and magnesium may be present. The method, to date, has been used for determining fluoride in amounts of 20 to 50 μg.

In addition to anions, many cations interfere in methods for the determination of fluoride. The principal effect is competitive reaction with the inorganic or organic indicators used to detect the excess metal which has not reacted with fluoride. Usually a lesser influence is competition for the fluoride by the other cations rather than complete reaction with the agent used for the determination. For example, the presence of aluminum ions decreases or eliminates the complexing of fluoride with iron(III) so that the latter ion's thiocyanate complex is not decomposed to the extent which the same amount of fluoride would cause in the absence of aluminum. Further examples are evident from a study of the relative stability of varied fluoride complexes cited in Section V-3. In this case, the solution to the problem of fluoride determination is to choose a detection system in which the metal ion forms a much stronger complex than any other metal that is suspected to be present in the sample.

Another possibility is the discovery of an agent, probably an organometallic complex ion, which forms a fluoride salt or a complex extractable into a water-immiscible organic solvent which will exhibit a property in the solvent which differs from the same property for the solvent or any other anion complexes which may be extracted. A start to this approach has been reported in the extraction of tetraphenyl antimony(V) fluoride. Other organometallics which deserve investigation are those of arsenic, tin, titanium, aluminum, boron, thorium, and zirconium. The use of a chromophoric grouping, instead of an unsubstituted aliphatic or aromatic organic radical probably would give rise to differences in spectral response. Another step, although an indirect determination, has been the extraction and fluorescent intensity measurement of uncomplexed aluminum ion as the morin or quercetin complex.

2. Pyrolysis Separations

The varied types of samples and compounds for which fluoride separation by steam pyrohydrolysis or fusion pyrolysis, where moist oxygen is used, are discussed in Section IV-3. It is evident that additional laboratories should investigate the applicability of these separation techniques to additional sample types. Still worthy of test with the techniques are soils, bones, animal tissues, vegetation, and several other types. It probably will be possible to develop fluxes and accelerators which should enable fluoride separation by this technique for many types of samples yet uninvestigated. It may be possible to evolve differentially the varied halides by temperature and flux control.

3. Scandium Chelates for Determination

Of the metals which form strong complexes or insoluble salts with fluoride, only beryllium and scandium remain to be investigated extensively. In two papers discussed earlier (Section IV-6), beryllium is used as a reactant. Since solid beryllium compounds are toxic if inhaled or ingested, the author cannot recommend further studies with this metal ion. Connick and Paul (158) recently reported that scandium forms a very stable monofluo complex, second in strength to the zirconium complex and stronger than any other trivalent ion's monofluo complex. As yet, analytical methods for fluoride using scandium as an intermediary in the fluoride determination are unpublished. Since this author has no experience with scandium chromophoric chelates or extractable chelates, no starting point is suggested for such colorimetric or solvent extraction investigations.

4. Buffers for Volumetric and Colorimetric Methods

In the titration of fluoride with thorium using a colorimetric indicator the hydrogen ion concentration is often controlled by the use of a buffer. For Alizarin Red S indicator, a monochloroacetate buffer is often utilized. In our monograph of 1954 (55), it was suggested that use of a formate buffer might help to reduce the effect of any oxidants in the sample that is being titrated. No one yet has investigated this buffer. With such a buffer it may be advantageous to use a thorium formate titrant and a high frequency conductance endpoint rather than a visual or spectrophotometric method. Earlier studies (95) indicated that thorium chloroacetate and other slow moving anion salts can be conductometrically titrated with fluoride. Excess acid in the thorium solution made the reverse conductometric titration unsatisfactory. Better preparation of such a salt, without excess acid, may allow for a satisfactory titration.

Another type of buffer, worthy of search, would be one which might complex other cations, or anions, other than fluoride or the metal used in the determination. This is a problem which involves some fair knowledge of the stability constants of varied metal complexes. For success, the stability constant of the metal chelating agent should be at most one-hundredth the value of the formation constant of the appropriate metal fluoride complex. The anion complexer should have a stability constant at least fifty times greater than the appropriate formation constant for the metal fluoride complex. The recent publication of a compilation of the formation constants available until 1957 (28) will aid in such a search but cannot be considered exclusive, since only a fraction of the possible systems have yet been studied.

5. Physical Methods for Determination

Among the techniques which, as yet, have not been really exploited analytically, is that of nuclear magnetic resonance. Until a few months ago this technique was used mainly in structural or fundamental studies; however, it has been indicated that mixtures of varied phosphoric acids, (ortho, meta, pyro) can be determined at least roughly. Since fluorine in compounds has one of the strongest signals for this technique and the position of the signal varies, depending on the grouping present, quantitative analyses of mixtures of organic fluorine compounds or admixtures with nonfluorinated organics should be possible. Unfortunately the high resolution instruments involving use of this property are as yet very expensive. Inorganic samples probably could be handled if ways are found to add all the fluoride in a sample, as hydrogen fluoride, to a water-immiscible olefin or other organic compound which reacts readily and rapidly with fluoride ion. The other halide ions probably would react also, thereby consuming a fair proportion of the active reagent. The products could be distinguished either directly, or separated by chromatographic methods.

Another technique, not extensively investigated, is quantitative infrared spectrophotometry of organic mixtures containing fluorinated components. Since numerous structural studies that use infrared spectrographic methods have been published, and fairly satisfactory correlations of band positions with type of fluorine linkage have been worked out (55,191,192), it would only require a bit of additional work to develop additional quantitative methods.

Use of the ion intensity measurements of mass spectrographic cracking patterns may deserve some additional investigations, as well as the publication of data known to be buried in the files of various companies. Solids could be handled similarly by fusion in high-temperature spectrometers. Unfortunately it is very difficult to reproduce the same quantitative breakdown of a compound into ionic fragments from instrument to instrument or in varying types of samples.

6. Other Systems for Determination

The use of metal, metal oxide, and metal–metal fluoride couples as one of a pair of electrodes whose potential or current response is a function of fluoride content, deserves further investigation. In the first field, the current passing between an aluminum (9,10) or zirconium (136) electrode and a platinum electrode has received some investigation (Section IV-7). Further study of both direct current measurement and titrations in varied media with these and titanium electrodes perhaps with a potential applied across the electrodes, may lead to methods with response less influenced by other halides, sulfates, or phosphates and perhaps operable in media of higher ionic strength and variable or low pH. The effect of varied buffers needs study to control the influence or hydrogen ion concentration. Since the direct response is a function of temperature, stirring, and other factors a flow system for direct measurement, as recently investigated for low levels in air samples (98), or a titration endpoint detection, probably will serve better than the original method (10).

Several other systems should be given further attention for the possible estimation of fluoride.

Holzbecker (97a) finds that the fluorescence of the salicylidene-*o*-aminophenol with aluminum at pH 5 can detect 0.005 μg. of aluminum and that fluoride quenches fluorescence of the complex. The quantitative aspects of the fluoride effect deserve study.

The enzymatic and catalytic approaches to the determination of fluoride perhaps have not received sufficient attention. The methods of these types, now available, require considerable control of several experimental variables. It may be possible to discover an enzyme system with relatively low temperature dependence which might be very sensitive to low fluoride levels.

VII. DETERMINATION OF ELEMENTAL FLUORINE

Analytical methods for the determination of elemental fluorine, F_2, depend on the oxidizing character of this element.

a. A gaseous sample containing fluorine is passed through pellets of sodium fluoride to remove hydrogen fluoride, then through dry sodium chloride, forming chlorine by oxidation. The chlorine is absorbed in caustic, forming hypochlorite, which is then treated with iodide and acetic acid. The iodine thus formed is titrated with thiosulfate (40,55).

b. The gas, after removal of hydrogen fluoride, is reacted with sodium bromide, and the intensity of color of the effluent is measured (55).

c. The gas sample is titrated into a known amount of bromine in bromine trifluoride, contained in an inert plastic until the red bromine color disappears (187).

d. A gas sample containing less than 30% of fluorine is reacted with an excess of aqueous neutral potassium iodide by shaking. The iodine formed is titrated with thiosulfate to estimate the fluorine content. By addition of excess standard base and back-titration to phenolphthalein with acid, the hydrogen fluoride content is determined on the same sample (55,151).

e. Low concentrations in air are estimated by passing a sample over silica gel treated with potassium bromide, carbonate, and fluorescein. Formation of a red color, due to eosin, reputedly detects under 0.5 μg. of fluorine per liter of air (161).

f. An older method (27,141), measures the volume reduction of a sample after reaction with liquid mercury in a nickel or copper tube following earlier removal of hydrogen fluoride.

g. A method for certain ranges, measures the pressure change of a stirred reactor vessel during titration with gaseous ethylene in the presence of solid sodium fluoride (107).

h. The change in molar flow at the exit of a reactor chamber into which known flows of sulfur dioxide and of samples containing fluorine are continually passed, due to formation of one mole of sulfuryl fluoride, SO_2F_2, from one each of fluorine and the reagent, allows continuous estimation of the fluorine content (157).

In addition to these methods for fluorine, similar oxidation-reduction methods have been used for the assay of bromine and chlorine trifluorides.

References

1. Adams, D. F., R. K. Koppe, and H. J. Dana, *Universal Air Pollutant Analyzer*, U. S. Department of Public Health contract, Report from State College of Washington, 1957. *Anal. Chem.*, **31**, 1249 (1959).
2. American Public Health Association, *Standard Methods for the Examination of Water, Sewage, and Industrial Wastes*, 10th ed., A.P.H.A. New York, 1955, pp. 98–107.
3. Armstrong, W. D., and L. Singer, *Anal. Chem.*, **26**, 1047 (1954).
4. Armstrong, W. D., and L. Singer, *Micro Determination of Fluoride in Biological Materials and the Biochemical Role of Fluoride*, U. S. Department of Defense, Surgeon General's Office, 1957.
5. Association of Official Agricultural Chemists, *Official and Tentative Methods of Analysis*, 8th ed., A.O.A.C., Washington, D. C., 1955, pp. 39, 52–55, 415, 423, 491, 576.
6. Atteberry, R. W., and G. E. Boyd, *J. Am. Chem. Soc.*, **72**, 4805 (1950).
7. Aynsley, E. E., *School Sci. Rev.*, **38**, 270 (1957).
8. Babko, A. K., and P. V. Khodulina, *J. Anal. Chem.*, *U.S.S.R.*, **7**, 281 (1952).
9. Baker, B. B., *Anal. Chem.*, **30**, 1085 (1958).
10. Baker, B. B., and Morrison, J. D., *Anal. Chem.*, **27**, 1306 (1955).
11. Ballczo, H., G. Doppler, and A. Lanik, *Mikrochim. Acta*, **1957**, 809.
12. Ballczo, H., and H. Schiffner, *Z. anal. Chem.*, **152**, 3 (1956); *Mikrochim. Acta*, **1956**, 1829.
13. Banerjee, G., *Anal. Chim. Acta*, **13**, 409 (1955).

14. Banks, R. E., F. Cuthbertson, and W. K. R. Musgrave, *Anal. Chim. Acta*, **13**, 442 (1955).
15. Bartlet, J. C., D. Kavanagh, and R. A. Chapman, *Can. J. Technol.*, **33**, 348 (1955).
16. Beck, M. T., *Acta Chim. Acad. Sci. Hung.*, **4**, 233 (1954).
17. Belcher, R., *Österr. Chemiker-Ztg.*, **55**, 158 (1954).
18. Belcher, R., and S. J. Clark, *Anal. Chim. Acta*, **8**, 222 (1953).
18a. Belcher, R., M. A. Leonard, and T. S. West, *Talanta*, **2**, 92 (1959).
18b. Belcher, R., M. A. Leonard, and T. S. West, *J. Chem. Soc.*, **1959**, 3577.
19. Belcher, R., and A. M. G. MacDonald, *Mikrochim. Acta*, **1957**, 510.
20. Belcher, R., and C. L. Wilson, *New Methods in Analytical Chemistry*, Reinhold, New York, 1955, p. 229.
21. Bellack, E. J., *J. Am. Water Works Assoc.*, **50**, 4, 530 (1958).
22. Bellack, E., and P. J. Schouboe, *Anal. Chem.*, **30**, 2032 (1958).
23. Bennett, C. E., and F. J. Debbrecht, Am. Chem. Soc. Meeting, Miami, April 1957.
24. Berquin, Y., *Chim. anal.*, **38**, 367 (1956).
25. Bergmann, F., and R. Segal, *Biochem. J.*, **62**, 542 (1956).
26. Beveridge, J. S., B. J. MacNulty, G. F. Reynolds, and E. A. Terry, *Analyst*, **79**, 190, 267 (1954).
27. Bigelow, L. A., *Chem. Revs.*, **40**, 52–115 (1947).
28. Bjerrum, J., G. Schwarzenbach, and L. G. Sillen, *Stability Constants. II. Inorganic Ligands*, The Chemical Society, London, Spec. Publ. No. 7, 1958, Table 51, pp. 88–93.
29. Bloch, L., *Chem. Weekblad.*, **51**, 65 (1955).
30. Bouman, J., *Chem. Weekblad.*, **51**, 33 (1955).
31. Brandt, W. W., and A. A. Duswalt, Jr., *Anal. Chem.*, **30**, 1120 (1958).
32. Bredemann, G., *Biochemie et Physiologie des Fluors*, 2nd ed., Akademie Verlag, Berlin, 1956, pp. 186–236.
33. Brunisholz, G., *Helv. Chim. Acta*, **37**, 1546 (1954).
34. Brunisholz, G., and J. Michod, *Helv. Chim. Acta*, **37**, 598, 874 (1954).
35. Bullard, H. L., A. S. Ostroskí, and W. S. Stringham, *U.S. Atomic Energy Commission*, GAT-213 (1957).
36. Bumstead, H. E., and J. C. Wells, *Anal. Chem.*, **24**, 1595 (1952).
37. Cabral, J. M. P., and H. Götte, *Z. Naturforsch.*, **10B**, 440 (1955).
37a. Caley, E. R., and G. R. Kahle, *Anal. Chem.*, **31**, 1880 (1959).
38. Chaikin, S. W., G. I. Glassbrook, and T. D. Parks, U.S. Pat., 2,741,544 (Apr. 10, 1956) (to Stanford Research Institute).
39. Chilton, J. M., and A. D. Horton, *Anal. Chem.*, **27**, 842 (1955).
40. Compton, J. D., *U.S. Atomic Energy Commission*, A-3513 (1946).
41. Couceiro, R. G., daC., *Anales real soc. espan. fis. y quim. (Madrid), Ser. B*, **50**, 799 (1954); through *Chem. Abstracts*, **49**, 8734 (1955).
42. Cropper, F. R., *Analyst*, **76**, 370 (1951).
43. Curry, R. P., and M. G. Mellon, *Anal. Chem.*, **28**, 1567 (1956).
44. D'Amore, G., and G. Faraone, *Ann. chim., (Rome)*, **47**, 142 (1957).
45. Danielsen, M. E., *Univ. Bergen Arbok, Naturvitenskap Rekke*, No. 9

(1954); **No. 15** (1955); through *Chem. Abstracts*, **49**, 12193 (1955); **51**, 2206 (1957).

46. Dean, J. A., M. H. Buehler, and L. J. Hardin, *J. Assoc. Offic. Agr. Chemists*, **40**, 949 (1957).
47. Debal, E., R. Levy, and H. Moureu, *Mikrochim. Acta*, **1957**, 396.
48. Degtyarenko, Ya. A., *Ukrain. Khim. Zhur.*, **22**, 813 (1956); through *Chem. Abstracts*, **51**, 7232 (1957).
49. Devonshire, L. N., and H. H. Rowley, *Proc. Oklahoma Acad. Sci.*, **34** (1953), 159 (1955).
50. Diamond, W. J., *Appl. Spectroscopy*, **12**, 10 (1958).
51. Dowdall, J. P., D. V. Sinkinson, and H. Stretch, *Analyst*, **80**, 491 (1955).
52. Dykes, F. W., G. L. Booman, M. C. Elliott, and J. E. Rein, *U.S. Atomic Energy Commission*, IDO-14405 (1957).
53. Eger, C., and A. Yarden, *Bull. Res. Counc. Israel*, **4**, 305 (1954).
54. Eger, C., and A. Yarden, *Anal. Chem.*, **28**, 512 (1956).
55. Elving, P. J., C. A. Horton, and H. H. Willard, "Analytical Chemistry of Fluorine and Fluorine-Containing Compounds," J. H. Simons, ed., *Fluorine Chemistry*, Vol. II, Academic Press, New York, 1954, pp. 51–211.
56. Emi, K., and T. Hayashi, *J. Chem. Soc. Japan, Pure Chem. Sect.*, **77**, 1656 (1956); *Anal. Abstr.*, **4**, 3159 (1957).
57. Epars, L., *Bull. schweiz Akad. med. Wiss.*, **10**, 276 (1954).
58. Eucken, A., and A. Bertram, *Z. physik. Chem.*, **B31**, 361 (1936).
59. Evans, D. G., and J. C. Tatlow, *J. Chem. Soc.*, **1955**, 3021.
60. Fabre, R., R. Truhaut, and A. Roquette, *Compt. rend.*, **240**, 226 (1955).
61. Fellenberg, Th. von, *Mitt. Gebiete Lebens. Hyg.*, **42**, 267 (1951).
61a. Fine, L., and E. A. Wynne, *Microchem. J.*, **3**, 515 (1959).
61b. Fisher Scientific Co., Bulletins on Lanthanum and Thorium Chloranilates, 1958–1959.
62. Fletcher, M. H., and R. G. Milkey, *Anal. Chem.*, **28** 1408 (1956).
63. Francis, R. L., *Offic. Bull. N. Dak. Water Works Conf.*, **19**, No. 6/7, 4 (1951/1952).
64. Frazier, R. E., *J. Am. Water Works Assoc.*, **57**, 560 (1955).
65. Frazier, R. E., and H. P. Kramer, *J. Am. Water Works Assoc.*, **47**, 563 (1955).
66. Freier, H. E., B. W. Nippoldt, P. B. Olson, and D. G. Weiblen, *Anal. Chem.*, **27**, 146 (1955).
67. Fukamauchi, H., M. Sekiguchi, and K. Iiyoshi, *Bunseki Kagaku*, **6**, 229 (1957); *Chem. Abstracts*, **52**, 11,646a (1958).
68. Funasaka, W., M. Kawane, and T. Ichikawa, *Japan Analyst*, **3**, 505 (1954); through *Chem. Abstracts*, **49**, 15,607 (1955).
69. Funasaka, W., M. Kawane, T. Kojima, and K. Ishihara, *Japan Analyst*, **4**, 607 (1955); *Chem. Abstracts*, **50**, 16,554 (1956).
70. Funasaka, W., M. Kawane, and T. Hashino, *J. Chem. Soc. Japan, Ind. Chem. Sect.*, **53**, 326 (1950); through trans. *CIA/FDD/U-4702*.
71. Funasaka, W., M. Kawane, and T. Kojima, *Mem. Fac. Eng. Kyoto Univ.*, **18**, 44 (1956); through *Chem. Abstracts*, **50**, 10,603 (1956).
72. Fuwa, K., *Japan Analyst*, **3**, 98 (1954); *Chem. Abstracts*, **48**, 9864 (1954).

73. Gamble, L. W., W. E. Price, and W. H. Jones, Am. Chem. Soc. Meeting, Miami, April 1957.

74. Gelman, N. E. et al., *Doklady Akad. Nauk S.S.S.R.*, **123**, 468 (1958); *Chem. Abstracts*, **53**, 3985*f* (1959).

75. Gillies, G. M., N. J. Keen, B. A. J. Lister, and D. Rees, *Atomic Energy Research Establ. G. Brit., AERE-C/M-225* (1954).

76. Gladyshev, V. P., and G. A. Tolstikov, *J. Anal. Chem., U.S.S.R. (English Translation)*, **12**, 590 (1957).

77. Goodyear Atomic Corp., *U.S. Atomic Energy Commission, GAT-115*, Rev. 1 (1957).

78. Grant, C. I., and H. M. Haendler, *Anal. Chem.*, **28**, 415 (1956).

79. Greenspan, J., and A. S. Carlson, U.S. Pat. 2,797,983 (July 2, 1957).

80. Grimaldi, F. S., B. Ingram, and F. Cuttitta, *Anal. Chem.*, **27**, 918 (1955).

81. Grutsch, J. F., et al., *J. Dental Research*, **32**, 463 (1953).

82. Guntz, A. A., and M. Arène, *Chim. anal.*, **39**, 360 (1957).

83. Guntz, A. A., and M. Arène, *Chim. anal.*, **40**, 453 (1958).

84. Gwirtsman, J., R. Mavrodineanu, and R. R. Coe, *Anal. Chem.*, **29**, 887 (1957).

85. Haff, L. V., C. P. Butler, and J. D. Bisso, *Anal. Chem.*, **30**, 984 (1958).

86. Hall, R. J., *Analyst*, **82**, 663 (1957).

87. Hardin, L. J., *J. Assoc. Offic. Agr. Chemists*, **36**, 237 (1953).

88. Harris, W. E., *Anal. Chem.*, **30**, 1000 (1958).

89. Hennart, C., and E. Merlin, *Anal. Chim. Acta*, **17**, 463 (1957).

89a. Hensley, A. L., and J. E. Barney, II, Abstract 13, Amer. Chem. Soc. Meeting, Atlantic City, September 1959, p. 5B.

90. Herder, J. J. den, and J. A. C. van Pinxteren, *Pharm. Weekblad*, **93**, 1013 (1958).

91. Hering, H., J. Hure, and S. Legrand, *French Atomic Energy Commission, CEA-26* (1949).

92. Higashino, T., and Musha, S., *Japan Analyst*, **4**, 3 (1955); through *Chem. Abstracts*, **50**, 4711 (1946); *Anal. Abstr.*, **2**, 2416 (1955).

93. Hillebrand, W. F., G. E. F. Lundell, H. A. Bright, and J. I. Hoffman, *Applied Inorganic Analysis*, 2nd ed., Wiley, New York, 1953, pp. 737–748, 938–948, 978.

94. Horton, A. D., P. F. Thomason, and F. J. Miller, *Anal. Chem.*, **24**, 548 (1952).

95. Horton, C. A., *Ph.D. Thesis*, University of Michigan, 1949, Univ. Microfilms, Pub. No. 2205.

96. Horton, C. A., to be published.

97. Horton, C. A., and J. Gurney, unpublished work.

97a. Holzbecker, S., *Collections Czechoslov Chem. Communs.*, **19**, 241 (1954).

98. Howard, O. H., and C. W. Weber, *Arch. Ind. Hyg. and Occupational Med.*, **19**, 365 (1959).

99. Hunter, G. J., B. J. MacNulty, and E. A. Terry, *Anal. Chim. Acta*, **8**, 351 (1953).

100. Icken, J. M., and B. M. Blank, *Anal. Chem.*, **25**, 1741 (1953).

101. Irsa, A. P., and L. Friedman, *J. Inorg. & Nuclear Chem.*, **6**, 77 (1958).

102. Ishida, R., *Repts. Govt. Chem. Ind. Research Inst.*, *Tokyo*, **51**, 339 (1956); *J. Chem. Soc. Japan, Pure Chem. Sect.*, **77**, 241 (1956).
103. Johannesson, J. K., *New Zealand J. Sci. Technol.*, **36B**, 626 (1955).
104. Johannesson, J. K., *Chem. & Ind. (London)*, **1957**, 480.
105. Kadič, K., and Z. Rezáč, *Chem. listy*, **49**, 570 (1955).
106. Kamada, M., T. Ŏnishi, and M. Ŏta, *Bull. Chem. Soc. Japan*, **28**, 148 (1955).
107. Katz, S., and J. T. Barr, *Anal. Chem.*, **25**, 619 (1953).
108. Klement, R., W. Fresenius, and G. Jander, *Handbuch der Analytichen Chemie. Elements of Group VII. I. Hydrogen, Fluorine*, Springer, Berlin, 1950, Part III, Vol. VII a, pp. 132–245.
109. Knudson, G. E., Ph.D. Thesis, State U. of Iowa, 1954; through *Dissertation Abstr.*, **15**, 1717 (1955).
110. Koehler, F. A., and W. A. Levier, *Science*, **124**, 175 (1956).
111. Krahulec, L., *Českolov. hyg. epidemicl. mikrobiol. imunol.*, **4**, 376 (1955); through *Chem. Abstracts*, **49**, 15,621 (1955).
112. Kubli, H., *Helv. Chim. Acta*, **30**, 453 (1947).
113. Kubota, H., and J. G. Surak, *Anal. Chem.*, **31**, 283 (1959).
114. Kubota, K., *Folia Pharmacol. Japon.*, **48**, No. 1, Proc., 38 (1952); through *Chem Abstracts*, **47**, 1875 (1953).
115. Kunin, R., and R. J. Myers, *J. Am. Chem. Soc.*, **69**, 2874 (1947).
116. Kuyper, A. C., *Anal. Chem.*, **28**, 922 (1956).
117. Lafferty, R. H., Jr., and R. Winget, *U.S. Atomic Energy Commission, AECD-3825* (1946).
118. Lamar, W. L., and P. G. Drake, *J. Am. Water Works Assoc.*, **47**, 563 (1955).
119. Lambert, J. L., *Anal. Chem.*, **25**, 271 (1953).
120. Lambert, J. L., *Anal. Chem.*, **26**, 558 (1954).
121. Lang, B. G., O. C. Sieverding, and E. K. Borman, *Am. J. Public Health*, **46**, 860 (1956).
122. Lasiewicz, K., *Pramyal Chemiczny (Chem. Ind.)*, **10**, 36 (1954); *U.S. Atomic Energy Commission, AEC-tr-2352* (1955).
122x. Laszlovsky, J., *Magyar Kém. Folyóirat*, **60**, 209 (1954).
122a. Lee, J. E., Jr., J. H. Edgerton, and M. T. Kelley, *Anal. Chem.*, **28**, 1441 (1956).
122b. Liddell, H. F., *Analyst*, **79**, 752 (1954).
122c. Linsay, F. K., and J. S. D'Amico, *Ind. Eng. Chem.*, **43**, 1085 (1951).
123. Lothe, J. J., *Anal. Chem.*, **28**, 949 (1946).
124. Lubyanskaya, M. G., *Zavodskaya Lab.*, **22**, 921 (1956).
125. McBee, E. T., *U.S. Atomic Energy Commission, A-1511* (1944).
126. MacNulty, B. J., G. J. Hunter, and D. G. Barrett, *Anal. Chim. Acta*, **14**, 368 (1956).
127. MacNulty, B. J., G. F. Reynolds, and E. A. Terry, *Nature*, **169**, 888 (1952); *Analyst*, **79**, 190 (1954).
128. MacNulty, B. J., and L. D. Woolard, *Anal. Chim. Acta*, **14**, 452 (1956).
129. Ma, T. S., *Anal. Chem.*, **30**, 1557 (1958).
130. Mader, C., *Chemist-Analyst*, **44**, 86 (1955).
131. Massoth, F. E., *U.S. Atomic Energy Commission, GAT-234* (1958).

132. Mavrodineanu, R., and J. Gwirtsman, *Contribs., Boyce Thompson Inst.*, **17**, 489 (1954).
133. *Ibid.*, **18**, 181 (1955).
133a. *Ibid.*, **18**, 419 (1956).
134. *Ibid.*, **19**, 289 (1958).
135. Megregian, S., *Anal. Chem.*, **26**, 1161 (1954).
136. Megregian, S., *Anal. Chem.*, **29**, 1063 (1957).
137. Megregian, S., "Fluorine," in *Colorimetric Determination of Nonmetals*, D. F. Boltz, ed., Interscience, New York-London, 1958, pp. 231–59.
138. Megregian, S., and F. J. Maier, *J. Am. Water Works Assoc.*, **44**, 239 (1952).
138a. Menis, O., D. L. Manning, and R. G. Ball, *Anal. Chem.*, **30**, 1772 (1958).
139. Mercer, P. D., and H. O. Pritchard, *J. Chem. Soc.*, **1957**, 2843.
140. Miles, F. T., *U.S. Atomic Energy Commission*, *A-752* (1943).
141. Miyahara, Y., *Botyu Kagaku*, **18**, 176 (1953).
142. Moelants, L., *Compt. rend. congr. intern. chim. ind. 27ᵉ Congr., Brussels*, **1954**, 1; *Chem. Abstracts*, **50**, 9940 (1956).
143. Moffett, K. D., J. R. Simmler, and H. A. Potratz, *Anal. Chem.*, **28**, 1356 (1956).
144. Nakanishi, H., and S. Nagao, *Japan Analyst*, **1**, 86 (1952).
145. National Lead Co. of Ohio, *U.S. Atomic Energy Commission*, *FMPC-69*, *70* (1952), Vol. II, pp. 23,81,85.
146. Newman, A. C. D., *Anal. Chim. Acta*, **19**, 471 (1958); **19**, 580 (1958).
147. Nichols, M. L., and A. C. Condo, Jr., *Anal. Chem.*, **26**, 703 (1954).
148. Nielsen, H. M., *Anal. Chem.*, **30**, 1009 (1958).
149. Nielsen, J. P., and A. D. Dangerfield, *A. M. A. Arch. Ind. Health*, **11**, No. 1, 61 (1955).
150. Nommik, H., *Acta Polytech.*, *Chem. Met. Ser.*, **3**, No. 7, 7 (1953); through *Chem. Abstracts*, **48**, 4364 (1954).
151. Oak Ridge National Laboratory, *U.S. Atomic Energy Commission, TID-7015* (1957).
152. Onstott, E. I., and W. P. Ellis, *Anal. Chem.*, **28**, 393 (1956).
153. Oshesky, G. D., *Wright Aeronautical Development Center Rept.*, *WADC-TR-55-421*, (1956).
154. Ovsepyan, E. N., and M. G. Ekimyan, *Izvest. Akad. Nauk Armyan. S. S. R. Ser. Fiz.-Mat., Estestvan i Tekh. Nauk*, **8**, No. 5, 41 (1955); through *Chem. Abstracts*, **50**, 9932 (1956).
155. Ovsepyan, E. N., and V. M. Tarayan, *Nauch Trudy Erevan Univ.*, **53**, 85 (1956); *U.S. Atomic Energy Commission*, *AEC-tr-3219* (1958).
156. Ozhigov, E., M. A. Rafienko, and A. Ya. Vinogradova, *J. Anal. Chem. U.S.S.R.*, **11**, 375 (1956).
157. Pappas, W. S., and C. W. Weber, Amer. Chem. Soc. Meeting, Chicago, Sept. 1958.
158. Paul, A. D., *U.S. Atomic Energy Commission*, *UCRL-2926* (1955). See also *J. Am. Chem. Soc.*, **81**, 4185 (1959).
159. Peixoto-Cabral, J. M., *Z. Naturferach*, **10B**, 440 (1955).
160. Percival, W. C., *Anal. Chem.*, **29**, 20 (1957).
161. Peregud, E. A., and B. S. Boĭkina, *Zhur. Anal. Khim.*, **12**, 513 (1957);

through *U.S. Atomic Energy Commission Nuclear Sci. Abstr.*, **11**, No. 12,684, 1408 (1957); *J. Anal. Chem.*, *U.S.S.R.*, *(English Translation)*, **12**, 531 (1957).

162. Pollard, F. H., and C. J. Hardy, *Anal. Chim. Acta*, **16**, 135 (1957).
163. Popov, A. I., and G. E. Knudson, *Anal. Chem.*, **26**, 892 (1954).
164. Powell, R. H., and O. Menis, *Anal. Chem.*, **30**, 1546 (1958); *U.S. Atomic Energy Commission, ORNL-2512* (1958).
165. Powell, W. A., and J. H. Saylor, *Anal. Chem.*, **25**, 960 (1953).
166. Price, M. J., and O. J. Walker, *Anal. Chem.*, **24**, 1593 (1952).
167. Radimer, J. J., S. H. Smiley, and R. H. Lafferty, Jr., *U.S. Atomic Energy Commission, A-4022* (1946).
168. Raines, M. M., O. I. Pirogova, and M. V. Andreyeva, *Zavodskaya Lab.*, **21**, 151 (1955); *Chem. Abstracts*, **49**, 14,568 (1955).
169. Reed, T. M., III, *Anal. Chem.*, **30**, 221 (1958).
170. Remmert, LeM. F., T. D. Parks, A. M. Lawrence, and E. H. McBurney, *Anal. Chem.*, **25**, 450 (1953).
171. Revinson, D., and J. R. Harley, *Anal. Chem.*, **25**, 794 (1953).
172. Řežáč, Z., and Z. Kubec, *Chem. průmysl*, **6**, 195 (1956); through *Chem. Abstracts*, **50**, 16,554 (1956).
173. Rowley, R. J., J. G. Grier, and R. L. Parsons, *Anal. Chem.*, **25**, 1061 (1953).
174. Ruff, O., *Chemie des Fluors*, Springer, Berlin, 1920.
175. Samachson, J., N. Slovik, and A. E. Sobel, *Anal. Chem.*, **29**, 1888 (1957).
176. Sano, H., *Japan Analyst*, **5**, 289 (1956); through *Anal. Abstr.*, **4**, 102 (1957).
177. Sato, K., and Y. Osumi, *Osaka Kôgyô Gijutsu Shikenjo Kihô*, **7**, 232 (1956); *Chem. Abstracts*, **52**, 18,073f (1958).
178. Savchenko, A. Ya, *J. Anal. Chem. U.S.S.R.*, **10**, 343 (1955).
179. Savinelli, E. A., *Ph.D. Thesis*, University of Florida, 1955.
180. Schall, E. D., and H. G. Williamson, *J. Assoc. Offic. Agr. Chemists*, **38**, 454 (1955).
181. Schnell, E., and E. G. Rochow, *J. Am. Chem. Soc.*, **78**, 4178 (1956).
182. Schöniger, W., "New Ideas in Organic Microanalysis," in C. N. Reilley, ed., *Advances in Analytical Chemistry and Instrumentation*, Interscience, New York-London, 1960.
183. Schultz, H. A., *Anal. Chem.*, **29**, 1840 (1957).
184. Sen, S., *Z. anal. Chem.*, **153**, 168 (1956).
185. Shaw, J. H., *Fluorination as a Public Health Measure*, A.A.A.S., Washington, D.C., 1954, p. 203.
186. Shaw, W. M., *Anal. Chem.*, **26**, 1212 (1954).
187. Sheft, I., H. H. Hyman, and J. J. Katz, *Anal. Chem.*, **25**, 1877 (1953).
188. Shehyn, H., *Anal. Chem.*, **29**, 1466 (1957).
189. Shell, H. R., and R. L. Craig, *U.S. Bur. Mines Rept. Invest.* **5158** (1956).
191. Simons, J. H., ed., *Fluorine Chemistry*, Vol. I, Academic Press, New York, 1950.
192. *Ibid.*, Vol. II, 1954.
193. Singer, L., and W. D. Armstrong, *Anal. Chem.*, **26**, 904 (1954).
194. Singer, L., and W. D. Armstrong, *Anal. Chem.*, **31**, 105 (1959).

195. Smith, F. A., and D. E. Gardner, *U.S. Atomic Energy Commission, UR-390* (1955).

196. Sommer, L., *Chem. listy*, **47**, 906 (1953); *Anal. Abstracts*, **2**, 78 (1955) *Chem. Abstracts*, **48**, 3848 (1954).

197. Specht, R. C., *Anal. Chem.*, **28**, 1015 (1956).

198. Spindler, D. C., and M. F. Smith, *Anal. Chem.*, **30**, 1330 (1958).

199. Sporek, K. F., *Anal. Chem.*, **30**, 1030 (1958).

200. Stacey, M., *The Application of Gas Chromatography to Fluorine Chemistry*, Birmingham University, England, 1956.

201. Stevenson, C. E., *U.S. Atomic Energy Commission, IDO-14443* (1958).

202. Susano, C. D., J. C. White, and J. E. Lee, Jr., *Anal. Chem.*, **27**, 453 (1955).

203. Szabo, Z. G., M. T. Beck, and K. Toth, *Naturwissenschaften*, **43**, 156 (1956); *Magyar Kém. Folyóirat*, **64**, 35 (1958).

204. Talipov, Sh. T., Z. T. Sofeïkova, and T. B. Amirkhanova, *Trudy Sredneaziat. Gosudart. Univ., Khim. Nauki, (Tashkaut)*, **33**, No. 4, 75 (1952); through *Chem. Abstracts*, **50**, 1521 (1956).

205. Talipov, Sh. T., and I. L. Teodorovich, *Doklady Akad. Nauk Uzbek. S.S.S.R.*, **8**, 32 (1953); through *Chem. Abstracts*, **49**, 10,123 (1955); *Anal. Abstracts*, **2**, 1804 (1955).

206. Talipov, Sh. T., I. L. Teodorovich, and N. P. Shestakova, *Trudy Sredneaziat. Gosudarst. Univ. (Tashkaut)*, **33**, No. 4, 83 (1952); through *Chem. Abstracts*, **50**, 1526 (1956).

207. Tamura, Z., and M. Miyazuki, *Japan Analyst*, **5**, 566 (1956).

208. Tedesco, P. H., *Mon. farm. y terap. (Madrid)*, **58**, 439 (1952); *Rev. fac. cienc. quim., Univ. nacl. La Plata*, **24**, 195 (1952); through *Chem. Abstracts*, **47**, 2637, 3176 (1953).

209. Tiedemann, E., *Z. anal. Chem.*, **146**, 415 (1955); *ibid.*, **150**, 1 (1956).

210. Treadwell, F. P., and W. T. Hall, *Analytical Chemistry*, Vol. II, 9th English ed., Wiley, New York, 1951, p. 397.

211. University of California, Radiation Laboratory, *U.S. Atomic Energy Commission, UCRL-2647* (1954); *ibid.*, *UCRL-2841* (1955).

212. Venkataramanan, K., N. Krishnaswamy, and T. Ramakrishnan, *Indian J. Med. Research*, **39**, 211, 218 (1951).

213. Venkateswarlu, P., and D. N. Rao, *Anal. Chem.*, **26**, 766 (1954).

214. Vigier, R., *Bull. soc. chim. France*, **1957**, 160.

215. Vogelenzang, E. H., *Pharm. Weekblad*, **25**, 905 (1956).

216. Vřesťál, J., J. Havíř, J. Brandštetr, and S. Kotrlý, *Chem. listy*, **51**, 1677 (1957); through *Chem. Abstracts*, **52**, 978 (1958).

217. Vřesťál, J., et al., *Collections Czechoslov. Chem. Communs.*, **23**, 886 (1958).

218. Wagner, W., C. J. Hull, and G. E. Markle, *Advanced Analytical Chemistry*, Reinhold, New York, 1956, Chap. 15, pp. 225–229.

219. Wakimoto, S., *J. Chem. Soc. Japan*, **77**, 1489 (1956); *Nippon Kagaku Zasshi*, **77**, 1489 (1956); through *Chem. Abstracts*, **52**, 2660 (1958).

220. Wall, R. F., *Ind. Eng. Chem.*, **50**, 65A, July 1958.

221. Warf, J. C., W. D. Cline, and R. D. Tevebaugh, *Anal. Chem.*, **26**, 342 (1954).

222. Wayman, D. H., *Anal. Chem.*, **28**, 865 (1956).

223. Willard, H. H., and J. A. Dean, *Anal. Chem.*, **22**, 1264 (1950).
224. Willard, H. H., and C. A. Horton, *Anal. Chem.*, **22**, 1190 (1950).
225. *Ibid.*, **24**, 862 (1952).
226. Willard, H. H., and O. B. Winter, *Ind. Eng. Chem., Anal. Ed.*, **5**, 7 (1933).
227. Yasuda, S. K., and J. L. Lambert, *Anal. Chem.*, **30**, 1485 (1958).
228. Young, R. S., *Industrial Inorganic Analysis*, Wiley, New York, 1953, pp. 117–128.
229. Zenin, A. A., *Gidrokhim. Materialy*, **22**, 115 (1954); through *Chem. Abstracts*, **49**, 14,568 (1955).
230. *Ibid.*, **24**, 68 (1955); through *Chem. Abstracts*, **51**, 17,589 (1957).
231. Zipkin, I., W. D. Armstrong, and L. Singer, *Anal. Chem.*, **29**, 310 (1957).
232. Zymny, E., *Glas-Emeil-Keramo-Tech.*, **5**, No. 10, 365 (1954); through *Chem. Abstracts*, **49**, 782 (1955).

New Ideas In Organic Microanalysis

Part I.   C—H, O, N, Halogens, S, and Other Elements

Wolfgang Schöniger, *Sandoz Ltd., Basel, Switzerland*

I. INTRODUCTION

Since Pregl developed quantitative organic microanalysis about 50 years ago, these methods have become well known all over the world. In the first decades microanalytical procedures were used only in a few laboratories, mainly at universities, and done by most qualified people—often by the director of the institute, himself, because he had been the one who had been trained by Pregl at Graz. Since these early times the Pregl methods have become very important tools of the organic chemist and today nearly every chemistry department and every large company have their own microanalytical laboratories doing all the analyses required for efficient research work. The original methods have been modified and simplified, and new procedures have been developed. The purpose of the following pages is to provide information on modifications and new methods in the field of elementary organic microanalysis and to review them critically. Also new procedures shall be recommended which have been tested either in the author's laboratory or elsewhere.

II. BALANCES

Today practically no one employs the original free swinging microbalance, the so-called "assay balance," which was recommended by Pregl. It should be mentioned, however, that in cases where the most exact and reliable weighings are necessary, the undamped microbalance is still the best one available (1). More commonly damped balances are used, since they offer sufficient accuracy and reproducibility of results (e.g., Ainthworth, Ch. Baker, Oertling, Stanton, Bunge, Sartorius). A new type of microbalance, which was introduced by the Mettler Instrument Corp., is based on the principle of weighing by substitution. The maximum load (20 g.) is placed on both sides of the asymmetric beam. When a load is put on the pan the analyst must remove an equivalent weight from the load side to bring the balance to equilibrium. To determine a weight with a Mettler balance, one follows this procedure:

Determine zero as usual and correct where necessary. After arresting the balance, place the substance to be weighed on the pan and close the sliding window. Partially release the pans (move the arrest lever as far to the right as it will go) and set the approximate weight by adjusting the weight control knobs. Now release completely, (turn the lever to the left) and wait until the projected scale comes to rest, or in the case of time weighing, until the exact point of time has been reached. At this point, adjust to the second and third decimal places by quickly turning the micrometer knob, and then read the weight. Do not keep your hand on the micrometer knob or attempt to turn it with the movement of the optical scale in order to locate the point of rest, for the heat radiated by the hand is sufficient to influence the balance.

Absorption tubes used for the C—H determination are weighed in a similar manner. After removing the tubes from the combustion apparatus (if gloves are used for this purpose only the tips need be cleaned and it is not necessary to wipe the whole absorption tube) deposit them beside the balance. Check and, where necessary, correct the zero, and after 3 min. from the time the tubes were set down beside the instrument, place the water absorption tube on the balance. The mechanical weights are properly set, and after an additional 2 min. release the balance and determine the exact weight. Now the carbon dioxide tube is placed on the balance and is finally weighed after the elapse of another 2 min. period. It is not extremely important to observe the times noted here, since these are dependent on the skill of the analyst, but rather to weigh always at exactly the same times as is necessary when operating other balances. Balances of this type, as well as other damped balances, are used in the author's laboratories, and no difference in accuracy and reproducibility has been noted.

The balance room should be air conditioned at all times. The optimum conditions are 21 to 25°C. and 45 to 55% R.H. The outlets of the system should be situated so that there is no apparent movement of air. The type of table upon which the balance is mounted is most important. In order to eliminate shocks and vibrations and to preserve the precision and sensitivity of the balance, different systems for vibration-free mounting have been described. Steyermark (2,3) recommends two systems. The newer one consists of a heavy, reinforced concrete inertia block (c.a. 800 lb.) which rests upon compressed springs. The table of Gysel and Strebel (4) can also be used if there is sufficient space in the weighing room and if no heavy machines are running in the neighborhood. Another setup, (5) which is based on the research work of Howard (6) and a report by Kirner (7), where the balances are mounted on stone plates, has been very useful in the author's laboratories. These plates rest on three tetrahedrons consisting of golf balls and which are held in position by iron rings. Instead of the golf ball tetrahedrons, three supports which consist of one wooden hemisphere resting on three golf balls can also be recommended. The rings are attached to an iron plate which is put on a support fixed in the wall. These units are protected from disturbances by the operator by means of woodwork which is completely separated from the support.

III. DETERMINATION OF CARBON AND HYDROGEN

The most important determination in the organic analytical laboratory is that of carbon and hydrogen. With this method it is possible to obtain, with one analysis, the two values which are important and significant to every compound. Realizing this, Pregl at first developed the micro method for the determination of carbon and hydrogen, a procedure which in its original form is still successfully used by many analysts.

In the past few years many important modifications and also completely new methods have been described, which may be classified into three main groups: (1) modifications in the conditions for the combustion; (2) modifications in the way in which nitrogen oxides are removed; and (3) new methods for the determination of the combustion products—carbon dioxide and water.

1. Modifications of Conditions for Combustion

The so-called "universal filling" of Pregl ($CuO/PbCrO_4$, Ag, and PbO_2) is very useful, but it is important to work exactly according to the directions given by him in order to obtain accurate and reliable results, particularly with "difficultly burning" compounds. A big step forward was made by Reihlen (8) who introduced combustion catalysts, such as the Vinosites. They consist of mixtures of different metal oxides (Cu, Pb, Cr, Mn, Ag) that facilitate combustion of organic matter at relatively low temperatures (500 to 700°C.). Mainly, they catalyze the oxidation of carbon monoxide and methane. In the last few years methods have been developed which permit still lower combustion temperatures by the use of catalysts other than those of the type just mentioned. There are two such methods which have been tested in the author's laboratories over a long period and are now in constant use for routine analysis.

Körbl (9) introduced the use of the thermal decomposition product of silver permanganate as a catalyst. Silver permanganate, itself, is easily prepared in a pure state and the decomposition proceeds with deflagration at 150°C. A voluminous black product is obtained which can be used directly for filling the combustion tube. Further heating at 500°C. leads to a material corresponding to the formula $AgMnO_2$; at temperatures of 790°C. and higher this product loses more oxygen (10,11). An improvement in the mechanical properties of this catalyst may be achieved when the decomposition of silver permanganate is carried out at 90 to 95°C. for 24 hr. In this case no deflagration occurs and the catalyst particles retain the shape and size of the original crystals (12), even when heated to 500°C. in the combustion tube. This catalyst is used only in a layer, 3 to 4 cm. long, in the combustion tube. Since it contains very finely dispersed metallic silver, no additional absorbent for the halogens (with the exception of fluorine) and sulfur is necessary (13). For the analysis of fluorinated compounds (14) a layer of Pb_3O_4 on pumice, 3.5 cm. long, (15) must be introduced in the combustion tube behind the catalyst, and the whole filling heated to 550°C. by a single furnace.

Večeřa and Synek (16,17) introduced cobalto–cobaltic oxide on asbestos as a catalyst, and they claim some advantage over the above mentioned thermal decomposition product of silver permanganate.

Horáček and Körbl (18) have prepared a series of similar catalysts by the reaction of ferrous, manganous, cerous, or cobaltous salts with silver nitrate in ammoniacal or strongly alkaline solutions. The precipitates formed consist of the higher oxides of the appropriate metals containing finely dispersed metallic silver. Very short layers of all these catalysts proved to be highly effective for the complete combustion of organic compounds at 550°C. The absorption capacity for halogens and sulfur is also very high. It seems that in the field of catalysis of the combustion of organic matter new substances still can be found.

Another approach to secure complete combustion was made by the introduction of high temperature furnaces working above 800°C., as used by Belcher and Ingram (19–22) in their "empty tube" combustion method, which permits combustion without an oxidizing filling or catalyst. In this method the sample is burned in a fast stream of oxygen. A modification of it has been described by Kirsten (23), in which he has fitted a nickel tube into the combustion tube, which becomes oxidized and burns the sample at 1000°C. in a fast stream of oxygen. The introduction of such methods made it possible to develop apparatus for automatic combustion with the advantage that all compounds can be burned in the same way. Using the original Pregl method, this is impossible since every compound must be burned individually. Also these methods can be further developed because today it is possible to attain much higher temperatures.

Finally it is pertinent to mention methods which permit the determination not only of carbon and hydrogen, but also the simultaneous determination of other elements. These procedures are based on the so-called pyrolysis principle, first used by Marek (24).

The compound to be analyzed is weighed out into a quartz test tube, not into a platinum boat. This tube is placed in a quartz combustion tube with its open end directed toward the high temperature section of the combustion tube, which is heated by a furnace to a temperature of 850 to 950°C. The full flame of a gas burner is applied at the open end of the test tube and slowly moved back toward the sample, and a current of oxygen, 35 to 50 ml./min., is passed through the combustion tube. Korshun (25) has shown that under these conditions oxidation of the hydrogen in the organic compound is practically 100% complete, and that of the carbon 95 to 100% complete within the test tube or at its opening in a 2 to 3 cm. long zone which is heated by the gas flame. The section of the combustion tube heated by the long stationary furnace (8 to 10 cm. long) is sufficient to ensure complete oxidation of the remaining unoxidized pyrolytic products.

This procedure may be used for solids and liquids. Liquids of sufficiently high boiling point are weighed directly into the test tube with the aid of a capillary pipet, care being taken to avoid contact with the walls of the test tube. Hygroscopic solid compounds are weighed into a test tube with a ground-in stopper, dried, and reweighed. The stopper is removed just before insertion into the combustion tube. Volatile liquids are weighed into capillaries in the usual manner and the sealed end broken off immediately before placing the capillary into the test tube. Highly volatile liquids (e.g., pentane) are placed into the test tube in sealed capillaries, which are opened within the combustion tube by heating the tube at the site of the sealed tip of the capillary. A sudden rush of the vapors through the heated zone into the combustion tube has to be avoided, otherwise the results will, as a rule, be low due to incomplete combustion. According to Korshun and Klimova (26,27) less nitrogen oxides are produced than when the combustion is carried out in a boat. For the absorption of these nitrogen oxides, different reagents can be used (see p. 206). The real advantage of this pyrolysis procedure has already been mentioned, namely, that it is possible to determine certain other elements in addition to carbon and hydrogen.

For the simultaneous determination of carbon, hydrogen, and sulfur (28) an absorption tube filled with silver wool or silver on a pumice carrier (29) is attached to the combustion tube and kept at 650 to 700°C. Some halogen-containing compounds may give low results for carbon and hydrogen due to the formation of halogen-containing pyrolysis products which inhibit the quantitative oxidation of carbon monoxide among the combustion products (30). To overcome this difficulty a wad of silver wool, heated to 600°C., is placed between the test tube and the furnace. A platinum contact can also be used. In this case carbon, hydrogen, and halogen or sulfur can be determined simultaneously.

Compounds containing silicon are subjected to slow combustion (31), or an asbestos pad carrying chromium sesquioxide or vanadium pentoxide may be inserted into the test tube and tared with it (32). The asbestos quantitatively holds back all the silica formed and the metal oxides prevent the formation of silicon carbide. Additionally also halogen (33) or sulfur (34) can be determined.

For the analysis of phosphorus-containing compounds a similar arrangement has been recommended. The test tube is partially filled with granulated pumice which reacts well with phosphorus pentoxide. Taking the weight before and after the combustion gives the amount of phosphorus. If the sample also contains sulfur it is recommended to use powdered quartz etched with concentrated alkali to retain the phosphorus pentoxide (35). The sulfur is determined by using an absorption tube filled with silver wool.

For the simultaneous determination of carbon, hydrogen, and fluorine the following procedure is recommended (36). The test tube with the sample is placed inside a quartz sheath with a perforated bottom containing a layer of magnesium oxide 15 to 18 cm. in length and the whole assembly is then placed in the combustion tube. After the analysis the absorption tubes for carbon dioxide and water are taken off and the magnesium fluoride that is formed is subjected to pyrohydrolysis with water vapor at 1000°C. The resulting hydrogen fluoride is determined alkalimetrically or by titration with thorium nitrate. According to Mázor (15) the pyrolysis products are brought into contact with Pb_3O_4. After the analysis the resulting lead fluoride is extracted and the fluorine is determined gravimetrically as lead chlorofluoride.

2. Modifications in the Way in Which Nitrogen Oxides Are Removed

The most important source of error in the classical carbon and hydrogen determination is the lead dioxide which is used for the absorption of the nitrogen oxides. The reagent, at 180°C., absorbs the nitrogen oxides, but it retains also some water and carbon dioxide. Changes in the temperature of the lead dioxide furnace have, therefore, some influence on th result of the estimation. These conditions were studied by Lindner (37) and Boetius (38). In view of these early difficulties many attempts were made to find an acceptable substitute.

Principally there are two possible means for the removal of the nitrogen oxides, namely, the absorption and chemical reaction of the oxides of nitrogen, or the reduction to N_2 and/or N_2O. Both gases are neither absorbed in the water absorption tube nor in the carbon dioxide tube.   Many external absorbents have been suggested, such as concentrated sulfuric acid (39), concentrated sulfuric acid and potassium dichromate (40) or diphenylamine (41), and different preparations of manganese dioxide (42,43).   Only the last is of importance and is used.   Lindner (37) was the first to recommend the use of copper for the reduction of the nitrogen oxides to N_2.   Copper is also used in the methods published by Kainz (44) and Unterzaucher (45).   It has also been shown that nickel serves to reduce these oxides (46).   When use is made of these reagents it is necessary to burn the substance either in a stream of nitrogen, using metal oxides to provide the source of oxygen for the combustion of the organic matter, or in a stream of air.   Reagents which affect reduction of the oxides of nitrogen to N_2 and N_2O that are not retained in the carbon dioxide absorption tube have been recommended by Hussey and co-workers (47), (ammonium sulfamate) and Cross and Wright (48) (trihydroxyl ammonium phosphate).   Both reagents can be used under normal combustion conditions, with the sample being burned in a stream of oxygen.   The absorber with the reagent has to be placed between the water and carbon dioxide absorption tube. Care must be taken that no water vapor condenses in the capillaries of the water absorption tube.

3. New Methods for the Determination of the Combustion Products

Until 10 years ago only the gravimetric method of finish was employed for the determination of the carbon dioxide and water produced and only recently some more important modifications of the absorption tubes have been suggested (49–51).   Nevertheless it seems that the Pregl absorption tube is still preferred by a plurality of microanalysts.   Moreover, rubber (or better still, silicone) tubing connections are still regarded as being sufficiently reliable, although some authors recommend ground-joint connections for the tubes (52–54).

The first attempt to determine the combustion products titrimetrically was carried out by Lindner (37) in 1935.   This method never gained any importance until recently when Belcher published a new procedure for the carbon dioxide absorption (55) and a new reagent for the determination of water (56).   He recommends succinyl chloride as a hydrolytic reagent instead of the α-naphthoxydichloro-phosphine suggested by Lindner. The water reacts according to the equation

$$(CH_2COCl)_2 + H_2O \longrightarrow (CH_2CO)_2O + 2HCl$$

and the resulting hydrochloric acid can be titrated. Carbon dioxide is absorbed in excess barium hydroxide solution containing barium chloride and the excess is back-titrated after the absorption has taken place with hydrochloric acid in the presence of o-cresolphthalein indicator. One disadvantage of this method, especially in the determination of the water, is the blank value. This is due to the slight volatility of the reagent. Johansson (57) published, a few years ago, a method using the Karl Fischer titration for the water determination and a complicated iodometric procedure for carbon dioxide. A conductometric method for the carbon dioxide determination is given by Malissa (58). In combination with a rapid, high temperature combustion one carbon determination is completed within 3 min.

The most successful approach seems to be the iodometric determination developed by Unterzaucher (59), in which the carbon contact principle of the oxygen determination is employed to convert the oxygen of the carbon and hydrogen combustion products into carbon monoxide as follows:

The sample is burned in a stream of air, and pure nitrogen is used, after the combustion has taken place, as a carrier gas. The water is separated from the carbon dioxide by freezing it out at $-70°C$. in a special cooling device. Halogens are removed by metallic silver, sulfur with lead chromate. The absorption of the excess oxygen from the air used for the combustion and the decomposition of nitrogen oxides is by means of heated copper. After the carbon dioxide has been converted into carbon monoxide and titrated, the cooling trap containing the water is warmed and the water brought into reaction with the carbon to again get carbon monoxide. An analysis requires about 75 min. The author claims that using a 3 to 4 mg. sample the accuracy of the carbon determination is $\pm0.1\%$ absolute, of the water determination $\pm0.04\%$ absolute. Due to the very favorable calculating factors (1 ml. $0.02N$ $Na_2S_2O_3 = 50.04$ μg. C and 16.8 μg. H) this method can be highly recommended for ultramicro work.

During the past few years some methods have been described wherein the combustion products are determined by a gas volumetric or manometric procedure (60–64). Most of these methods work on the principle that water and carbon dioxide are fractionated by freezing out with dry ice/acetone and liquid air, respectively, and after the combustion is finished the partial pressures or the gas volumes are measured. The entire system is evacuated to 10^{-3} mm. Hg. One disadvantage of these manometric methods is that the manometers have to be prepared by the analyst himself (two liquid manometers) and then empirically calibrated. It can be expected, however, that in the near future manometers admitting an electric measurement will be developed. Such methods are very important for the analysis of compounds containing C^{14}. It is very easy to determine the C^{14} activity in a proportional counting tube after the carbon determination has been completed (65). A method for the wet combustion of organic compounds has been developed in our laboratories and has been in daily use for more than 3 years in our isotope department (66). Moreover, it is also possible to fractionate the combustion products by gas chromatography, and recently two such methods have been developed (273,274).

IV. DETERMINATION OF OXYGEN

Although the determination of the oxygen content in organic compounds is very important, a reliable method for a direct determination was developed only about 20 years ago. Since this micro method was published by Unterzaucher (67–70) a host of modifications has been reported.

In the past years, improvements, such as modifications of the following sections of the original Schütze–Unterzaucher procedure, have been published: (*1*) variations of the carbon filling; (*2*) procedures to eliminate the interference of disturbing elements present in the substance; (*3*) determination of the carbon monoxide formed on the carbon contact; (*4*) simultaneous determination of other elements; and (*5*) other methods.

1. Variations of the Carbon Filling

In the original Unterzaucher procedure a carbon contact (gas black of special grade) heated at $1120 \pm 5°C$. is used. Aluise and co-workers (71), Kirsten (72), Colson (73), Lacourt (74), Moelants and Wesenbeek (75) investigated the sources of blank values which were obtained when working according to the procedure described by Unterzaucher (e.g., 70).

It seems that the ash content of the carbon used, as well as the nature of the elements present in the ash are very important. It is also of some influence if the carbon is in an amorphous state or crystallized (graphitized) to some extent (76). Furthermore the temperature recommended by the author has to be controlled very carefully. For this purpose, a special furnace with a precise temperature controlling system has been developed by Schöniger (77). Because of the difficulties arising when working with this high temperature, the publications of Oliver (78), Oita and Conway (79) and Korshun and Bondarewskaya (80) seem to be important. They all report that a tube filling of platinized carbon successfully converts all oxygen-containing cracking products of the compound to be analyzed, to carbon monoxide at 900°C.

According to Oliver (78) this platinized carbon is prepared as follows: Dissolve 3 g. of platinum pieces in aqua regia and evaporate to a small volume. Add water and again evaporate. Dilute to about 50 ml. with water and add 3 g. of carbon. Evaporate to a paste and finally dry at 150°C. Break the mass into small pieces and heat it in a tube in an atmosphere of nitrogen at 900°C. for about 2 hr. Complete the reduction of the platinum chloride by passing hydrogen through the tube at the same temperature until the issuing gas is neutral to moist litmus paper.

The results reported by the authors and those given in a comparative study by Steyermark (81) are good.

2. Procedures to Eliminate the Interference of Disturbing Elements Present in the Substance

According to Unterzaucher (70), the method can be used without difficulty for organic substances that contain carbon, hydrogen, oxygen, nitrogen, chlorine, bromine, and iodine. Accurate oxygen values may be obtained if sulfur is present, but difficulties will sometimes be encountered. Fluorine and phosphorus cause considerable interference, the results are not satisfactory, and the apparatus can be damaged. On the other hand substances containing arsenic or mercury can be analyzed without any difficulty.

In the analysis of the heavy metal salts of organic acids (e.g., Fe, Cu, or Co containing compounds), the entire oxygen will be obtained in the results without any difficulty, because the metal oxides on which the salts are based are reduced to metals. The situation is different with respect to aluminium and magnesium salts which leave their metals behind in the sample boat in the form of the oxides. After weighing these oxides their oxygen content can be calculated and added to that found in the analysis. The situation seems to be similar with calcium salts. It is remarkable that, on the other hand, potassium and sodium salts behave in the same manner as the heavy metal salts. They yield the entire oxygen content directly if sufficient carbon is present. It is recommended, therefore, to add to the weighed sample an organic substance that does not contain oxygen and that will give sufficient carbon in the boat on being cracked. According to Unterzaucher (69) the induline base is suitable for this purpose.

Other authors also report that erroneous results can be obtained when the substances to be analyzed contain oxygen in amounts below 1% and yield considerably large amounts of hydrogen during the cracking process (petroleum products). To overcome the difficulties just mentioned, some suggestions recently have been made (85,86).

A. FLUORINE CONTAINING COMPOUNDS

Mázor (82) reported that any H_2F_2 formed when the substance is decomposed reacts with the silica of the combustion tube to give water. This reacts with the heated carbon contact to give carbon monoxide:

$$SiO_2 + 2H_2F_2 \longrightarrow SiF_4 + 2H_2O$$

$$2H_2O + 2C \xrightarrow{\ 1120°C.\ } 2CO + 2H_2O$$

To overcome this unwanted reaction a layer of magnesium nitride approximately 1 cm. long is introduced into the combustion tube in front of the carbon contact. It is heated, by the radiation of the carbon contact furnace, to 200 to 300°C. Any H_2F_2 formed during the combustion then reacts with the magnesium nitride:

$$Mg_3N_2 + 3H_2F_2 \longrightarrow 3MgF_2 + 3H_2 + N_2$$

The magnesium nitride is stable at the temperatures that are attained.

B. SULFUR CONTAINING COMPOUNDS

The sulfur error arises in that although most of the sulfur in a sample is converted to hydrogen sulfide, which can be scrubbed out by ascarite, some carbon disulfide and carbonyl sulfide are also formed, which cannot thus be removed. Reaction of carbon disulfide with iodine pentoxide forms carbon dioxide and gives, when the final determination is gravimetric, too high results. On the other hand, if carbonyl sulfide is formed the results will be low because the carbonyl sulfide contains part of the oxygen present in the sample. In order to avoid these sources of error different methods have been suggested.

The most promising method (79) seems to be that of passing the gas stream that emerges from the carbon contact over heated copper (500 to 900°C.). Probably the following reactions occur:

$$4Cu + CS_2 \longrightarrow 2Cu_2S + C$$
$$2Cu + COS \longrightarrow Cu_2S + CO$$
$$2Cu + H_2S \longrightarrow Cu_2S + H_2$$

Another modification for sulfur containing substances is suggested by Bürger (83). When hydrogen, as a carrier gas, is used instead of nitrogen all the sulfur present will be converted to hydrogen sulfide, which can easily be removed by passing the gases over ascarite. He claims that by this method all errors, due to sulfur present in the substance, can be avoided. Also the oxygen content in metalloorganics and metal salts, provided the metal components can be released from their oxides by hydrogen, can be determined.

Maylott and Lewis (84), and Dundy and Stehr (85) also carried out investigations on the interference of sulfur compounds. They recommend using a liquid nitrogen trap which is placed between the reaction tube and the oxidation tube. Any carbon disulfide and carbonyl sulfide is by this means prevented from entering the oxidation tube. Dixon (86) finds that by this procedure oxygen will be lost as carbonyl sulfide.

It seems that the use of copper at 900°C. is the best method of analyzing sulfur containing compounds.

C. PHOSPHORUS CONTAINING COMPOUNDS

Until now no procedure has been developed to make it possible to determine the oxygen content in substances containing phosphorus.

D. COMPOUNDS CONTAINING LITTLE OR NO OXYGEN

Dundy and Stehr (85) reported results for the oxygen content of hydrocarbon samples, which were reported to no oxygen, as high as 2.5% when working with the original Unterzaucher method. Dixon also (86) found similar errors and gave the explanation that the large quantity of hydrogen present in the pyrolysis gases, from hydrocarbons, reacts with iodine pentoxide to a small extent, according to the equation

$$I_2O_5 + 5H_2 \longrightarrow I_2 + 5H_2O$$

It is, therefore, recommendable to use a modified procedure when applying the oxygen determination to petroleum products. The sample is pyrolyzed as usual in a steam of pure nitrogen and the oxygen converted to carbon monoxide. Then the carbon monoxide is oxidized to dioxide and determined by one of the procedures given in the section under Sulfur Containing Compounds.

Another possibility for eliminating large quantities of hydrogen from the pyrolysis products is the procedure given by several authors (87,88), in which the interfering hydrogen is removed by diffusion through a heated palladium thimble.

3. Determination of the Carbon Monoxide Formed on the Carbon Contact

A. IODOMETRIC DETERMINATION

In his first publications Unterzaucher recommended the iodometric titration (e.g., 67) instead of the gravimetric determination described by Zimmermann (89) for semimicro analysis. In the beginning a special grade iodine pentoxide was used.

In the past few years it was found (90) that due to the different manufacturing temperatures of the iodine pentoxide preparations some authors used anhydroiodic acid (HI_3O_8) and others iodine pentoxide. HI_3O_8 allows the carbon monoxide to be determined iodometrically even in the presence of hydrogen, since this oxidant, in contrast to iodine pentoxide, does not react with hydrogen.

In view of the importance of these findings for the iodometric oxygen determination, the procedure for the preparation of HI_3O_8 shall be described: Add an excess of iodic acid or dehydrated iodic acid to boiling nitric acid, 60% by volume. Boil the solution with the undissolved excess for approximately 1 hr., after which time a saturated solution is obtained. Filter the solution through a glass filter and set it aside at room temperature for about 24 hr. Separate the brilliant crystals formed from the solution, wash them with 68% nitric acid and dry them at room temperature by first sucking pure air over them for about an hour. In this manner the adherent nitric acid is almost completely removed. Subject the product, for some time, to further drying, either at room temperature in a desiccator containing solid alkali and phosphorus pentoxide, or in an oven a 120°C.

The preparative work described should be carried out away from bright daylight, otherwise decomposition will occur, as can be seen from the crystals assuming a pink or reddish color. It should be pointed out that, after the decomposing influence of bright daylight was discovered and then avoided during the preparation of the reagent, the crystals were for the first time obtained without the slightest pinkish color. If the substance prepared according to this procedure is completely dry, it proves to be neither hygroscopic nor sensitive to light.

B. DETERMINATION OF CARBON DIOXIDE

Some authors (85,86,91–96) prefer the oxidation of carbon monoxide to dioxide and the determination of the latter either gravimetrically or volumetrically. The use of this method has the advantage that the temperature of the carbon contact can be lowered to 1000°C. because any carbon dioxide not being reduced to monoxide would be determined anyway.

It seems that the best way to oxidize the carbon monoxide is the reaction with copper oxide at temperatures over 600°C. (86). The carbon dioxide so formed, has to be dried by passing the gases over a desiccant. After the quantitative absorption in a Pregl absorption tube the carbon dioxide is determined gravimetrically. Oxidizing with either iodine pentoxide or HI_3O_8, as described earlier in the section under Iodometric Determination, has the disadvantage that the iodine formed is not so easily absorbed.

For the volumetric determination of the carbon dioxide obtained by one of the two reactions given above, a procedure described by

Ehrenberger and co-workers (97) seems to be recommendable. The carbon dioxide is absorbed in a special filtration vessel in an alkaline solution of barium chloride and titrated potentiometrically, continuously during the combustion. According to the authors correct oxygen values were also obtained in samples containing considerable amounts of halogen and sulfur.

C. OTHER PROCEDURES

A colorimetric determination of the carbon monoxide has been described by Walton and co-workers (98). Harris (99) recommended the combustion with helium as carrier gas and the determination of the carbon monoxide by measuring the thermal conductivity of the effluent gas. Other gases formed by the pyrolysis of the sample, e.g., nitrogen and hydrogen, cause interferences.

A manometric method for measuring carbon dioxide has been reported by Holowchak and Wear (100). The carbon dioxide is collected in a liquid nitrogen trap and, after the residual gases have been pumped out by means of a vacuum pump, is determined manometrically with a two liquid manometer in a standard volume.

Kôno and co-workers (101) developed a gravimetric method. They describe a procedure where the iodine formed by the reaction of carbon monoxide with iodine pentoxide is absorbed on a roll of silver net. By taking the weight before and after the analysis the amount of oxygen can be calculated. This method seems to have no advantage over the other procedures.

4. Simultaneous Determination of Other Elements

Studying the conditions under which the oxygen is converted to carbon monoxide, Korshun and Bondarewskaja (80) found that it is also possible to determine the halogen content in the same sample. The method is based on the probability of evolution of halogens as hydrogen halides during the pyrolysis of the sample, in contact with hydrogen. Since the formation of hydrogen halides occurs at the expense of hydrogen generated in the decomposition, difficulties are encountered if the sample contains little or no hydrogen. In this case a considerable quantity of hydrogen halides are also retained by the catalyst and are only slowly removed by the carrier gas. It is, therefore, recommended by the authors to mix the samples with standard hydrocarbons, e.g., paraffin wax, to supply the needed hydrogen. It seems that by combination with the procedure of Bürger (83) a potentially much more elegant solution of the simultaneous determination of oxygen and halogen might be achieved.

5. Other Methods

It should be mentioned that before the pyrolysis procedure, with subsequent conversion of all oxygen into carbon monoxide, was developed by Schütze (102), Zimmermann (89) and Unterzaucher (67–70), Ter Meulen (103) described the following macro method:

The substance is evaporated in a steam of hydrogen as the carrier gas and pyrolyzed at 1000°C. The resulting products are hydrated over a special nickel catalyst at 400°C. and the resulting water is determined gravimetrically. In the past years Smith and coworkers (104) described a modification of this method. They recommend a special nickel–thorium catalyst for the hydration, prepared as described by Russel and Fulton (105), and platinized quartz for the pyrolysis. They claim that in a series of consecutive determinations the time required for one determination is only 15 min. and that with small modification the method is also applicable to compounds containing nitrogen. Nitrogen can be hydrated to ammonia on the catalyst which is absorbed on the anhydrone in the water absorption tube. By filling this tube with sodium hydroxide pellets, according to Russel and Fulton it is possible to quantitatively retain all water produced, without error due to ammonia. If the catalyst is poisoned by sulfur—Russel and Marks have shown that 200 to 400 mg. of sulfur will be held back by the catalyst before it fails to give quantitative conversion of oxygen to water—it is recommendable to use a new charge of catalyst.

Instead of the gravimetric determination of the water Lindner (106) suggested the volumetric determination using naphthyl dichlorophosphine oxide as a reagent to react with the water vapor. The succinyl chloride introduced by Belcher and co-workers (107) should be a more reliable reagent for the same purpose.

Sheft and Katz (108) use BrF_2SbF_6 for the oxygen determination in inorganic compounds. They heat the sample in a special nickel reaction tube with the reagent up to a temperature of 500°C. Under these conditions oxygen is liberated as O_2 and determined manometrically. Preliminary experiments indicated that oxygen could also be quantitatively recovered from certain oxygen containing organic compounds. This procedure should be of importance for the analysis of compounds containing O^{18}.

Another completely new method which can be used also for the carbon and nitrogen determination in organic compounds has been described by Grosse and co-workers (109–111). The substance to be analyzed, is pyrolyzed in vacuum in a platinum reaction vessel; it is not necessary to accomplish quantitative combustion. A known amount of a heavy oxygen mixture of O_2^{16}, $O^{16}O^{18}$, and O_2^{18} is added. After the reaction is completed the isotope ratio in the gas sample is determined by means of the mass spectrometer. The amounts of oxygen, carbon, and nitrogen, follows from the simple mixture rule. For details of this procedure which, until now, was limited to liquid samples and to the semimicro scale, the original paper must be consulted.

DETERMINATION OF NITROGEN

Principally there are only two, generally used methods for the determination of nitrogen in organic substances. According to Dumas the compound to be analyzed is combusted in an atmosphere of carbon dioxide and the volume of nitrogen liberated is measured. According to Kjeldahl the organic material is destroyed with sulfuric acid, various catalysts have to be added, and the nitrogen is converted to ammonium acid sulfate. The ammonia is liberated and either titrated or determined colorimetrically.

1. Determination by Dry Combustion

The so-called micro Dumas method seems to be very simple when the original Pregl procedure is used and was believed to handle successfully all types of compounds. Nevertheless experience has taught that many substances require some modifications. From the large number of publications dealing with this method only the most important shall be mentioned.

A. MODIFICATIONS OF THE DUMAS–PREGL METHOD

One main disadvantage of this method is the fact that the substance has to be decomposed in an atmosphere of carbon dioxide.

The oxygen needed for complete combustion is supplied from cupric oxide. In the original Pregl method the substance had to be mixed with finely powdered cupric oxide in the combustion tube. For this reason the tube had to be taken out of the apparatus after each analysis. The method was, therefore, very time consuming.

The first real progress was achieved when Gysel (112,113) introduced the so-called by-pass. The combustion tube remains in the furnace and during the introduction of the sample the carbon dioxide flows in the reverse direction. The substance to be analyzed is mixed in the boat with a mixture of lead chromate and cupric oxide.

Zimmermann (114) described an automatic combustion train which gives excellent results. The sample still has to be mixed with powdered cupric oxide in the combustion tube before each analysis. The substance is burned in a closed system and a special mercury filled vessel has to be used for pressure regulation. The gaseous combustion products are collected in this vessel. After the decomposition, which takes place in a closed system, is completed, these gases are swept into the nitrometer by means of a rapid stream of carbon dioxide over the hot combustion tube filling. One determination can be completed in 25 min.

Two very rapid micro procedures, also based on the Dumas principle, have been described by Shelberg (115) and Schöniger (116). The sample mixed with powdered cupric oxide is precombusted in a separate exchangeable combustion tube which is connected with the apparatus by a ground glass joint. As many as four analyses can be made in 1 hr. Belcher and Bhatty (117) used this method for the nitrogen determination in coke on a semimicroscale with good results. Gustin (275) developed a completely automatic method based on the procedures just mentioned.

Hozumi and co-workers (118–120) tested different metal oxides (MnO_2, Co_2O_3, NiO, and CuO) which can be used to promote the oxidation of refractory organic nitrogen compounds. They found that the following arrangement is the best:

The sample is placed on a shallow platinum boat and inserted into the tube. A nickel boat containing approximately 150 mg. of Co_2O_3 is placed next to the platinum boat and the combustion is carried out at temperatures over 850°C. Since Co_2O_3 starts decomposing at 750°C. and liberates oxygen at a constant rate between 800 and 850°C., complete combustion is achieved.

This method is used with the following slight modifications in the author's laboratories and gives excellent results. The platinum boat with the sample is placed in a nickel boat (width 8 mm., height 5 mm., length 20 mm.). Approximately 200 mg. of a mixture of Co_2O_3 and lead chromate (4:1) is added to the substance. This boat is placed before the side arm of the combustion tube with the stop cock of the nitrometer closed. After 5 min. all air will be swept out by the carbon dioxide and the open end of the tube is closed. The nickel boat is pushed in place (4 cm. in front of the filling) with a magnet and the movable burner (900°C.) is started. Between the carbon dioxide supply and the combustion tube is the pressure equilibration vessel recommended by Zimmermann (114).

B. NEW METHODS

Unterzaucher (121,122) published a method where the substance is introduced in a platinum boat into the combustion tube and burned in a gas steam of carbon dioxide and oxygen. The combustion tube is filled with copper oxide and copper, which is at the end of the tube filling. Any excess of oxygen is removed by the copper. In the original method the mixture of oxygen and carbon dioxide is obtained by passing the latter through a 30% solution of hydrogen peroxide. Because is was impossible to obtain a controlled amount of oxygen by this procedure, Cropper and co-workers (123) and Manser and Egli (124) suggested to generate the oxygen electrolytically.

Ingram (125) combined this method with the "empty tube" principle already used by Belcher and Ingram (126) for the C—H determination.

Kirsten (127–129) pointed out that the reaction

$$C + CO_2 \longrightarrow 2CO$$

can be very useful for the combustion of compounds which are difficult to burn. The combustion tube is filled with granulated nickel oxide. This part of the tube is kept at 1000 to 1050°C. At the end of the tube a short layer of hopcalite, heated to 100°C., is placed to remove any carbon monoxide before the gases enter the nitrometer. Before the substance placed in a platinum boat is introduced, a capsule of platinum gauze filled with nickel oxide is inserted into the tube. Prior to the analysis the combustion tube is swept air-free

by means of a by-pass. The movable burner has a temperature over
1050°C. A modified nitrometer is also recommended. A simplified
procedure based on this method is described by Clark and Dando
(130).

2. Determination by Wet Combustion

Since Kjeldahl first published his method for the nitrogen determination about 75 years ago, a large number of publications have
appeared in the literature. This method is applicable to many
types of organic compounds although it is sometimes referred to as
being that for the determination of aminoid nitrogen.

A. PROCEDURES FOR THE KJELDAHLIZATION

Principally, the main problem lies in the fact that it is very hard
to transform every kind of organic bound nitrogen into ammonia.
According to its behavior, when digested, there are four main groups
of organic compounds (131); (1) compounds with N—H linkages,
(2) compounds with heterocycles, (3) compounds with N—N linkages, and (4) compounds with NO and NO_2 groups.

Because it is impossible to review all the papers that deal with the
Kjeldahl procedure which appeared in the past years only the most
important ones shall be mentioned.

Compounds which belong to groups (1) and (2) are relatively easy
to digest by adding a catalyst to the sulfuric acid. A great deal of
research work has been done to find the best catalysts. Reviews
on this subject have been published from time to time (132–135).

As it seems today, the important factors are the time needed for
digestion, the temperature, and the concentration of potassium sulfate. Mercury appears to be superior to other catalysts (e.g.,
copper, selenium). Therefore, the procedure recommended by
Steyermark (136), based on the collaborative studies under the direction of Willits and Ogg (137–139) is in the author's opinion the best
for compounds of groups (1) and (2).

Compounds with N—N, NO, and NO_2 linkages (groups (3) and (4))
must be reduced prior to digestion. This fact was first recognized by
Friedrich (140) who recommended the reduction of the substance
before the kjeldahlization with hydroiodic acid and red phosphorus.
According to Ogg and Willits (141), this method is satisfactory only

for the nitrogen–oxygen linkages and completely unsatisfactory when nitrogen is connected to another nitrogen atom.

Ma and co-workers (142) recently described a micro method applicable to aromatic nitro compounds. The sample is placed in a Kjeldahl flask and is dissolved in a mixture of acetic acid and methanol containing a little hydrochloric acid. Subsequently, it is reduced with zinc metal. Sulfuric acid is added, the organic solvents are distilled off, and the residue mineralized in the usual manner.

While this method is only useful for substances of group (4), the procedure given by Steyermark and co-workers (143) gives excellent values with a variety of substances including those containing N—N, N=N, NO and NO₂ groupings, where the nitrogen to nitrogen linkage is not part of the ring (nitrogen may be linked to oxygen as part of a ring). The method is not yet reliable for compounds where the nitrogen is connected to nitrogen as part of a ring. The authors hope that some modifications might be effective. For nitrates they recommend treatment with salicylic acid as has been suggested by Dickinson (144).

Because of its importance the accurate procedure for the determination of nitrogen in azo and nitro compounds, oximes, isoxazoles, hydrazines, and hydrazones, as described by the authors, shall be given (144a):

"From 5 to 8 mg. of sample, 0.2 ml. of 98 to 100% formic acid, and 0.1 ml. of concentrated hydrochloric acid, specific gravity 1.18, in a 30-ml. micro-Kjeldahl flask (preferably, Soltys type) . . ., are heated in a water bath (80° to 85°C.) until the sample is dissolved. To this are added 80 mg. of zinc dust (nitrogen-free), and the contents mixed by swirling for about 2 minutes, and heated in the water bath for 5 additional minutes. Then 40 mg. of iron powder (prepared by hydrogenation) are added and the flask is swirled for 2 minutes to effect mixing. To this are added 0.1 ml. of concentrated hydrochloric acid, specific gravity 1.18, and 0.15 ml. of ethanol, and the mixture is again heated for 5 minutes (water bath). Every 5 minutes a 0.1-ml. portion of concentrated hydrochloric acid is added, with swirling and heating in the water bath, until the iron is dissolved. While the flask is swirled under a hood, 1.0 ml. of concentrated sulfuric acid, specific gravity 1.84, is added (cautiously), and the contents are warmed until the evolution of gas (hydrogen chloride) has subsided. Then 0.65 gram of potassium sulfate, 0.016 gram of mercuric oxide, and, finally, 0.5 ml. of concentrated sulfuric acid, specific gravity 1.84, are added. (It is preferable to add the sulfuric acid in this manner rather than all at once, because the final 0.5 ml. can be use to wash down any materials adhering to the walls.)

The mixture is boiled on a micro-Kjeldahl digestion rack for 4 hours, making certain that boiling is vigorous enough so that refluxing takes place almost half-way up in the neck of the flask. The digest is transferred to the micro-Kjeldahl distillation apparatus (preferably the one-piece model) . . ., 7.5 ml. of sodium hydroxide–sodium thio-sulfate mixture . . . are added, and the ammonia is distilled out into boric acid solution (8 minutes with the delivery tube below the boric acid solution, 2 minutes with it above). The distillate is then titrated with 0.01N hydrochloric acid, using bromocresol green–methyl red mixture . . . as the indicator. A blank determination should be run using all of the materials, minus the sample, and going through the entire procedure. Any blank value so obtained should be subtracted."

B. METHODS FOR THE DETERMINATION OF AMMONIA

Distillation Apparatus. The apparatus as designed by Pregl is still widely used. An all-glass, one-piece model can also be recom-mended. Both types have been recommended by the Committee for the Standardization of Microchemical Apparatus, Division of Ana-lytical Chemistry, ACS (145). A simplified one-piece model is used in Europe (146).

Volumetric Procedures. The normal method is the absorption of the ammonia, liberated from the alkalized digestion liquid in an excess of standard acid and back-titration from the hot solution with standard alkali. Either methyl red or a mixture of methyl red with methylene blue can be used as an indicator for the titration.

Another method which is quite often used is the absorption of the ammonia in an aqueous solution of boric acid. After the distilla-tion is finished, the boric acid solution of ammonia is titrated with standard hydrochloric acid using bromocresol green–methyl red or methyl red–methylene blue as an indicator.

According to Belcher and Bhatty (147) it is possible to determine the ammonia directly after the digestion without distillation, if the substance to be analyzed does not have to be reduced as in section under Procedures for the Kjeldahlization. The sample is destroyed with sulfuric acid using a mixture of sodium sulfate and mercuric sulfate as a catalyst. After the digestion the solution is neutralized, the ammonia oxidized with hypochlorite, and a known volume of standard arsenite acid added. The excess of the latter is back-titrated with standard hypochlorite.

Colorimetric Procedures. Since these methods are normally used for the determination of very small amounts of nitrogen, it should only be mentioned that the ammonia can be determined either by Nessler's reagent (e.g., 148) or according to Van Slyke (e.g., 149) with hypochlorite and phenolate.

C. OTHER METHODS

A completely new way for the determination of nitrogen was found first by Ter Meulen (150,151) who hydrogenated the nitrogen by using nickel and thorium dioxide as a catalyst. Lacourt (152) transferred this method to the micro scale. Holowchak and co-workers (153) suggested a nickel-magnesium catalyst, which is recommended also by King and Faulconer (154). Gelman and Korshun (155) also published a method based on this principle. The sample is pyrolyzed in a quartz test tube and the resulting products are passed with a rapid stream of hydrogen through the combustion tube, with metallic iron at 400°C. serving as a catalyst.

Zinneke (156) modified the Kjeldahl procedure by combination of a special digestion apparatus with a combustion tube. The sample is digested with sulfuric acid and a mixture of selenium, cupric sulfate, mercuric oxide and sodium sulfate is used as a catalyst. He obtains ammonia and nitrogen, both of which are determined titrimetrically or volumetrically. If platinum black is added to the digestion mixture, nitrogen is gained from the ammonium sulfate formed and the total nitrogen content is determined only by volumetric methods.

Finally the procedures of Fedoseev and Ivashova (157) and Schöniger (158) shall be mentioned. The organic material is heated with magnesium powder in the absence of air. All nitrogen is converted to magnesium nitride. The reaction product is decomposed with acid and then subjected to the normal Kjeldahl distillation procedure. This method seems to be important with reference to the possibility of determining the sulfur as well as the chlorine (bromine) and the nitrogen content in an organic compound, it these elements are present together, using a single sample.

VI. DETERMINATION OF HALOGENS (Cl, Br, I) AND SULFUR

Despite the fact that the elements mentioned are in different groups of the periodic system, it is possible to discuss the methods for the quantitative analysis of these elements in organic compounds. The organic bound element that is to be determined has to be "mineralized," i.e., conversion into an inorganic form which can be easily determined by conventional methods. There are two possible procedures by which this may be accomplished, namely, (1) oxidation methods, and (2) reduction methods.

1. Oxidation Methods

A. COMBUSTION WITH OXYGEN

The Pregl method and a host of variations are generally applicable. The sample is burned in a stream of oxygen over a platinum contact. It is useless to describe all the papers which have appeared on this subject since they are already reviewed by several authors (159–163).

About 25 years ago Grote and Krekeler (164) reported a special combustion setup with a tube having two built-in quartz frits and which used temperatures above 1000°C. Belcher and Ingram (165) also applied their "empty tube technique" to the determination of these elements.

The method of Voight (166) has been further developed by Wickbold (167,168), to be an excellent procedure of general applicability. The sample is vaporized in a stream of oxygen and burned in a special hydrogen–oxygen burner which is placed in the combustion tube (see also Ehrenberger (169)).

In the past years a very simple method for the decomposition of organic compounds has gained widespread approval. This is the technique of burning samples in a closed flask filled with oxygen. Based on a macro method published by Hempel (276) and Mikl and Pech (170,171), for plant control purposes only (172), Schöniger (173,174) used this principle for micro determinations. The author showed that this procedure could be used in routine microanalysis for halogens and sulfur with an accuracy as good as, or better than, that of the slower, more complicated classical methods which have been mentioned above.

The principle of the procedure is that an absorption liquid, the kind depending on the element to be determined, is placed in a conical flask which is then filled with oxygen. The sample is wrapped in a piece of ashless filter paper (2.5 × 2.5 cm.) from which hangs a "fuse" consisting of a small strip of the same paper. This paper is inserted in a piece of platinum gauze attached to a platinum wire which in turn is sealed into the ground glass stopper of the flask. The fuse is then ignited and the stopper quickly inserted into the flask. The combustion is complete within a few seconds and the flask is then shaken for 5 to 10 min. to ensure complete absorption of the combustion products. The required ion may then be determined by any suitable procedure. With this method it is possible to determine not only halogens and sulfur, but also, as was shown by several authors, phosphorus (175–179), arsenic (177), boron (177,180), mercury (181), zinc, calcium, cadmium (180), and carbon -14 (182). A historical review of this method has been published by MacDonald (183).

B. DECOMPOSITION WITH OXIDIZING REAGENTS

The oldest and still most widely used method is the micro version of the Carius technique. The substance to be analyzed is destroyed by heating with nitric acid in a sealed, heavy-walled combustion tube at a temperature of 250 to 300°C. for several hours.

The oxidation of an organic compound with sodium peroxide in a crucible was first suggested by Pringsheim (184). Parr (185) used a closed system for the decomposition, the so-called Parr-bomb thus modifying the procedure so as to make it generally applicable. This principle was applied by several authors to the microanalysis of organic compounds. A few years ago Wurzschmitt (186) published a modification which represents significant progress in this field of analytical work. Ethylene glycol is added to the sample, before the sodium peroxide is introduced into the metal bomb. This reagent is oxidized at 50 to 60°C. by the sodium peroxide. By this means it is possible to ignite the decomposition at a low temperature.

2. Reduction Methods

A. CATALYTIC PROCEDURES WITH HYDROGEN

Ter Meulen was one of the first to introduce hydrogenation methods for the determination of these elements. For the sulfur determination he recommended the use of a platinum catalyst; for the halogens, according to his first publications, it is only necessary to decompose the substance in a stream of hydrogen mixed with ammonia at temperatures over 600°C. (187), or to use a special nickel catalyst at 300 to 400°C. (188). Lacourt (189,190) and Wiesenberger (191) found that when these hydrogenation methods are used, low results will sometimes result—especially in the determination of sulfur— because of the carbon residue in the sample boat. Irimescu (192) tried to improve the method. Kirsten (193), in the determination of sulfur, used a hydrogenation procedure. He suggested that the substance to be analyzed be first burned in a stream of oxygen and then the sulfur oxides that are formed, be reduced to hydrogen sulfide with a hydrogen–oxygen flame.

Summarizing the literature it can be stated that the hydrogenation methods based on the principles mentioned above cannot be applied to every kind of organic compound. For this reason they are not recommended.

B. PROCEDURES WITH REDUCING REAGENTS

Considerable progress in the method of analysis was achieved when Bürger (194,195) found that it is possible to use the well-known method of Vohl (196) for the detection of halogens and sulfur also for the quantitative determinations of these elements.

According to this procedure, modified later by Kainz and co-workers (197–199) for the halogens and by Zimmermann (200–203) for the sulfur, the substance to be analyzed is fused with potassium in a sealed tube. Schöniger (204) and Radmacher and Mohrbauer (205) used magnesium and lithium, respectively, for the same purpose.

This widely spread method is used especially for the sulfur determination in the modification as described by Zimmermann (200–203). After the reduction with potassium is finished, the sealed tube is broken off and the contents are dissolved in acid using a special distillation apparatus. The hydrogen sulfide generated is determined iodometrically as in the section under the determination of sulfur as sulfide.

It shall be mentioned that by using magnesium for this technique it is possible to determine two or three elements in one sample. Schöniger (204,206) and Fedoseev, and Ivashova (207,208) have shown that by proper means nitrogen, halogens, and sulfur can thus be determined. By heating a compound containing these elements in a nitrogen-free atmosphere with magnesium, the magnesium halides, nitride, and sulfide will be obtained. Digestion of these reaction products with acid gives hydrogen sulfide, which can be distilled off. The halides remain in the solution, the nitride gives ammonium sulfate if sulfuric acid has been used. The halide can then be determined by titration, and finally the ammonia is estimated according to Kjeldahl. It can be expected that procedure of this kind will gain importance in the near future.

Another reduction method which is of some value for the halogen determination is the reaction of the substance in solution with sodium. At first organic solvents were used (209,210), and later liquid ammonia was recommended (211). Also, sodium biphenyl was suggested for the reductive removal of halogen (212).

3. Determination of the Elements

A. HALOGENS

Chlorine and Bromine. All oxidation and reduction methods finally give the halides. These have been determined gravimetrically in the beginning, according to Pregl, by precipitation as silver halide, a method which is still used today in many laboratories.

Another gravimetric procedure is the direct absorption of the halide formed on metallic silver. By taking the weight of a silver gauze roll before and after the analysis the amount of halogen present can be determined. The best known method on this principle is described by Safford and Stragand (213). Different modifications of these procedures have been described, some authors recommend the use of specially prepared silver (214). Kirsten (215) examined the use of zinc for the absorption of the halogens.

Most frequently the absorption is made in alkaline solutions (e.g., sodium hydroxide with some hydrogen peroxide added) and the halide is determined titrimetrically. It seems to be of no use to list the host of methods and modifications which have been described, because excellent reviews have already appeared in journals and handbooks (e.g., 160,216,217). In the author's opinion the best method is the potentiometric titration using an automatic apparatus, if a large number of determinations are made every day. When only a few analyses per day are requested, one of the titrimetric procedures that uses an indicator should be applied. If the sample to be analyzed does not contain nitrogen, the acidimetric procedure according to Vieböck (218,219) can be used. Hydroxyl ions are titrated, resulting from the reaction of the halide with mercuric hydroxy cyanide. Excellent results have been obtained with the following simple methods:

For the chlorine determination an argentometric titration with an absorption indicator (220) is used. If bromine is to be determined the iodometric procedure as recommended first by Kolthoff (221,222) is applied. In cases where chlorine and bromine are present in the compound, the iodometric titration gives only the bromine content. A second combustion where the halogen is determined argentometrically gives the sum of chlorine and bromine. By calculation it is possible to find the chlorine content.

Iodine. For the determination of iodine there is only one method which can be highly recommended, namely, the multiplication procedure first introduced by Leipert (223) and Vieböck and Brecher (224). All iodine, regardless if it is present in the absorption liquid as free iodine, iodide, or hypoiodite, is oxidized to iodic acid with bromine. The excess of bromine is then destroyed with formic acid, a certain amount of iodide is added, and the liberated iodine titrated with thiosulfate.

Kainz (197) suggested for the oxidation a solution of chlorine in sodium acetate–acetic acid if only small amounts of iodine are present.

B. SULFUR

Present as Sulfate. All oxidation procedures, as previously mentioned, (see p. 224) will finally give by some means, sulfate. When the first micro methods for the sulfur determination were published (the Carius method and the catalytic combustion procedure), only gravimetric means of finish were recommended. Later different titrimetric methods were suggested without being generally recognized.

The method of Hallet and Kuipers (225), also recommended by Steyermark (226,217), is one of the most used. The sodium or potassium sulfate obtained after the Carius combustion is titrated in 50% alcoholic solution with standard barium chloride, using tetrahydroxyquinone as an indicator. Another titrimetric procedure has been suggested by Belcher and co-workers (227). After precipitation of the sulfate with 4-amino-4-chloro diphenyl an alkalimetric method is applied.

Today, the best method seems to be the titration of sulfate with barium perchlorate as introduced by Fritz and co-workers (228,229). This method quickly found wide approval and is recommended by many laboratories (230–232). The principle of this titration is the following: The sulfate formed by one of the combustion methods, as listed in the section under Combustion with Oxygen, is neutralized. Isopropanol is added to get on 80% solution. The sulfate is finally titrated with standard barium perchlorate (in 80% isopropanol) in the presence of thorin (or thorin–methylene blue, recommended by Wagner (232)). Sharp end points can be obtained if the amounts of phosphate, nitrate, chloride, and fluoride present in the titration liquid are not too large. This will not occur when micro analytical determinations are carried out. Inglis (233) pointed out that this method can also be used when the combustion has been carried out with sodium peroxide. Fritz and co-workers (229), too, arrive at the same conclusions. The solution has to be treated with a cation exchange resin before the titration.

Finally the complexometrical determination using o-cresolphthalein Complexon as indicator (234), and the titration with barium chloride and a conductometric end point indication (235) shall be mentioned.

When the sulfur oxides formed during the combustion are absorbed by silver (the mechanism of this reaction has been studied very accurately by Večeřa (236)), the silver sulfate can be determined either gravimetrically or after elution, titrimetrically. Such methods were published lately by Zinneke (237), Bladh and co-workers (238) and Večeřa and Šnobl (239).

For the determination of very small amounts of sulfate (e.g., in petroleum products after oxidation) a conductometric procedure is suggested by Hurdy and Mair (240). Bertolacini and Barney (241) have chosen a colorimetric way of finish, by using the reaction of the

sulfate formed with barium chloranilate, leading to the liberation of
the intensively colored chloranilic acid.

Present as Sulfide. For the reduction method as described by
Zimmermann, as in the section under Procedures with Reducing
Reagents, the following method has been chosen by the author.
The hydrogen sulfide generated is absorbed in a buffered solution of
cadmium acetate. The precipitated cadmium sulfide is transferred
into a solution of standard iodate and iodide. Acid is added and the
liberated hydrogen sulfide reduces an equivalent amount of iodine.
The excess of the latter is then titrated with thiosulfate. Dirscherl
(242) described minor modifications, designed to remove certain
sources of error.

Večeřa and Spěvák (243) use a colorimetric method, based on the
formation of Lauth's violet with p-phenylendiamine and ferric chloride, whereas Martin and Floret (244) determined the hydrogen
sulfide as methylene blue. This way of finish has already been suggested by Roth (245) for the determination of traces of sulfur in organic compounds. According to Trifonov and co-workers (246),
the hydrogen sulfide can also be estimated polarographically.

VII. OTHER ELEMENTS

1. Phosphorus

For the decomposition of organic compounds containing phosphorus the wet combustion with a mixture of sulfuric and nitric
acids in a Kjeldahl digestion flask is still the most frequently used
method. The oxidation with sodium peroxide in a bomb has been
recommended by several authors (247,248). Jureček and Jeník (249)
use fusion with magnesium in a sealed tube. The magnesium phos-
phide thus formed is decomposed with acid, the phosphine absorbed
in bromine water, and the resulting phosphoric acid determined by
one of the normal procedures.

Most recently the combustion in the closed flask as introduced
by Schöniger for the halogen and sulfur determination (250,251)
has been applied by several authors. The substance to be analyzed is decomposed in the usual way, as in section under Combustion
with Oxygen, and the resulting phosphoric acid can be estimated,
according to Fleischer and co-workers (252–254) either titrimetrically
or colorimetrically. Belcher and MacDonald (255) recommend a

modification of the well-known quinoline phosphomolybdate method
and Merz (256) uses the colorimetric way of finish. He also points
out that with this procedure the simultaneous determination of
phosphorus and the halogens (chlorine, bromine, or iodine) is possible, if these elements are present in a compound.

The phosphoric acid formed by one of the above mentioned combustion procedures can be determined either gravimetrically as ammonium phosphomolybdate (the formula of this precipitate has been
found empirically by Pregl (257)), or colorimetrically. The latter
method is based on the work of Taylor and Miller (258), and Roth
(259) who found that in a mixture of molybdic and phosphomolybdic
acids, only the latter is reduced to heteropoly blue if treated with
reducing reagents. Since both methods are well known standard
procedures they shall only be mentioned in passing.

2. Arsenic, Antimony, Boron

Jureček and Jeník (260–262) also used the reduction with magnesium for the determination of arsenic and antimony. After the min-
eralization the arsenic acid can be estimated iodometrically or alternatively, colorimetrically after arsine is absorbed in a pyridine solution of silver diethyldithiocarbamate. For the estimation of antimony a colorimetric procedure is recommended.

Corner (253) has shown that the closed flask method can also be
used for the determination of organically bound arsenic. In a modified apparatus the sample is at first burned as usual. Arsenite, as
well as arsenate, is formed. The author recommends the distillation of all the arsenic as trichloride, after reduction to the lower
valency state with hydrazine dihydrochloride. It should also be
possible to apply the potentiometric titration as described by Lévy
(263) to this procedure.

Boron may be estimated after a closed flask combustion, as has
been reported by Corner (253) and found to be true in the author's
laboratories. The neutralized absorption liquid is treated with
mannitol, thus obtaining a di–diol complex of the boric acid, which
can be titrated with standard alkali (264).

3. Selenium, Silicon, Metals

Kainz and Resch (265) recommend for the determination of selenium, the decomposition with sodium peroxide and an iodometric

finish, whereas Kondo (266) suggested the gravimetric determination of the black selenium, after the selenic acid has been reduced with hydrazine. The silicon content of organosilicon compounds can be determined as previously described (see p. 205) together with the carbon and hydrogen. Alternatively the sample can be evaporated with 25% oleum and fumic nitric acid containing 20% of oxides of nitrogen: the residual silica is weighed (267). Fusion with sodium and potassium carbonates has also been suggested for the decomposition. The melt is dissolved and the solution, after neutralization, is treated with ammonium fluoride and is titrated acidimetrically (263).

According to Southworth and co-workers (269) the closed flask method can be applied to the determination of mercury. After the combustion the mercury is absorbed in concentrated nitric acid, the pH of the solution is adjusted to 7.5, and the mercury is titrated amperometrically with ethylenedinitrilotetraacetic acid.

Recently, Belcher and co-workers (270) have shown, as has already been mentioned, that the flask combustion method can also be used for the micro determination of other elements in organic compounds.

The determination of metals in organic compounds has been reviewed by Belcher and co-workers (271) and more recently by Sykes (272).

References

1. Benedetti-Pichler, A. A., *Mikrochim. Acta*, 1956, 565.
2. Steyermark, A., E. D. Ingalls, and J. W. Wilkenfeldt, *Anal. Chem.*, 28, 517 (1956).
3. Steyermark, A., *Microchem. J.*, 2, 21 (1958).
4. Gysel, H., and W. Strebel, *Mikrochim. Acta*, 1954, 782.
5. Schöniger, W., *Mikrochim. Acta*, 1959, 382.
6. Howard, H. C., *Ind. Eng. Chem.*, 13, 231 (1921).
7. Kirner, W. R., *Ind. Eng. Chem., Anal. Ed.*, 9, 300 (1937).
8. Reihlen, H., *Mikrochemie*, 23, 285 (1937/1938).
9. Körbl, J., *Mikrochim. Acta*, 1956, 1705.
10. Körbl, J., *Chem. listy*, 49, 858 (1955).
11. Šatava, V., and J. Körbl, *Chem. listy*, 51, 27 (1957).
12. Knižáková, E., and J. Körbl, *Chem. listy*, 52, 750 (1958).
13. Körbl, J., *Chem. listy*, 49, 1532 (1955).
14. Horáček, J., and J. Körbl, *Chem. listy*, 51, 2132 (1957).
15. Mázor, L., *Mikrochim. Acta*, 1957, 113.
16. Večeřa, M., and L. Synek, *Chem. listy*, 51, 2266 (1957).

17. Večeřa, M., D. Šnobl, and L. Synek, *Mikrochim. Acta*, **1958**, 9.
18. Horáček, J., and J. Körbl, *Chem. & Ind. (London)*, **1958**, 401.
19. Belcher, R., and G. Ingram, *Anal. Chim. Acta*, **4**, 118 (1950); *Mikrochemie ver. Mikrochim. Acta*, **36/37**, 690 (1951).
20. Belcher, R., and C. E. Spooner, *J. Chem. Soc. (London)*, **1943**, 313.
21. Ingram, G., *Analyst*, **73**, 548 (1948).
22. Ingram, G., *Chem. & Ind. (London)*, **1956**, 103.
23. Kirsten, W., *Mikrochemie ver. Mikrochim. Acta*, **35**, 217 (1950).
24. Marek, I., *J. prakt. Chem.*, **1911**, 713.
25. Korshun, M. O., *Zhur. Anal. Khim.*, **7**, 96 (1952); through *Brit. Abstr.*, **C**, No. 3801 (1952).
26. Klimova, V. A., and M. O. Korshun, *Zhur. Anal. Khim.*, **6**, 230 (1951); through *Brit. Abstr.*, **C4**, No. 288 (1952).
27. Korshun, M. O., and V. A. Klimova, *Zhur. Anal. Khim.*, **4**, 292 (1949); through *Chem. Abstracts*, **44**, 2884f (1950).
28. Korshun, M. O., and N. S. Sheveleva, *Zhur. Anal. Khim.*, **7**, 104 (1952); through *Brit. Abstr.*, **C4**, No. 3803 (1952)
29. Sokolova, N. V., *Zhur. Anal. Khim.*, **11**, 728 (1956); through *Anal. Abstr.*, **4**, No. 3991 (1957).
30. Korshun, M. O., and N. S. Sheveleva, *Zhur. Anal. Khim.*, **11**, 376 (1956); through *Z. anal. Chem.*, **155**, 431 (1957).
31. Klimova, V. A., M. O. Korshun, and E. G. Bereznickaja, *Doklady Akad. Nauk S.S.S.R.*, **84**, 1175 (1952); through *Chem. Abstracts*, **46**, 11036f (1952).
32. Klimova, V. A., M. O Korshun, and E. G. Bereznickaja, *Doklady Akad. Nauk S.S.S.R.*, **96**, 81 (1954); through *Chem. Zentr.*, **1955**, 2265.
33. Klimova, V. A., and E. G. Bereznickaja, *Zhur. Anal. Khim.*, **11**, 292 (1956); through *Chem. Abstracts*, **50**, 15,338e (1956).
34. Klimova, V. A., and E. G. Bereznickaja, *Zhur. Anal. Khim.*, **12**, 424 (1957); through *Chem. Zentr.*, **1958**, 7221.
35. Korshun, M. O., and E. A. Terenteva, *Doklady Akad. Nauk S.S.S.R.*, **100**, 707 (1955); through *Chem. Zentr.*, **1956**, 3958.
36. Korshun, M. O., N. E. Gelman, and K. I. Glazova, *Doklady Akad. Nauk S.S.S.R.*, **111**, 1255 (1956); through *Anal. Abstr.*, **5**, No. 1542 (1958).
37. Lindner, J., *Mikroanalytische Bestimmung des Kohlenstoffs und Wasserstoffs mit grundlegender Behandlung der Fehlerquellen in der Elementaranalyses*, Verlag Chemie, Berlin, 1935.
38. Boetius, M., *Ueber die Fehlerquellen bei der mikroanalytischen Bestimmung des Kohlenstoffs und Wasserstoffs*, Verlag Chemie, Berlin, 1931.
39. Bürger, K., *Die Chemie*, **55**, 260 (1942).
40. Elving, P. J., and W. R. McElroy, *Ind. Eng. Chem., Anal. Ed.*, **13**, 660 (1941).
41. Irimescu, J., and B. Popescu, *Z. anal. Chem.*, **128**, 185 (1948).
42. Belcher, R., and G. Ingram, *Anal. Chim. Acta*, **4**, 401 (1950).
43. Ingram, G., *Mikrochim. Acta*, **1953**, 71.
44. Kainz, G., *Mikrochemie ver. Mikrochim. Acta*, **35**, 569 (1950).
45. Unterzaucher, J., *Mikrochemie ver. Mikrochim. Acta*, **36/37**, 706 (1951).
46. Kainz, G., and F. Schöller, *Z. anal. Chem.*, **148**, 6 (1955).

47. Hussey, A. S., J. H. Sorensen, and D. D. de Ford, *Anal. Chem.*, **27**, 280 (1955).
48. Cross, C. K., and G. F. Wright, *Anal. Chem.*, **26**, 886 (1954).
49. Kirsten, W., *Mikrochim. Acta*, **1953**, 41.
50. Körbl, J., *Collection Czechoslov. Chem. Communs.*, **20**, 993 (1955).
51. Mitsui, T., *Bull. Res. Inst. Food Science, Kyoto Univ.*, **39**, 11 (1953); through *Chem. Abstracts*, **47**, 12120b (1953).
52. Fischer, F. O., *Anal. Chem.*, **21**, 827 (1949).
53. Kuck, J. A., and P. L. Altieri, *Mikrochim. Acta*, **1956**, 1550.
54. Kuck, J. A., P. L. Altieri, and M. Arnold, *Mikrochim. Acta*, **1956**, 1544.
55. Belcher, R., J. H. Thompson, and T. S. West, *Anal. Chim. Acta*, **19**, 309 (1958).
56. Belcher, R., J. H. Thompson, and T. S. West, *Anal. Chim. Acta*, **19**, 148 (1958).
57. Johansson, A., *Anal. Chem.*, **26**, 1183 (1954).
58. Malissa, H., *Mikrochim. Acta*, **1957**, 553.
59. Unterzaucher, J., *Mikrochim. Acta*, **1957**, 448.
60. Anderson, R. C., Y. Delabarre, and A. A. Bothner-By, *Anal. Chem.*, **24**, 1298 (1952).
61. Christman, D. R., N. E. Day, P. R. Hansell, and R. C. Anderson, *Anal. Chem.*, **27**, 1935 (1955).
62. Kirsten, W., *Anal. Chem.*, **26**, 1097 (1954).
63. Naughton, J. J., and M. M. Frodyma, *Anal. Chem.*, **22**, 711 (1950).
64. Schöniger, W., *Mikrochim. Acta*, **1957**, 545.
65. Rutschmann, J., *Helv. Chim. Acta*, **40**, 433 (1957).
66. Rutschmann, J., and W. Schöniger, *Helv. Chim. Acta*, **40**, 428 (1957).
67. Unterzaucher, J., *Ber.*, **73**, 391 (1940).
68. Unterzaucher, J., *Mikrochemie ver. Mikrochim. Acta*, **36/37**, 706 (1951).
69. Unterzaucher, J., *Analyst*, **77**, 584 (1952).
70. Unterzaucher, J., *Bull. soc. chim. France*, **20**, C.71 (1953).
71. Aluise, V. A., R. T. Hall, F. C. Straats, and W. W. Becker, *Anal. Chem.*, **19**, 347 (1947).
72. Kirsten, W., *Mikrochemie ver. Mikrochim. Acta*, **34**, 152 (1949).
73. Colson, A. F., *Analyst*, **79**, 784 (1955).
74. Lacourt, A., *Mikrochim. Acta*, **1954**, 735.
75. Moelants, L. J., and W. Wesenbeek, *Mikrochim. Acta*, **1954**, 738.
76. Schöniger, W., *Mikrochim. Acta*, **1956**, 863.
77. Schöniger, W., *Mikrochim. Acta*, **1954**, 320.
78. Oliver, F. H., *Analyst*, **80**, 593 (1955).
79. Oita, I. J., and H. S. Conway, *Anal. Chem.*, **26**, 600 (1954).
80. Korshun, M. O., and J. A. Bondarewskaya, *Doklady Akad. Nauk S.S.S.R.*, **110**, 220 (1956); through *Chem. Zentr.*, **1958**, 7221.
81. Steyermark, A., *J. Assoc. Offic. Agr. Chemists*, **41**, 299 (1958).
82. Mázor, L., *Mikrochim. Acta*, **1956**, 1757.
83. Bürger, K., *Mikrochim. Acta*, **1957**, 313.
84. Maylott, A. O., and J. B. Lewis, *Anal. Chem.*, **22**, 1051 (1950).
85. Dundy, M., and E. Stehr, *Anal. Chem.*, **23**, 1408 (1951).

86. Dixon, J. P., *Anal. Chim. Acta*, **19**, 141 (1958).
87. Campanile, V. A., J. H. Bradley, E. D. Peters, E. J. Agazzi, and F. R. Brooks, *Anal. Chem.*, **23**, 1421 (1951).
88. Canales, A. M., and T. D. Parks, *Anal. Chim. Acta*, **15**, 25 (1956).
89. Zimmermann, W., *Z. anal. Chem.*, **118**, 258 (1939).
90. Unterzaucher, J., *Mikrochim. Acta,* **1956**, 822.
91. Berret, R., and P. Poirier, *Bull. soc. chim. France*, **16**, D.539 (1949).
92. Gouverneur, P., M. A. Schreuders, and P. N. Degens, *Anal. Chim. Acta*, **5**, 293 (1951).
93. Imaeda, K., *J. Pharm. Soc. Japan*, **78**, 30 (1958); through *Chem. Abstracts*, **52**, 6065*i* (1958).
94. Korshun, M. O., *Zavodskaya Lab.*, **10**, 241 (1941); through *Chem. Abstracts*, **35**, 7315[9] (1941).
95. Korshun, M. O., and N. E. Gelman, *Zavodskaya Lab.*, **12**, 500 (1946); through *Chem. Abstracts*, **41**, 890c (1947).
96. Spooner, C. E., *Fuel in Science and Practice*, **26**, 15 (1947).
97. Ehrenberger, F., S. Gorbach, and W. Mann, *Mikrochim. Acta*, **1958**, 778.
98. Walton, W. W., F. M. McCulloch, and W. H. Smith, *J. Res. Natl. Bur. Standards*, **40**, 443 (1948).
99. Harris, C. C., D. M. Smith, and J. Mitchell, Jr., *Anal. Chem.*, **22**, 1297 (1950).
100. Holowchak, J., and G. E. C. Wear, *Anal. Chem.*, **23**, 1404 (1951).
101. Kôno, T., K. Sato, M. Suzuki, and I. Isobe, *J. Agr. Chem. Soc. Japan*, **29**, 963 (1955); **31**, 587 (1957).
102. Schütze, M., *Z. anal. Chem.*, **118**, 241 (1939).
103. Ter Meulen, H., *Rec. trav. chim.*, **51**, 509 (1922).
104. Smith, R. N., J. Duffield, R. A. Pierotti, and J. Mooi, *Anal. Chem.*, **28**, 1161 (1956).
105. Russel, W. W., J. W. Fulton, and M. E. Marks, *Ind. Eng. Chem., Anal. Ed.*, **5**, 384 (1933).
106. Lindner, J., and W. Wirth, *Ber.*, **70**, 1025 (1937).
107. Belcher, R., J. H. Thompson, and T. S. West, *Anal. Chim. Acta*, **19**, 148 (1958).
108. Sheft, I., and J. J. Katz, *Anal. Chem.*, **29**, 1322 (1957).
109. Grosse, A. V., S. G. Hindin, and A. D. Kirshenbaum, *Anal. Chem.*, **21**, 386 (1949).
110. Grosse, A. V., and A. D. Kirshenbaum, *Anal. Chem.*, **24**, 584 (1952).
111. Kirshenbaum, A. D., A. G. Steng, and A. V. Grosse, *Anal. Chem.*, **24**, 1361 (1952).
112. Gysel, H., *Helv. Chim. Acta*, **22**, 1088 (1939).
113. Gysel, H., *Helv. Chim. Acta*, **35**, 802 (1952).
114. Zimmermann, W., *Mikrochemie ver. Mikrochim. Acta*, **31**, 42 (1943).
115. Shelberg, E. F., *Anal. Chem.*, **23**, 1492 (1952).
116. Schöniger, W., *Mikrochemie ver. Mikrochim. Acta*, **39**, 229 (1952).
117. Belcher, R., and M. K. Bhatty, *Fuel*, **37**, 159 (1958).
118. Hozumi, K., and S. Kinoshita, *J. Pharm. Soc. Japan*, **76**, 1157 (1956); through *Anal. Abstr.*, **4**, No. 2993 (1957).

119. Hozumi, K., K. Imaeda, and S. Kinoshita, *J. Pharm. Soc. Japan,* **76,** 1161 (1956); through *Anal. Abstr.,* **4,** No. 2993 (1957).
120. Hozumi, K., and S. Kinoshita, *J. Pharm. Soc. Japan,* **76,** 1167 (1956); through *Anal. Abstr.,* **4,** No. 2993 (1957).
121. Unterzaucher, J., *Chem.-Ingr.-Tech.,* **22,** 128 (1950).
122. Unterzaucher, J., *Mikrochemie ver. Mikrochim. Acta,* **36/37,** 706 (1951).
123. Cropper, F. R., R. H. Reed, and R. Rothwell, *Mikrochim. Acta,* **1954,** 223.
124. Manser, W., and A. Egli, *Helv. Chim. Acta,* **37,** 1048 (1954).
125. Ingram, G., *Mikrochim. Acta,* **1953,** 131.
126. Belcher, R., and G. Ingram, *Anal. Chim. Acta,* **4,** 118 (1950).
127. Kirsten, W., *Anal. Chem.,* **19,** 925 (1947).
128. Kirsten, W., *Mikrochemie ver. Mikrochim. Acta,* **39,** 245 (1952).
129. Kirsten, W., *Anal. Chem.,* **29,** 1084 (1957).
130. Clark, S. J., and B. Dando, *Mikrochim. Acta,* **1955,** 1012.
131. Kainz, G., *Österr. Chemiker-Ztg.,* **57,** 242 (1956).
132. Bradstreet, R. B., *Chem. Revs.,* **27,** 331 (1940).
133. Bradstreet, R. B., *Anal. Chem.,* **26,** 185 (1954).
134. Kirk, P. L., *Anal. Chem.,* **22,** 354 (1950).
135. Lieb, H., and W. Schöniger, Nachweis und Bestimmung einzelner Elemente, in Hoppe-Seyler/Thierfelder, *Handbuch der physiologisch- und pathologisch-chemischen Analyse,* 10th ed., Vol. III, Springer, Berlin, 1955, p. 240.
136. Steyermark, A., *Quantitative Organic Microanalysis,* Blakiston, New York, 1951, pp. 134–155.
137. Willits, C. O., M. R. Coe, and C. L. Ogg, *J. Assoc. Offic. Agr. Chemists,* **32,** 118 (1949).
138. Willits, C. O., and C. L. Ogg, *J. Assoc. Offic. Agr. Chemists,* **31,** 565 (1948).
139. Willits, C. O., and C. L. Ogg, *J. Assoc. Offic. Agr. Chemists,* **33,** 100, 179 (1950).
140. Friedrich, A., E. Kuhaas, and R. Schnürch, *Z. physiol. Chem.,* **216,** 68 (1933).
141. Ogg, C. L., and C. O. Willits, *J. Assoc. Offic. Agr. Chemists,* **35,** 288 (1952).
142. Ma, T. S., R. E. Lang, and J. D. McKinley, *Mikrochim. Acta,* **1957,** 368.
143. Steyermark, A., B. E. McGee, E. A. Bass, and R. R. Kaup, *Anal. Chem.,* **30,** 1561 (1958).
144. Dickinson, W. E., *Anal. Chem.,* **26,** 777 (1954).
144a. Reprinted from *Analytical Chemistry,* Vol. 30, Page 1563, 1958.
145. Steyermark, A., H. K. Alber, V. A. Aluise, E. W. D. Huffman, J. A. Kuck, J. J. Moran, and C. O. Willits, *Anal. Chem.,* **23,** 523 (1951).
146. Schöniger, W., and A. Haack, *Mikrochim. Acta,* **1956,** 1369.
147. Belcher, R., and M. K. Bhatty, *Mikrochim. Acta,* **1956,** 1183.
148. Schaffer, F. L., and J. C. Sprecher, *Anal. Chem.,* **29,** 437 (1957).
149. Van Slyke, D. D., and A. Hiller, *J. Biol. Chem.,* **102,** 499 (1933).
150. Ter Meulen, H., *Bull. soc. chim. Belgique,* **49,** 103 (1940).
151. Ter Meulen, H., and J. Heslinga, *Neue Methoden der organisch-chemischen Analyse,* Akad. Verlagsgesellschaft, Leipzig, 1927, pp. 20–27.
152. Lacourt, A., and C. F. Chang, *Bull. soc. chim. Belgique,* **49,** 167 (1940).

153. Holowchak, J., G. E. C. Wear, and E. L. Baldechwieler, *Anal. Chem.*, **24**, 1754 (1952).
154. King, R. W., and W. B. M. Faulconer, *Anal. Chem.*, **28**, 255 (1956).
155. Gelman, N. E., and M. O. Korshun, *Zhur. Anal. Khim.*, **12**, 128 (1957); through *Anal. Abstr.*, **5**, No. 543 (1958).
156. Zinneke, F., *Angew. Chem.*, **64**, 220 (1952).
157. Fedoseev, P. N., and N. P. Ivashova, *Zhur. Anal. Khim.*, **7**, 116 (1952); through *Brit. Abstr.*, **C**, No. 3804 (1952).
158. Schöniger, W., *Mikrochim. Acta*, **1955**, 44.
159. Gouverneur, P., *Anal. Chim. Acta*, **2**, 510 (1948).
160. Kainz, G., *Österr. Chemiker-Ztg.*, **58**, 8 (1957).
161. Körbl, J., *Ind. Chemist*, **34**, 563 (1958).
162. Ogg, C. L., *Anal. Chem.*, **28**, 766 (1956).
163. Willitts, C. O., *Anal. Chem.*, **21**, 132 (1949).
164. Grote, W., and H. Krekeler, *Z. angew. Chem.*, **46**, 106 (1933).
165. Belcher, R., and G. Ingram, *Anal. Chim. Acta*, **7**, 319 (1952).
166. Voight, J., *Z. angew. Chem.*, **35**, 654 (1922).
167. Wickbold, R., *Angew. Chem.*, **64**, 133 (1952).
168. Wickbold, R., *Angew. Chem.*, **69**, 530 (1957).
169. Ehrenberger, F., *Mikrochim. Acta*, **1959**, 192.
170. Mikl, O., and J. Pech, *Chem. listy*, **46**, 382 (1952).
171. Mikl, O., and J. Pech, *Chem. listy*, **47**, 904 (1953).
172. Pech, J., private communication.
173. Schöniger, W., *Mikrochim. Acta*, **1955**, 123.
174. Schöniger, W., *Mikrochim. Acta*, **1956**, 869.
175. Belcher, R., and A. M. G. MacDonald, *Talanta*, **1**, 185 (1958).
176. Cohen, L. E., and F. W. Czech, *Chemist-Analyst*, **47**, 86 (1958).
177. Corner, M., *Analyst*, **84**, 41 (1959).
178. Fleischer, K. D., B. C. Southworth, J. H. Hodecker, and M. M. Tuckerman, *Anal. Chem.*, **30**, 152 (1958).
179. Merz, W., *Mikrochim. Acta*, **1959**, 456.
180. Belcher, R., A. M. G. MacDonald, and T. S. West, *Talanta*, **1**, 408 (1958).
181. Southworth, B. C., J. H. Hodecker, and K. D. Fleischer, *Anal. Chem.*, **30**, 1152 (1958).
182. Götte, H., R. Kretz, and H. Baddenhausen, *Angew. Chem.*, **69**, 561 (1957).
183. MacDonald, A. M. G., *Ind. Chemist*, **35**, 33 (1959).
184. Pringsheim, H., and J. A. Gibson, *Ber.*, **38**, 2459 (1905).
185. Parr, S. W., *J. Am. Chem. Soc.*, **30**, 764 (1908).
186. Wurzschmitt, B., *Mitrochemie ver. Mikrochim. Acta*, **36/37**, 769 (1951).
187. Ter Meulen, H., and J. Heslinga, *Neue Methoden der organisch-chemischen Analyse*, Akad. Verlagsgesellschaft, Leipzig, 1927, pp. 39–41.
188. Ter Meulen, H., *Rec. trav. chim.*, **47**, 698 (1928).
189. Lacourt, A., *Bull. soc. chim. Belgique*, **43**, 93 (1934).
190. Lacourt, A., *Mikrochemie*, **23**, 308 (1938).
191. Wiesenberger, E., *Mikrochemie ver. Mikrochim. Acta*, **29**, 73 (1943).
192. Irimescu, J., and E. Chirnoaga, *Z. anal. Chem.*, **128**, 71 (1948).
193. Kirsten, W., *Mikrochemie ver. Mikrochim. Acta*, **35**, 174 (1950).

194. Bürger, K., *Z. angew. Chem.*, **54**, 479 (1941).
195. Bürger, K., *Die Chemie*, **55**, 245 (1942).
196. Vohl, H., *Dinglers Polytech. J.*, **168**, 49 (1863).
197. Kainz, G., *Mikrochemie ver. Mikrochim. Acta*, **35**, 469 (1950).
198. Kainz, G., *Mikrochemie ver. Mikrochim. Acta*, **38**, 167 (1951).
199. Kainz, G., and A. Resch, *Mikrochemie ver. Mikrochim. Acta*, **39**, 1, 75 (1952).
200. Zimmermann, W., *Mikrochemie ver. Mikrochim. Acta*, **31**, 15 (1943).
201. Zimmermann, W., *Mikrochemie ver. Mikrochim. Acta*, **33**, 122 (1947).
202. Zimmermann, W., *Mikrochemie ver. Mikrochim. Acta*, **35**, 80 (1950).
203. Zimmermann, W., *Mikrochemie ver. Mikrochim. Acta*, **40**, 162 (1952).
204. Schöniger, W., *Mikrochim. Acta*, **1954**, 74.
205. Radmacher, W., and P. Mohrbauer, *Z. anal. Chem.*, **141**, 419 (1954).
206. Schöniger, W., *Mikrochim. Acta*, **1955**, 44.
207. Fedoseev, P. N., and N. P. Ivashova, *Zhur. Anal. Khim.*, **11**, 233 (1956); through *Z. anal Chem.*, **155**, 289 (1957).
208. Fedoseev, P. N., and N. P. Ivashova, *Zhur. Anal. Khim.*, **13**, 230 (1958); through *Z. anal. Chem.*, **166**, 48 (1959).
209. Irimescu, J., and E. Chirnoaga, *Z. anal. Chem.*, **125**, 32 (1942).
210. Rauscher, W. H., *Ind. Eng. Chem., Anal. Ed.*, **9**, 296 (1937).
211. Beckman, H., *Chem. Eng. News*, **37**, 34 (1959).
212. Liggett, L. M., *Anal. Chem.*, **26**, 748 (1954).
213. Safford, H. W., and G. L. Stragand, *Anal. Chem.*, **21**, 625 (1949).
214. Mitsui, T., and H. Sato, *Mikrochim. Acta*, **1956**, 1603.
215. Kirsten, W. J., *Mikrochim. Acta*, **1957**, 289.
216. Roth, H., *Pregl-Roth, Quantitative organische Mikroanalyses*, 7th Ed., Springer-Verlag, Wien, 1958.
217. Steyermark, A., *Quantitative Organic Microanalysis*, Blakiston, New York, 1951.
218. Belcher, R., A. M. G. MacDonald, and A. J. Nutten, *Mikrochim. Acta*, **1954**, 104.
219. Vieböck, F., *Mikrochemie*, **11**, 465 (1932).
220. Wagner, H., and F. Bühler, *Mikrochemie ver. Mikrochim. Acta*, **36/37**, 641 (1951).
221. Kolthoff, M., *Ind. Eng. Chem., Anal. Ed.*, **9**, 75 (1937).
222. Kainz, G., *Mikrochemie ver. Mikrochim. Acta*, **36/37**, 1002 (1951).
223. Leipert, T., *Biochem. Z.*, **261**, 436 (1933).
224. Vieböck, F., and C. Brecher, *Ber.*, **63**, 3207 (1930).
225. Hallett, L. T., and J. W. Kuipers, *Ind. Eng. Chem., Anal. Ed.*, **12**, 360 (1940).
226. Steyermark, A., E. Bass, and B. Littman, *Anal. Chem.*, **20**, 587 (1948).
227. Belcher, R., A. J. Nutten, and W. I. Stephen, *Mikrochim. Acta*, **1953**, 51.
228. Fritz, J. S., and S. S. Yamamura, *Anal. Chem.*, **27**, 1461 (1955).
229. Fritz, J. S., S. S. Yamamura, and M. J. Richard, *Anal. Chem.*, **29**, 158 (1957).
230. Alicino, J. F., *Microchem. J.*, **2**, 83 (1958).
231. Erdey, L., L. Mázor, and T. Meisel, *Mikrochim. Acta*, **1958**, 140.

232. Wagner, H., *Mikrochim. Acta*, **1957**, 19.
233. Inglis, A. S., *Mikrochim. Acta*, **1956**, 1834.
234. Anderegg, G., H. Flaschka, R. Sallmann, and G. Schwarzenbach, *Helv. Chim. Acta*, **37**, 113 (1954).
235. Ottosson, R., and O. Snellman, *Acta Chem. Scand.*, **11**, 185 (1957).
236. Večeřa, M., and D. Šnobl, *Chem. listy*, **50**, 1941 (1956).
237. Zinneke, T., *Z. anal. Chem.*, **132**, 175 (1951).
238. Bladh, E., K. J. Karrman, and O. Andersson, *Mikrochim. Acta*, **1958**, 60.
239. Večeřa, M., and D. Šnobl, *Mikrochim. Acta*, **1958**, 28.
240. Hurdy, J. A., and R. D. Mair, *Anal. Chem.*, **27**, 802 (1955).
241. Bertolacini, R. J., and J. E. Barney, *Anal. Chem.*, **29**, 281 (1957).
242. Dirscherl, A., *Mikrochim. Acta*, **1957**, 421.
243. Večeřa, M., and A. Spěvák, *Chem. listy*, **51**, 2037 (1957).
244. Martin, F., and A. Floret, *Chim. anal.*, **40**, 120 (1958).
245. Roth, H., *Mikrochemie ver. Mikrochim. Acta*, **36/37**, 379 (1951).
246. Trifonov, A., C. P. Ivanov, and D. N. Pavlov, *Collection Czechoslov. Chem. Communs.*, **19**, 1133 (1954).
247. Burton, J. D., and J. P. Riley, *Analyst*, **80**, 391 (1955).
248. Fennell, T. R. F. W., M. W. Roberts, and J. R. Webb, *Analyst*, **82**, 639 (1957).
249. Jureček, M., and J. Jeník, *Chem. listy*, **51**, 1312 (1957).
250. Schöniger, W., *Mikrochim. Acta*, **1955**, 123.
251. Schöniger, W., *Mikrochim. Acta*, **1956**, 869.
252. Cohen, L. E., and F. W. Czech, *Chemist-Analyst*, **47**, 86 (1958).
253. Corner, M., *Analyst*, **84**, 41 (1959).
254. Flesicher, K. D., B. C. Southworth, J. H. Hodecker, and M. M. Tuckerman, *Anal. Chem.*, **30**, 152 (1958).
255. Belcher, R., and A. M. G. MacDonald, *Talanta*, **1**, 185 (1958).
256. Merz, W., *Mikrochim. Acta*, **1959**, 456.
257. Pregl, F., *Quantitative Organic Microanalysis*, translated from the 2nd rev. German ed. by E. Fyleman, J. & A. Churchill Ltd., London, 1924.
258. Taylor, A. E., and C. W. Miller, *J. Biol. Chem.*, **18**, 215 (1914).
259. Roth, H., *Mikrochemie ver. Mikrochim. Acta*, **31**, 290 (1944).
260. Jeník, J., *Chem. listy*, **51**, 1316 (1957).
261. Jureček, M., and J. Jeník, *Chem. listy*, **49**, 341 (1955).
262. Jureček, M., and J. Jeník, *Chem. listy*, **50**, 84 (1956).
263. Levy, R., *Compt. rend.*, **283**, 2320 (1954).
264. Roth, H., *Z. anal. Chem.*, **141**, 404, 414 (1954).
265. Kainz, G., and A. Resch, *Mikrochemie ver. Mikrochim. Acta*, **40**, 332 (1952).
266. Kondo, A., *Japan Analyst*, **6**, 583 (1957).
267. Kreshkov, A. P., S. V. Syavtsillo, and V. T. Shemyatenkova, *Zavodskaya Lab.*, **22**, 1425 (1956); through *Anal. Abstr.*, **4**, No. 1858 (1957).
268. Šiř, Z., and R. Komers, *Chem. listy*, **50**, 88 (1956).
269. Southworth, B. C., J. H. Hodecker, and K. D. Fleischer, *Anal. Chem.*, **30**, 1152 (1958).
270. Belcher, R., A. M. G. MacDonald, and T. S. West, *Talanta*, **1**, 408 (1958).

271. Belcher, R., D. Gibbons, and A. Sykes, *Mikrochemie ver. Mikrochim. Acta*, **40,** 76 (1952).
272. Sykes, A., *Mikrochim. Acta*, **1956,** 1155.
273. Duswalt, A. A. and W. W. Brandt, *Anal. Chem.*, **32,** 272 (1960).
274. Sundberg, O. E. and C. Maresh, *Anal. Chem.*, **32,** 274 (1960).
275. Gustin, G. M., *Abstracts* **11B**, 136th Meeting, ACS, Atlantic City, N. J., Sept. 1959; *Microchem. J.*, **4,** 43 (1960).
276. Hempel, W., *Z. angew. Chem.*, **5,** 393 (1893).

Theory of Electrode Processes

W. H. REINMUTH, *Columbia University, New York, N. Y.*

I. INTRODUCTION

The present review is intended to survey recent work in the theory of electrode processes with particular emphasis on those fields which hold interest for the electroanalytical chemist. A number of topics have been slighted, some such as the hydrogen evolution reaction corrosion, and electrokinetic phenomena because they seemed of lesser importance to the analyst; others such as coulometry, polarized electrode potentiometry, because they have received such excellent recent discussions; still others such as conductimetry and membrane potentials because they are not strictly concerned with electrode processes.

The present discussion is divided into three major sections dealing with the nature of electrode reactions, experimental techniques, and the effects of experimental variables on electrode processes. Subjects considered in the last category include the nature of the reactant, the electrode material, the solvent, surface active materials and the supporting electrolyte.

II. ELECTRODE REACTIONS

The theory of electrode reactions has been a matter of concern to chemists since the time of Faraday. Not only is the study of the subject a worthy endeavor in its own right but the information obtainable is of vital interest to chemists in other fields as well as in practical applications. The electrode reaction can be broken down arbitrarily into three steps. In the first, the reactive species arrives at the electrode surface by chemical reaction, diffusion, or the like. In the second, a charge transfer occurs at the electrode–solution interface. The third step is the reverse of the first. The second step is controlled by the potential. Generally by moving to extremes of anodic or cathodic potentials for oxidation or reduction, respectively, we can cause reaction at the surface to become essentially instantaneous. The reaction is then limited by the first of these steps. At less extreme potentials the second step becomes the controlling factor. Unless the second step is totally irreversible, i.e., unless the reverse of the electrode reaction can be neglected, the third step also becomes important in this intermediate potential region. Even when the reaction is irreversible, the third step influences the observed results when the product formed can react chemically with the initial reactant. In order to describe an electrode reaction completely, then, it is necessary to specify both qualitatively and quantitatively the nature of each of these three stages.

1. Charge Transfer

Reaction theory in general concerns itself with two questions—the nature of systems at equilibrium and the processes by which they attain that state. If the charge transfer process is sufficiently rapid in both directions, then equilibrium is achieved between reactants and products and the reaction is said to be reversible in the thermodynamic sense. If the reaction proceeds appreciably in only one direction, it is said to be totally irreversible.   Cases in between are deemed quasi-reversible.   In the first case information can be obtained only about initial and final products.   In the other cases more information can be obtained but at the cost of greater theoretical complexity.

Treatment of reversible systems rests on the very firm ground of thermodynamics.   The Nernst equation and its innumerable modifications can be applied with confidence to any system in which equilibrium is attained.   The major problem of the chemist, in such systems, then reduces to the task of assuring himself that the equilibrium condition is satisfied, producing theoretical equations which relate his experimental observations to the Nernst equation or an equivalent, and then designing experiments which will produce the necessary data.   The types of information obtainable are standard potentials or free energies of reaction, activities and activity coefficients of species in solution, and effects of various factors upon these quantities. With polarography and potentiometry in particular, complexity constants, acid–base dissociation constants, hydrogen ion activities, and the like can be determined with relative ease.

Aside from routine applications of these principles to specific problems, most of the recent work dealing with reversible systems resolves itself into two major categories.   The first of these is the quest for new electrochemical techniques, and is intimately concerned with the problem of obtaining information more accurately and with greater confidence than was obtained under equilibrium conditions. For many systems, conventional polarography and potentiometry are adequate, but as the systems become more complex, more complicated techniques must be employed.   Since, with these techniques, the question of equilibrium or nonequilibrium hinges on an understanding of the latter as well as the former, their discussion will be postponed for the present.

The second category of recent work is the application of the basic principles to particularly novel or challenging systems.   Three examples will be cited.   Haissinsky and co-workers (73,74), Rogers and co-workers (34,174), and later Nicholson (161) have considered the problem of the activities of metals in less than monolayer deposits. The classical view is, of course, that the activity of any bulk phase is unity.   This model, however, often breaks down when a small deposit of the metal of interest is plated on another.   From the nature of the breakdown it is possible to infer valuable information about the nature of metal–metal bonds. For example, if the activity of the deposit decreases at low surface coverage, it indicates that the bond of the depositing metal with the substrate is stronger than that with itself. In principle it is even possible to determine the range of bonding energies and the effect of surface pretreatment on them.

A line of research pursued by Laitinen and his co-workers (118) has been the determination of the electromotive series in fused salt media. The results not only give valuable information about the nature of solvation in these media but also indirectly shed light on the peculiarities associated with our most familiar solvent water.

Electrochemistry texts generally classify electrodes as belonging to the first, second, or third types. The silver–silver ion electrode is an example of the first. The potential is directly related to the couple undergoing reaction. The second is typified by the silver–silver chloride electrode. Here chloride, "once removed" from the electrode reaction, is the potential determining species. The texts go on to give an example of the third kind generally involving two precipitates, always with the statement that such electrodes are sluggish and unreliable. Schmid and Reilley (185) with their pM electrode involving mercury–mercuric EDTA–metal EDTA not only produced an electrode which will make the analyst eternally grateful, but also made the first practical application of a very old principle.

Further examples of this sort would not be hard to cite but the interested reader will have no difficulty in discovering them for himself.

In the realm of quasireversible and irreversible reactions the questions are much more complex and by no means resolved.

A fundamental difficulty arises in the description of any nonequilibrium system, namely, that many of the variables we are able to measure are strictly defined only in terms of measurements at equilibrium. Potential in the thermodynamic sense, activity, temperature, and many others have this restriction and it is the first of these which is particularly bothersome to the electrochemist. Does a nonequilibrium potential have any meaning; is it related to the thermodynamic one; can one define a potential he can not measure? These and similar questions which penetrate to the basic philosophy of physical reality are ones which must be answered satisfactorily and yet, are not. Lange (125), Parsons (164), Grahame (69), and others have considered the vexing problems of definition of potential under these conditions. These authors agree in many details but yet there are subtle differences between them.

Superimposed on this difficulty is the even more general problem of valid approach to any chemical kinetic situation. One may cite two basic approaches. The first is the empirical one which in electrochemical systems is due to Tafel. It is observed that in general the rates of electrochemical reactions have an approximately exponential dependence on potential. This fact, if it be so accepted, permits a reasonable number of valid predictions but is of little help if one wishes to inquire into the factors affecting the dependence. To perform meaningful experiments in this area it is necessary to have a more extensive model and preferably one which offers more general predictions.

Since thermodynamics has served so well in equilibrium studies it was only natural that the attempt should have been made to apply it to nonequilibrium situations. Eyring's absolute rate theory is the most often quoted formulation of this idea. In its simplest form it predicts the exponential dependence of rate of reaction on potential and in more erudite extensions it predicts successfully, at least in some cases, the second order corrections to this dependence produced by changes in the structure of the solution in the vicinity of the electrode surface. Until relatively recently, however, few workers have attempted to apply this theory to its fullest extent, that is, for the purpose of predicting absolute reaction rates. The difficulty with such an extension is, of course, that in order to pursue it one must have a picture of the mechanism of reaction and such pictures have come only with recent advances in experimental methodology. An electrode reaction has three major complications. First, it proceeds in an inhomogeneous medium, the solvent, about which one can make only the crudest of approximations without introducing impossible mathematical complexities. Second, the reaction is a heterogeneous one occurring at a boundary between a conducting metal and a dielectric containing mobile charges, a most complicated situation. Thirdly, it generally proceeds by an electron-transfer rather than by rupture and formation of bonds. With all these complications it is small wonder that widely divergent views are held by various workers. The most extensive recent theoretical investigations have been by Marcus (144) and by Hush (85). These authors agree that because of the rapidity of electron-transfer the solvent and ligand shell around the reactive species cannot immediately reorient to its new surroundings in the activated complex but they disagree very strongly as to

how to take account of this fact.   At the present the outcome of the
controversy awaits further experimental work.   Because of the approximations necessarily involved in the results of both treatments,
exact agreement with experiment would be fortuitous.

A question which is often of major importance is when, and whether,
it is important to take account of rates in electrode processes, i.e., is
the particular system under observation behaving reversibly or not?

In general, the method of observation tends to disturb the system
under consideration.   Since reversibility depends on the possibility
of the system readjusting itself to an equilibrium state through rapid
charge-transfer reaction, it depends on the relative magnitudes of the
disturbance and the rate of the charge-transfer process,   In a potentiometric measurement the disturbing factor is a very slight one, the
current necessary to activate the current sensitive device in the potentiometer.   In chronopotentiometry the disturbing current may be
many orders of magnitude larger and thus reversibility is more difficult
to achieve.   Not only the magnitude of the disturbance but the
length of time for which it is observed are important.   In potentiometry one may wait minutes or hours, in polarography the experiment covers the lifetime of a drop, a few seconds; in a.c. polarography
a cycle covers a few milliseconds.   Three factors, then, the chemical
system, the magnitude of disturbance, and the time of observation
determine reversibility.

Further complication arises from the fact that reversibility is
defined in terms of concentrations at the electrode surface and, in
general, these are not the same as in the bulk of the solution.   Since
concentrations at the surface can generally not be measured directly,
they must be inferred from a theoretical model.   This can be done
only when the means by which the reactive species are supplied at the
electrode surface is known.

2. Mass Transfer

There are a number of methods by which reactants can be supplied
to the electrode surface.   The most commonly encountered of these
is diffusion, movement of the species through a concentration gradient
which is generally set up by the reaction at the surface.   Diffusion is
a particularly advantageous mode of mass transfer because it obeys
well-known and often easily solved equations, Fick's laws, and because it can be made to occur very reproducibly.

Convection is the mode of transfer in which the solution moves and the reactant is carried along. It occurs with moving electrodes or in stirred solutions. It results in higher currents and greater sensitivity than pure diffusion, but theoretically it is much more difficult to treat exactly, and practically it is much more difficult to obtain reproducibly. The theoretical problem is not nearly so severe as the practical one because the system often behaves as though the electrode had a thin stationary layer around it in which only diffusion occurs. Although the simple Nernst diffusion layer assumption gives results consistent with experiment, it has often been proven that it is based on a much oversimplified view of conditions at the electrode surface so that it must be applied with caution in new situations.

Migration is the movement of charged species in an electric field. It is generally undesirable because it makes currents dependent on the resistance of the solution and thus on the concentration of all ionic species present. It can be suppressed by adding large excesses of electrolytes to lower the resistance.

The fourth mode of supply to the electrode surface is by chemical reaction. A simple example is the dehydration of formaldehyde prior to its reduction. Kinetic phenomena are inherently more dependent on subtle factors than is diffusion so that the results in kinetic cases are less reproducible: but, on the other hand, this offers a means by which these phenomena may be studied.

In some cases species can react only when they are adsorbed on the electrode. In such cases the amount of reaction often becomes limited by the surface area of the electrode rather than by concentrations of the species of interest in solution. From an analytical standpoint this is undesirable, but again is valuable in the study of adsorption phenomena.

The charge-transfer process may be reversible in the thermodynamic sense no matter which of these modes of supply is operative. Ambiguity arises, however, when the term reversible is applied to the over-all electrode reaction. Though the charge-transfer may be reversible, if a chemical reaction preceding it is not, the over-all process is irreversible. Unfortunately, many workers seem not to make a distinction between these two cases. For that reason the present author prefers to reserve the terms reversible and irreversible for the entire process and to designate the charge-transfer process by the terms Nernst-controlled for the reversible cases and charge-transfer controlled for the irreversible case. This terminology will be used in the remainder of the present work.

III. ELECTROCHEMICAL TECHNIQUES

Polarography is the most widely applied of the available experimental techniques. Its value is well demonstrated by its sustained popularity. However, for both the analyst and the less practically oriented researcher it has a number of disadvantages. In analytical applications they include its relatively low resolution, sensitivity, and potential range. Problems of resolvability arise in two cases; when two waves occur at nearly the same potential and when a small wave is preceded by a large one. In either case, taking the derivative of the wave improves the situation. This or its equivalent can be done in several ways. Some of these methods introduce the complication that only Nernst-controlled processes are observable. All introduce the complication that any factor which influences the slope of a conventional wave influences the height of the derivative peak. Thus reproducibility becomes more difficult to achieve.

Problems of sensitivity stem from the continual renewal of the drop surface. This introduces a continuous residual current necessary to charge the double layer at the drop surface. The magnitude of this current becomes comparable with that for reaction when the reactant concentration is about $10^{-5}M$. This has led to development of techniques in which the two components of current could be separated and to techniques in which either the charging current could be lowered or the reaction current made higher for a given system.

The problem of potential range is inherent in the ease of oxidation of mercury. In choosing other electrodes to avoid this problem one is led to other techniques to recoup losses in reproducibility incurred in forsaking mercury.

In the study of electrode reactions per se still other shortcomings are evident. The theory is unwieldy and very inexact, even in the simplest cases. This has led to refinements of the theory and to a quest for techniques which better lend themselves to theoretical analysis. The researcher is faced with chemical systems which can be roughly divided into two overlapping categories. First there is the simple, generally fast, reaction in which the major question is a quantitative measure of the rate. Second there is the multistep, generally slow, reaction in which the major question is one of mechanism. For both of these cases polarography is often inadequate. In the first, the difficulties arise because diffusion is relatively slow and thus becomes the limiting step at very low reaction rates. This means that reactions having fast rates, show no kinetic characteristics. In the second case, since the potential essentially changes not at all over the lifetime of a drop, it is impossible to investigate the electrochemical characteristics of intermediates or products.

The following discussion will be divided into four parts dealing firstly with conventional polarography and related methods, secondly with techniques particularly useful for simple reactions, thirdly with techniques useful for complex reactions, and fourthly with some example of results achieved with these techniques.

1. Polarography

The difficulties involved in the mathematical treatment of the dropping mercury electrode (DME) can be appreciated by perusal of the recent review article by Markowitz and Elving (145). Unfortunately some of the interpretations of these authors are dubious. Despite their protestations, for example, the treatments of McGillavry and Rideal (152) and of Ilkovic (86) are completely equivalent and lead to exactly the same results for concentrations and currents. Both of these approaches lead to rigorous solutions of the problem of diffusion to an expanding plane, though admittedly not always couched in mathematically precise terms. The difficulty with the expanding plane approximation is two-fold. First, near time zero the physical picture is one of a very thin column of solution sitting on a small electrode. As time increases the electrode expands and the column of liquid thickens as solution is transported to the electrode. At time zero the rate of transport is infinite and remains very high compared to that at the actual expanding sphere throughout early drop life. This causes the theoretical current to be high compared with that actually observed. The second difficulty with the plane approximation is that it seriously underestimates the amount of solution in close proximity to the electrode by neglecting the "pie-shaped" wedges present at the actual sphere. This effect is most important where drop curvature is greatest and leads to theoretical currents which are too low. Fortunately, both of these errors are worst at times early in drop life where currents are smallest and hence least important. Moreover they tend to cancel each other.

Many attempts have been made to improve on the original equation. Lingane and Loveridge (131), Strehlow and Von Stackelberg (191), Kambara and Tachi (96), and Matsuda (148) have made corrections ranging from completely empirical to reasonably rigorous for the spherical nature of the electrode. Markowitz and Elving (146) made correction for the fact that the concentration of the solution in the vicinity of the drop is decreased by electrolysis by prior drops. Matsuda took account of the shielding effect of the capillary tube on the upper portion of the drop. That this factor may be more important than is generally realized is indicated by Grahame's observation of anomalous frequency dependence for double layer capacitance using conventional shielded capillaries (69). Other possible corrections are still open to the mathematically minded, including movement of the drop center relative to the solution, lateral movement of the drop surface relative to the solution, change of drop shape during growth and change of rate of drop growth due to back pressure. Some of these factors have received experimental study. Bresle (24) directly measured rate of flow of mercury by dislodging drops at predetermined times. Bahary and Reinmuth (3) studied growth rate and shape by means of photography. One concludes that the effect of deviations of these factors from ideality is quite small.

As each new correction is suggested, its proponents invariably find data to substantiate their views. Independent workers, Meites (154) and Hans (75) for example, find, however, that their results do not seem to favor consistently any particular form of correction. The corrections generally do seem better than the original Ilkovic equation, but since they all contain more terms and often adjustable parameters as well, this may not reflect greater validity. There is still need for comparative tests of these theories using values of diffusion coefficients obtained independently.

Currents limited by chemical reaction have been considered in detail in recent years. The pioneering work of Brdicka and Weisner (21, 212) has been greatly extended and there are now available calculations dealing with almost every conceivable combination of diffusion, preceding and following chemical reaction. Koutecky and his co-workers (111) have made numerous contributions but others including

Von Stackelberg (206,207), Kuta (114,115), and Smutek (189) have also been active.

A number of workers have considered the form of the complete polarographic current–potential curve and the transition between reversible and irreversible processes. Tanaka and Tamamushi (197) extended the original Nernst diffusion layer treatment of Eyring and co-workers (48) to include cases of reaction preceded by rapid chemical equilibrium. Delahay (39) approximated the DME as a stationary plane. More recently Matsuda and Ayabe (149) extended the expanding plane approximation of Koutecky. All these treatments lead to essentially the same conclusions, although, because of its greater rigor, the last is to be preferred. Oldham, Kivalo, and Laitinen (163) have made a Lingane–Loveridge type correction to the equation for the complete reversible wave. This correction for most applications is negligible though these authors clearly demonstrated its correctness. Koutecky and Cizik (112) have made more sophisticated spherical corrections for the irreversible wave. As with the limiting currents there have been several experimental investigations which adequately confirmed the predictions of theory with regard to functional dependence on variables, the most complete one being that of Kivalo, Oldham, and Laitinen (104). The closest approach to an independent experimental verification of these equations is Randles' recent study (166). He compared the results from conventional and a.c. polarography for the same system (Vanadium II–III) under the same conditions and obtained good agreement between kinetic parameters derived from the two methods using Koutecky and Cizik's equation for conventional polarography. It would seem that more intercomparisons of this type would be very valuable in deciding the merits of various methods and their associated theories.

The relatively low limiting currents at the DME can be circumvented to some extent by simply increasing the concentration of the reactive species as Laitinen and co-workers have shown (104). Their method of working at the foot of an abnormally high polarographic wave is the polarographic equivalent of the potential–current density investigations which have been made since the time of Tafel.

One can increase the rate of mass transfer not only by increasing the concentration but by changing the mode of transfer from diffusion to convection by moving electrode, solution, or both. The simplest and earliest approach is the rotating platinum electrode of

Kolthoff and Laitinen (119). A major advance in the rotating electrode field was Lee's rotating mercury electrode (128). The most recent contribution is the rotating dropping mercury electrode of Kolthoff and Stricks (192). This electrode gives much greater sensitivity than the DME at the cost of some mechanical complication. It essentially turns the whole polarographic wave into a maximum. Because of the complicated conditions at the electrode surface and the necessity for the presence of surface active substances its major use probably lies in analysis rather than kinetic studies.

Another member of the same category is the streaming electrode devised by Heyrovsky (80) and given a thorough theoretical treatment by Weaver and Parry (211). Still another is the rotating disk of Levich (129).

The most energetic proponents of the stirred solution have been Jordan and his co-workers (93). These workers have used a number of experimental arrangements in which extremely high flow rates of solution past the electrode could be achieved. Although they are not practical for routine analytical application they offer a number of interesting possibilities in kinetic studies, especially in cases in which products formed in the electrode reaction would interfere with its continuance but here are swept away.

2. Techniques for Fast Reactions

To investigate the kinetic behavior of a simple electrochemical system requires some form of perturbation to drive it from its quiescent equilibrium position. The larger the magnitude of the perturbation the more time is required for return to equilibrium and thus the greater time is available for observation. On the other hand, large perturbations may produce unwanted effects as well. This consideration proves an important one in experimental practice. Several methods have been used but fundamentally they are all based on the notion of perturbing the system by small rapid changes of current or potential and observing the resultant phenomena. Two major categories can be distinguished, (a) those techniques in which a system at equilibrium is subjected to a step-functional change in voltage, potential, or current and the form of the resulting current or potential–time curve is analyzed, the so-called relaxation methods; and (b) methods in which small alternating (sinusoidal or square wave) potentials are imposed on normal d.c., and the a.c. components of the resulting potentials or currents are measured.

The relaxation methods have been used extensively by Gerischer and his co-workers in Germany, and by Delahay and his co-workers in this country. Three techniques have been employed in which the applied transient is one of constant cell voltage (voltostatic), constant electrode potential (potentiostatic), or constant current (galvanostatic). The voltostatic which is perhaps the easiest to apply experimentally, was perfected by Vielstich and Delahay (202). Unfortunately, part of the constant applied voltage is dissipated in ohmic potential drop in the cell and since the current varies with time the potential of the electrode becomes a complex function of time. The issue is also clouded by the fact that an appreciable fraction of the current, particularly early in the electrolysis, is not faradaic but goes to charging the electrical double layer. The major limitation of the technique is the difficulty in separating and analyzing the faradaic component of current. The problems become more pronounced at very short times and hence as higher rates of reaction are studied. A less obvious source of difficulty is that the theory of the method can only be handled simply when the voltage step is 2 to 5 mv. or less. These factors combine to place an upper limit of 10^{-1} cm. sec.$^{-1}$ on the rate constants which can be measured by the method. This, of course, compares very favorably with the 10^{-5} value observable polarographically, but the potentiostatic technique extends this range by an order of magnitude.

The potentiostatic method developed by Gerischer (62) uses a three electrode system in which the potential between the working electrode and a nonpolarized reference electrode is held constant by a fast responding potentiostat (62). Using fast oscilloscopic techniques, the time of investigation can be as short as a few microseconds. Experimentally, a number of difficulties are encountered at the upper limit. As in all relaxation methods, the data are extrapolated to time zero where complications due to mass transport phenomena are not present. Near time zero, however, the double layer capacitance must be charged. This places a number of practical limitations on the shortest times which can be measured. First, since the resistance of the potentiostat and associated circuitry is finite, a finite time is required to charge the double layer. In addition, the finite response speed of the potentiostat and the appreciable ohmic potential drop between the working and reference electrodes limits the precision of potential control at short times.

A method of circumventing some of these problems is by use of constant current (12) rather than constant potential. The circuitry is simple and though there is an error in potential measurement due to ohmic potential drop between reference and working electrode, that error is a constant one at a given current density and can be corrected. Careful consideration, however, indicates that the problems have been by no means eliminated. The time required to charge the double layer is relatively long because of the limitation of a constant charging current. Berzins and Delahay's original estimate of the upper limit of applicability was to rate constants of 1000 cm. sec.$^{-1}$, later revised to 100 cm. sec.$^{-1}$. It would appear that even this estimate might be too high by a factor of 10 or 100 in view of practical difficulties. The technique does have one advantage over the potentiostatic one. From a single potentiostatic experiment it is possible to obtain only the rate constant for the electrochemical reaction at a single potential. With the galvanostatic technique, since the potential varies during the experiment, it is possible to determine the rate of change of the rate constant with potential and thus the electron-transfer coefficient. Of course, the same information can be obtained potentiostatically by taking measurements at several different potentials, but, particularly with solid electrodes, this is often not easy to accomplish because of changes in surface character of the electrode.

Booman and Crittenden (17) have used a technique related to the potentiostatic one in which not the current, but its integral is measured over short times. Since the current is not observed directly there is difficulty in extrapolating to time zero but the method would seem to have merit in some applications.

The most sophisticated of the relaxation techniques is the double impulse method developed by Gerischer (59). This combines the best features of the galvanostatic and potentiostatic techniques by following a constant current pulse with a potentiostatic period. During the current pulse, the double layer is charged. The potentiostatic segment of the curve can then be studied without the usual difficulties due to charging of the double layer. The technique seems to be limited by the practical electronic problem of providing controlled current bursts of submicrosecond duration.

The relaxation techniques have a number of advantages. Theory and treatment of data are relatively simple. In addition, the faradaic process can be fairly well separated from the capacitive charging of the double layer. The upper limit of observable rates is extremely high. On the other hand, these advantages are achieved at the expense of a high degree of experimental complexity. Potentiostats and galvanostats of high response speed must be coupled with oscillographic observation of results. The a.c. techniques, in large measure, avoid the experimental difficulty by applying small alternating components of potential on the normal d.c. and then measuring the resulting a.c. components of current. Techniques for measuring these a.c. components are generally much more readily available and adaptable than those required for relaxation techniques.

The first of these techniques to receive attention was that employing sinusoidal potentials. As early as 1898, Warburg noted some of the properties of the circuit element represented by an electrode–solution interface at which a reaction is occurring. It was not until the late 1940's however, that this knowledge was applied to kinetic studies. Early workers viewed the equivalent circuit of the Warburg (faradaic) impedance as a resistance and capacitance in series, the polarization resistance and the pseudo-capacity. It should be emphasized that this model is an arbitrary one based purely on convenience. The most careful analysis based on it is probably that due to Grahame (72). Since the method of derivation assumes only linear circuit elements and no d.c. components to the current, the results can only be expected to give a first approximation to the true faradaic current. Unfortunately, except for the reversible case, the complexity of more rigorous derivations is forbidding. For the reversible case, they have been presented by Breyer and Hacobian (29), and in more detailed form by Senda and Tachi (186).

Several experimental approaches have been used. The most accurate is undoubtedly the bridge method pioneered in this application by Randles. Bridge a.c. measurements have been used concurrently, of course, by many workers in studies of the nonfaradaic components of current and double layer structure. The bridge method essentially gives measurements not only of current but of phase angle as well. Breyer and co-workers (25–29) measure directly the current and thus obtain no information concerning phase angle. Watanabe and co-workers (209) have measured only the capacitive component by a resonance method. In principle phase angle is an important variable for two reasons. First, currents due to charging the double layer and faradaic processes add vectorially, rather than arithmetically as in d.c. methods, because they are out of phase. To correct for "background" then, resolution is important. Also, in addition to faradaic processes, reversible processes of adsorption produce currents. It happens that the adsorption processes most strongly affect capacitance, whereas faradaic processes most strongly affect resistance, though both influence the over-all current to about the same extent. Thus, phase angle contributes some information on the relative magnitudes of their contributions. On the other hand, bridge methods require more care in manipulation and are not so suitable for routine analytical use or automatic monitoring as methods in which current is measured directly.

For reversible waves and small amplitudes of a.c., the current through the faradaic impedance gives the derivative of a conventional polarographic wave. This allows investigation of small peaks in close proximity to large ones and so is analytically advantageous. The current increases with the square root of the frequency but increasing frequency actually lowers the signal to noise ratio because of the vectorial addition of the double layer charging current. For totally irreversible waves, essentially no response is observed. This is a double edged sword. It means that no interference results from the presence of these species in determination of a reversible couple, but it also means that irreversible reductions cannot be investigated. Randles and Somerton (167), and Vetter (201) made early determinations of rate constants for electrochemical reactions. Gerisher used the method for studying chemical reactions preceding electron transfer. For kinetic studies the method is quite limited by the continuously changing potential. This factor makes accurate separation of faradaic and capacitive double layer effects almost completely impossible above 10^4 cps.

Though most work, in order to simplify theory, has assumed the faradaic impedance to be a linear circuit element and hence to generate no harmonics, some workers have used the generation of harmonics to advantage. For example, Müller and co-workers (160) determined half-wave potentials of reversible polarographic waves by looking for potentials at which generation of harmonics was a minimum. They did this visual inspection of an oscilloscope trace, a relatively insensitive method. Van Cakenberghe (200) and more recently Elving and Bauer (8) have directly measured the second harmonic component of current and determined transfer coefficients in this manner. Unfortunately, the results of Elving and Bauer differ quite markedly from earlier results of Gerischer and of Delahay, who use other methods of comparable systems. Since the latter workers do obtain consistent results and the theory of their method involves less onerous assumptions, suspicion falls on Elving and Bauer's results. The difficulty may be one of several. Elving and Bauer assume that the ration of oxidized to reduced form at the surface is given by the Nernst equation (despite their statements to the contrary) and further assume that the superimposition of a.c. potential has no effect on these concentrations. The first of these conditions implies no adsorption of oxidized or reduced forms, an assumption which remains to be proven. The second condition is not easily dismissed either, for Fournier (50) has shown that the superposition of an alternating potential can materially alter the characteristics of the d.c. polarogram. Kambara and Tachi (193), and Kambara (95) have given theoretical interpretations of the Fournier polarogram. The effect of superposition is essentially one of faradaic rectification and the result is a drawing out of the d.c. polarogram about its point of symmetry.

Just as superimposing a.c. potentials on d.c. leads to derivatives or pseudo-derivatives of d.c. polarograms, superimposing small a.c. currents on d.c. leads to derivatives or pseudo-derivatives of normal chronopotentiograms. Recently Snead and Remick (190), and Takemori, Kambara, Senda, and Tachi (194) have revived this method which was originally discussed by Rosebrugh and Lash-Miller (175) in 1910.

Several difficulties emerge in use of sine wave techniques. Whereas with relaxation methods the current passes in only one direction and thus the net direction of reaction is known, in sine waves the facts are not quite so clear. With complicated reaction schemes the danger exists of obtaining apparent values of rate constants and transfer coefficients which may not be simply interpretable.

The practical difficulties of the sine wave technique center around the difficulty in resolution of the capacitive and faradaic components of current. To minimize this problem some workers have used square waves instead. The capacitive component decays early in the square wave step and by measuring current only after the initial decay.

difficulties from this source can be circumvented to a large extent. Barker and Jenkins (4,5) were among the earliest to make use of this principle. The theory of the method was developed by Kambara (95) and by Barker (5). The method gives essentially the same information as the sine wave method.

Recently, Barker (5) developed a new technique which he terms r.f. polarography. In this method a small radiofrequency (100 kc. to 10 mc.) sine wave is 100% modulated with an audio frequency square wave all superimposed on the normal d.c. polarizing voltage. The audio frequency component of the resulting current is measured. This component results from the rectifying effect of the faradaic impedence on the r.f. signal. Because the frequency of the r.f. component is so high the method offers, in principle, the possibility of determining very high reaction rates (20 cm. sec. $^{-1}$). The difficulties, however, are the same as those in the method of Van Cakenberghe. Results again differ (for transfer coefficients in particular) quite markedly from those obtained by seemingly more reliable methods. The method, however, certainly warrants further development on its merits as an analytical tool and it is to be hoped that the theoretical ambiguities will soon be resolved. Barker has suggested yet another technique—f.m. polarography—in which, not the amplitude, but the frequency of the applied r.f. signal would be used to tune in reactions of a given rate to the partial or complete exclusion of those at higher or lower rates.

All of the relaxation and a.c. methods cited above have common faults. They are useful for the characterization of electrode reactions only when these reactions have relatively simple kinetic schemes. In addition, the techniques are not useful for systems which are totally irreversible, in some cases because of theoretical and in other cases practical difficulties.

3. Techniques for Complex Reactions

In order to investigate the kinetics of complex reactions it is advantageous to vary the potential of an electrode over a wide range in a short time. This is so because the hope of finding intermediates in a complicated reaction scheme is that they will be reactive at potentials at which the starting material is not. Thus they must be generated at the potential of reaction of the reactant and then sought at other potentials before they can undergo further reaction. A number of methods are available for this purpose. The simplest experimentally, is probably the application of a large amplitude sine wave potential. In Silverman and Remick's technique (187) the resulting current is displayed on the horizontal plates of an oscilloscope and the potential is plotted on the vertical. In Heyrovsky's method (81) a sine wave current rather than potential is applied to the cell and the potential is displayed versus time or applied current, or the derivative of potential is displayed versus time or applied current. These displays yield peculiarly distorted Lissajou figures which are very useful for qualitative studies because of the simplicity of the apparatus required. They have been used for quantitative analytical applications but any number of other methods including conventional polarography would seem better suited to that purpose. Their use in kinetic studies has been limited by the fact that many workers are loathe to apply a method for which no quantitative theoretical treatment is available. It need hardly be noted, however, that much valuable information can none the less be obtained.

A more widely accepted method is the Randles-Sevcik (168,188) oscillographic method in which a saw-tooth voltage is applied and the current observed. These two workers as well as Delahay (43), Delahay and Berzins (13), and Matsuda and Ayabe (150) have considered the theory for a plane electrode. This theory applies also to electrodes of other shapes at oscillographic rates of scan. Frankenthal and Shain (51), and Reinmuth (171) have considered spherical electrodes and Nicholson (162) has considered cylinders. Loveland and Elving (140), Shain and co-workers (177), and Kemula and co-workers (101,102) have applied the technique to analysis and the elucidation of electrode kinetics. By comparison of forward and reverse scans the degree of reversibility can be ascertained. By variation of peak current with rate of potential scan the mode of mass transfer can be determined. For study of the kinetics of fast reactions, fast rates of scan can be employed and the results displayed oscillographically. However, since the capacitive current is directly proportional to the rate of scan and faradaic current is proportional to the square root, in terms of inherent accuracy as well as simplicity of equipment, analytical work is best done at slow scan rates (5 v./min.) and observed with conventional polarographic equipment using a hanging drop. Sensitivity is somewhat greater than for conventional polarography.

Another method which has come back into fashion after a 50 year lapse is chronopotentiometry—the passage of constant current and observation of the resulting current time curve. The method yields results very similar to those of conventional polarography except that for the fact that the variable current in polarography is equivalent to the variable square root of time in chronopotentiometry. The advantages over polarography are three-fold. In chronopotentiometry one can vary current density over a several thousand-fold range and thus investigate kinetically limited waves in detail. The analogous variable in polarography, drop time, can be changed only by a factor of two or three. The second advantage is that of being able to reverse the current during a chronopotentiogram and so observe both anodic and cathodic processes. The third advantage, and a major one it is in kinetic studies, is the relative simplicity of exact theoretical treatment. Gierst and Juliard (67), Delahay and co-workers (44, 45), and Kambara and Tachi (97) have contributed to the theory and made kinetic studies. Reilley and co-workers (169) have considered the analytical applications. For analytical purposes the technique offers little advantage over conventional polarography and, in fact, has somewhat lower sensitivity and reproducibility with standard equipment. It does offer advantages in use with solid electrodes with respect to reproducibility.

The Kalousek (94) technique in which a large amplitude square wave is superimposed on the conventional d.c. polarogram has been all but ignored by other workers. An audio frequency square wave is applied to the electrode. The voltage for one half cycle is held constant and that for the other half cycle is varied at its conventional polarographic rate. The current during one or the other half cycle is observed. The result is a polarogram which resembles a conventional one except that it is, for reversible reductions, more sensitive by a factor of approximately twenty (depending on the square root of the frequency). Depending upon the reference voltage, the wave may be anodic, cathodic, or mixed even thouth the solution originally contains only one species. Reversibility in this sense requires that the direction of the reaction be reversible on passing from one half cycle to the other, a potential change which may be as large as a volt or more, so that the restriction is not nearly so severe as in the case of the small potential a.c. techniques. A practical difficulty which has been discussed by Buchanan and by Tachi and Okuda is the somewhat peculiar behavior of the DME with respect to drop-time under the influence of large amplitude a.c. potentials.

4. Some Experimental Studies

Exemplifying the simple fast reaction are reductions of simple metal ions and complex ions which need not undergo prior dissociation. The earliest studies of these systems were those of Randles with small sine wave techniques (165). Later Randles and Somerton (167), Vetter (201), and Gerischer (60) advanced this work. Randles, for example, reported that the rate constants for reduction of cadmium decreased with gelatin coverage of the electrode and that the rate of reduction of zinc increased when polarizable anions were added to the solution. Both of these substances give reversible waves in conventional polarography.

The sine wave technique is less satisfactory in cases in which chemical reaction may precede electron transfer because the measured variables are relatively insensitive to such complications. Gierst and Juliard (67) found chronopotentiometry eminently suited to such applications; Delahay and co-workers (44–46) also made contribution. Mamantov and Delahay (38) concluded, for example, that reduction of zinc tetrammine required prior dissociation while that of copper bisethylenediammine did not.

Gerischer and co-workers (63) and Mehl and Bockris (153) have concerned themselves with simple metal deposition reactions. Here electron transfer is extremely rapid and potentiostatic methods have been employed. They concluded that the deposition process is a two step reaction; reduction to an adsorbed metal atom on the surface followed by diffusion across the surface to lattice sites. Gerischer (63) also concluded from his studies that the adsorbed atom concentration on the surface changes with potential and that therefore the bonds with the surface are partially ionic in character.

In the analysis of complex reactions large sine wave and saw-tooth potential scans have been used very successfully. Excellent recent examples can be found in the work of Kemula and co-workers (101,102). They observed that reduction of nitrobenzene led to phenyl hydroxylamine. This, when reoxidized, gave nitrosobenzene and various chemical reactions were possible between reactants and products. They found in some cases that with very rapid scan rates new waves appeared, waves apparently due to intermediates impossible to observe ordinarily because their rate of decomposition is so rapid. Imai (87) studied the reduction of cadmium in the presence of oxygen by saw-tooth polarography and found peculiarly enhanced currents which he attributed to the formation of colloidal cadmium hydroxide, the hydroxyl ion coming from reduction of the oxygen. Elving and co-workers have essentially repeated this work (98).

Vlcek (205) has applied the Kalousek square wave technique in conjunction with conventional and large sine wave polarography to the study of nickel cyanide. His interesting results lead to the conclusion that the reduction proceeds with the formation of a zero valent nickel complex and its subsequent decomposition.

IV. ELECTRODE MATERIALS

There have been, in recent years, a number of investigations on the effect of the nature of the electrode on electrochemical processes occurring at its surface. The many possible forms of influence can be divided into two arbitrary categories, one depending on the physical characteristics of the electrode and the other on its characteristics as a chemical reagent.

Insofar as the electrode is not chemically involved in an electrochemical reaction it can not influence the *equilibrium* products of that reaction. However, it can influence the rate of reaction and, if the electrode process is not reversible, the nature of the products as well.

The most obvious point of influence on the rate of reaction is the surface area of the electrode. It is well known that differences in hydrogen overvoltage on smooth and platinized platinum electrodes can be explained in terms of their effective surface areas even when the projected surface areas are equal. Unfortunately, there is no single unambiguous value of the surface area of most solid electrodes simply because the value obtained depends on the method of measurement chosen. For example, an electrolysis taking place over a period long enough that the thickness of the diffusion layer is large compared with surface unevenness would be influenced by the projected geometric area, while for electrolysis in short times the total area should be used. This factor becomes important in such techniques as chronopotentiometry at high current densities and has been suggested as an explanation of the anomalous frequency dependence of differential capacitance measurements at solid electrodes (181). In part, because of the ambiguity of definition of surface area and in part, because of the difficulty in preparing reproducible solid metal surfaces very little work has been done on determination of these surface areas. Bowden and Rideal (20), and Wagner (208) early described methods involving essentially measurement of double layer capacities and more recently Brodd and Hackerman (30) have compared areas determined from this type of measurement with areas determined by low temperature gas adsorption and found that the two methods gave comparable values.

Unevenness at the electrode can produce other types of influence on the reaction. If the electrode reaction were followed by a second order chemical reaction in competition with a first order process e.g., the Kolbe synthesis, an uneven electrode surface might well favor the second order process. An uneven surface also creates inhomogeneous electrical fields in such a way that reaction might be favored at selected "active" sites. For the most part, one can merely conjecture about the importance of these effects. Recently, however, Gerischer and Krause (59) have compared rates of reaction of liquid and solid mercury at low temperature. They found no appreciable difference in the case of deposition of mercury. It would seem that further studies of this sort should lead to much useful information on surface roughness.

It has long been recognized that the homogeneous nature of liquid-metal surfaces offers unique advantages in the study of electrochemical processes. Near room temperature, however, the available selection is severely limited. Several groups of workers have tried Wood's metal and gallium with such conspicuous lack of success that most of the work has never been published. The major problem with such materials seems to be oxide formation (68). Recently, Grahame (71) has succeeded in making double layer capacitance measurements with very pure gallium. Work with this electrode should prove most interesting because, through comparison with results on mercury, it permits direct investigation of the effect of the chemical nature of the electrode on reaction without the added complication from physical surface effects found in solids.

Particularly at solid electrodes it is often true that electrolysis of the solvent or supporting electrolyte occurs concurrently with, or in preference to, the reaction of species of interest. When such cases occur, the question invariably arises as to whether the end product is the result of a primary electrochemical reaction of the reactive species, or of a chemical reaction involving hydrogen atoms or other intermediates in the oxidation or reduction of the solvent.

At the mercury electrode the electrochemical reaction seems generally to be a direct one. At solid electrodes evidence is not nearly so conclusive. Apparently many anodic substitutions are the result of secondary chemical reactions but most reductions and some oxidations are primary reactions. Those unschooled in the theory of electrochemical preparations often control current density in an effort to obtain comparable reaction conditions at different electrodes. The critical variable is, of course, potential and the relationship between it and current density is often tied directly to the solvent decomposition potential which is very much dependent on electrode material.

As has been pointed out, the structure of the double layer at the electrode surface can have an important influence on the electrode process. The nature of the electrode material determines to a large extent the nature of this layer. This influence has several causes. First, the potential of zero charge of the electrode is a direct function of the electronic work function of the electrode material. This idea has been expressed by many authors, most recently by Rüetschi and Delahay (179). A second source of influence is the fact that specific adsorption of electrocapillary active ions often seems to depend on bond or quasibond formation between the electrode and the adsorbed species (18). Insofar as bond strengths differ from one metal to another, double layer structure should differ. Unfortunately, thus far there seems to be little, if any, data of sufficient accuracy on electrodes, other than mercury, to determine the importance of this factor. A third influence on double layer structure is through the adsorption of solvent at the electrode surface. Bockris and Conway (15) have recently given a theoretical treatment of this factor for copper electrodes. They note the higher heat of adsorption of water on solids than on mercury and suggest that this accounts for the relatively high double layer resistance and abnormal dependence of current on frequency at solid electrodes as opposed to mercury.

In many cases, so-called inert electrodes do in fact undergo at least limited chemical or electrochemical reaction. In the course of this reaction coatings may be produced on the electrode surface which can affect reaction. With platinum electrodes, for example, the presence of oxide or adsorbed oxygen films was postulated as early as 1929 and evidence consistent with such postulates appeared much earlier than that. Extensive electrochemical studies of these films have been made over many years. As excellent one is that of Kolthoff and Tanaka (106). It has only been very recently, however, that Anson and Lingane (2) by direct chemical analysis obtained persuasive evidence that the films were platinous and platinic oxides rather than adsorbed atomic or molecular oxygen. This film formation has two major ramifications. Firstly, the presence of the film passivates the electrode. Secondly, it offers an indirect mechanism by which electrode reactions can take place. Kolthoff and Nightengale (107) studied the effect of pretreatment of platinum electrodes on the potential of a ferrous–ferric couple. They concluded, in agreement with previous workers (119,132) that the presence of an oxide film increases reversibility of some electrode reactions. On the other hand Kolthoff and Tanaka's work shows that oxidation of adsorbed hydrogen is inhibited by the film. Ross and Shain (176) have associated the potential drifts observed during titrations with the same film formation. Lee, Adams, and Bricker (127) independently reached much the same conclusions in studies including gold and palladium as well as platinum electrodes and Baumann and Shain (9) also studied gold electrodes. The last authors noted that chromate reduction was inhibited by oxide films on a platinum electrode. They suggested gold as an alternative to platinum for "inert" electrodes.

Strangely enough, although oxide films on platinum have been studied actively for many years the analogous case of halide films on the more commonly used mercury electrode has received but scant attention, although passivization of mercury electrodes under conditions of anodic polarization in chloride media was known as early as 1936 (178), and Boult and Thirsk studied the physical structure of the film in 1954 (19), it has only been quite recently that Kuwana and Adams (116,117), and Kemula and co-workers (99) have made use of the phenomenon to extend the useful range of mercury electrodes in chronopotentiometry and hanging drop polarography to potentials as anodic as those available with platinum. Though Kuwana and Adams reported oxidation of a number of organic compounds in the presence of the film, Kemula (100) had much less success with such cases and the published work was limited to oxidation of deposited metals. Certainly the phenomenon deserves more attention than it has received, not only as an analytical tool and as a model for studying effects of surface films on reactivity, but also as a model for studying the nature of the passivization process.

The passivization phenomenon is, of course, of vital practical interest. Unfortunately, studies are plagued by the irreproducible surfaces of solid metals of commercial importance. Probably because of the experimental difficulties, there is still considerable disagreement concerning the mechanisms by which the phenomenon occurs, as is witnessed by the tenor of papers presented at the recent international symposium (89).

Strong oxidizing agents may, in some cases, be reduced by chemical reaction with the electrode followed by electrochemical reduction of the oxidized electrode material. Kivalo and Laitinen (105) proposed this mechanism for reduction of several platinum complexes at the DME. Their scheme seems unlikely for the particular cases they chose in view of the arguments of Nikolajeva and Frumkin (57), but this type of mechanism may be valid in other cases.

V. EFFECTS OF STRUCTURE ON REACTIVITY

One of the more challenging aspects of modern electrochemistry is the question of the effect of structure on reactivity. Of very great importance in the interpretation of the reactions of inorganic complexes is the symmetry principle formulated by Libby (130). He showed with arguments based on the Franck–Condon principle that the relative rates of electron-transfer and solvation or ligand shell rearrangement must be of the order of 200:1 or greater. Thus the coordination sphere must rearrange to conform to the changed electronic structure either before or after electron-transfer. This may present a considerable barrier to reaction. On this basis Libby stated that electron-exchange should be rapid for cases in which the geometrical configuration in initial and final states is the same within the zero point vibrational amplitude. Thus ferri–ferrocyanide and manganate–permanganate, in which this condition is satisfied, have rapid electrode reactions. For electron-exchange in solution this principle implies that the symmetrical state should be readily accessible to the most stable states of both the oxidized and reduced forms. For an electrode reaction, however, the restriction is not so stringent. All that is necessary is that there be a state of the product which is reasonably stable, not that it be in rapid equilibrium with the lowest energy state of the product. For example, the exchange reaction between hexammine cobalt(II) and (III) in solution is slow, despite the fact that the complexes are identical in constitution because the former is an outer and the latter an inner orbital complex (Co–N bond distances vary 0.6 A. between the two (31)). The inner orbital cobalt(II) configuration, however, though lying in energy above the outer orbital complex is still evidently metastable so that the electron-transfer is reversible but rapidly followed by irreversible internal rearrangement of the initially formed inner orbital to the more stable outer orbital complex (120).

Lyons (141,142) and Vlcek (204) have extended these ideas; Lyons with particular reference to deposition reactions and Vlcek with reference to reactions in which both oxidized and reduced forms are soluble. In cases in which the two forms have no stable or metastable symmetric states they considered the next further removed possibilities, those of unstable symmetric states or chemical reactions preceding electron-transfer which might lead to symmetric states.

Since the actual physical electron-transfer process is very rapid, a slow electron-transfer process must be interpreted as being one in which the rearrangement of configuration which is a prerequisite for the electron-transfer occurs only slowly.

Vlcek, on the basis of Taube's (198) characterization of complex reactions in solution, suggests that complexes with vacant inner d orbitals are reduced by accepting electrons into these orbitals when the resulting structures are stable. If the inner orbitals are filled, then outer d positions can take electrons often followed by internal rearrangement. If inner d orbitals are vacant but resulting structures are unstable, there may be transient acceptance of electrons followed by internal rearrangement. With labile complexes there may be dissociation leading to a vacant orbital prior to electron-transfer. On the basis of present evidence the first alternative is favored whenever possible. Which of the last three possibilities will occur in any given situation depends on the specific energetics of the case.

These energetics are determined not only by the nature and oxidation state of the central ion but also by the ligands around it. Thus, as Libby pointed out, it is possible to catalyze exchange (or electrode) reactions by putting the metal species in a medium in which symmetry may be more easily achieved. Vlcek makes the interesting observation that the nature of the substituents has no apparent influence on reducibility except insofar as it affects the electronic structure. This fact, if true, indicates that the coordination sphere does not offer a barrier to electron-transfer to the central ion.

Grahame (70) has pointed out that there is a fundamental difference between deposition and reductions in which both species are soluble in solution. In the latter case there must be electron-transfer whereas the former reaction could occur without the electrons ever leaving the metallic phase. Despite the possibility of this occurrence it remains to be proven that such a mechanism is ever operative. First, such a mechanism would require complete desolvation prior to reaction, a process which seems energetically out of the realm of possibility. Second, there seems to be considerable evidence favoring stepwise addition of electrons. Kleinberg, Davidson, and co-workers (33,126,151) have found much evidence for intermediate oxidation states in the oxidation of magnesium, aluminum, and beryllium. Imai and Sunahara (88) found evidence for zinc(I). Sanborn and Orleman (180) found evidence for nickel(I) and some of the work of Imai (87) can be interpreted as indicating the presence of cadmium(I), though such an interpretation was not made by that author. Vlcek (203) has also shown that the reduction of nickel cyanide proceeds through a zero valent complex. To be sure, positive evidence in favor of direct one step reduction would be much more difficult to obtain so that these cases need not indicate that stepwise reduction by electron-transfer is a general phenomenon. Nevertheless, the facts do seem to mitigate against a picture of the deposition process as simple as that suggested by Grahame.

The effect of structure on the reduction of organic compounds is not nearly so well characterized as that of the inorganics, undoubtedly because the electronic structures of these species do not lend themselves so readily to simple interpretation. Indeed, a major portion of the work which has been done is concerned with aromatic hydrocarbons, species for which information about electronic energy levels is available.

Maccoll (143) first made a correlation between electronic spectra and polarographic half-wave potentials for this class of compounds. This correlation was refined and extended by Watson and Matsen (210), and by Bergman (10). The frequency of the p band in these spectra can be shown to be a measure of the energy required to put an electron in the lowest energy unoccupied molecular orbital.

Hoijtink and co-workers (82,83), Basu (6,7), and Fernandez-Alonso and Domingo (49) have made the same type of correlation but using quantum mechanically calculated electronic energies rather than experimental estimates.

Correlations of these types would be expected to be most useful for reversible reactions where only the initial and final states need be considered. Even in these cases it is assumed that entropy contributions are not very different for the members of the series compared. In irreversible cases the correlation will be successful only insofar as the transition states are similar for each member of the series. This implies not only the necessity for the same reaction mechanism throughout the series compared but also the same environment for reaction, that is the effect of double layer structure at the electrode surface must be considered. Rogers and co-workers (172) have cited cases where this influence was not considered. A further complication which should not be overlooked is adsorption prior to reaction.

Unfortunately, for most organic compounds electronic energy calculations are not available. For such cases one can hope to relate reactivity only qualitatively with structure or at best to use the Hammett or other modified free energy function. Many authors have made such correlations and they seem applicable in a wide number of cases. The same dangers are inherent in these treatments as in those discussed above. Iredale (90) has correlated nuclear quadrapole coupling frequencies for iodo compounds with polarographic half-wave potentials. These frequencies are roughly related to the ionic character of the C–I bond. Presumably correlation could also be made with other physical constants related to Hammett σ values (91).

Relatively few studies of steric and other related structural characteristics on reactivity have been attempted. Elving and co-workers (47) have done work along these lines with various haloorganics. More recently Lambert and Kobayashi (124) have made similar studies.

VI. EFFECT OF SOLVENT

Water is the most important solvent for electrochemical studies but many others have been tried. The considerations which govern choice of solvent are numerous. First, there is the obvious requirement that the resulting solution must have a reasonably low resistance. Instrumentally this is not so great a problem as it once was because of the advent of three electrode systems and ohmic drop compensators. Nevertheless, it eliminates a large number of otherwise inviting solvents.

Second, the solvent should dissolve the species of interest. In the study of organic compounds in particular, alcohols, dioxane, acetonitrile, acetic acid, dimethyl formamide, and others can be used to advantage. In techniques in which the electrode surface is not constantly renewed insoluble products of reaction sometimes foul the electrode surface and produce undesired side effects. For this reason results in organic solvents are often more readily interpretable than those in water. With inorganic salts the opposite problem occurs. Hydrated cations are often not readily reduced. Organic solvents and fused salt media can then be employed to advantage, though the experimental difficulties of working in the latter systems are challenging.

The useful potential range of any solvent is limited by its ease of oxidation and reduction. For the reduction of alkali metals, for example, acetonitrile offers much wider possibilities than water, particularly with the use of solid electrodes. Some organics, the reactions of which are obscured by hydrogen discharge in water, can be studied effectively as well. In addition, in less reactive solvents than water reactive intermediates become more stable and hence are more easily studied.

Electrochemical studies in nonaqueous solvents have been applied to the study of two major problems, the nature of the solvent per se, and the nature of the solvation process in these solvents. One of the more interesting studies in the former category is that of Jordan and co-workers (92). These authors corrected diffusion coefficients of oxygen obtained polarographically in sucrose–water and glycerol–water mixtures for the varying activity of oxygen in the solvent. They found that with these corrections, the Stokes–Einstein equation was obeyed until the concentration of water became so high that its "ice-like" structure could be maintained.

There have been several studies in the latter category. One is that of Bruss and DeVries (32). These authors made a systematic study of a large number of metal ions in various solvents. They concluded that the major effect of solvent in these cases was the change of dielectric constant. In some cases the Stokes-Einstein relation was well obeyed by the diffusing species, in other cases linear plots were obtained between diffusion coefficient and reciprocal square root of viscosity but they did not extrapolate to the origin. Kolthoff and Coetzee (108) made extensive investigation into the relative behavior of metal ions in acetonitrile and water. These authors based their explanations of the differences largely on the relative basicity of the two solvents. They found that particularly with ions strongly hydrated in water (e.g., cobalt and nickel), reduction was easier in acetonitrile. On the other hand, cuprous copper and silver which complex with acetonitrile are more difficult to reduce. Schaap and co-workers (182) found that in ethylenediamine the relative ease of reduction of a number of metal ions correlated well with the stabilities of their ethylenediamine complexes in water. Thus it would seem that in any given case specific solvent interaction, solvation, and dielectric constant can all play important roles.

For organic reductions, specific interactions of solvent with reducible species are much less likely. Thus in aprotic solvents solubility effects seem generally determinative. In proton donating solvents acidity often plays an important role since most organic redox reactions are strongly proton dependent.

VII. SALT EFFECTS

Almost invariably, techniques for the study of electrode reactions require the presence in solution of large excesses of supporting electrolytes. Thus it becomes important to inquire how, and to what extent these salts affect the electrode process. One may first distinguish between effects on the electrode reaction per se and those on the mass transfer process.

In very low concentrations of salts or in their absence the mode of mass transfer is no longer solely diffusion in the case of ions but there is a noticeable contribution from migration of these charged species in the ohmic electric field. Although isolated examples have been reported, it would seem that this factor might be more commonly used to advantage as a diagnostic criterion in the study of mechanisms of reactions. From an analytical viewpoint, of course, the phenomenon is undesirable because the observed currents depend on the inert salt concentration as well as the concentration of reducible species if the supporting electrolyte is not in sufficiently large excess. For conventional polarography it is well recognized that a fifty-fold excess of salt is generally sufficient. It does not seem to be commonly appreciated, however, that for kinetic techniques in which the current density is much higher, particularly chronopotentiometry, that much larger excesses may be required and that considerable differences between theory and experiment can result from overlooking this insidious detail. In very high salt concentrations the viscosity of the solvent may change materially, generally in the direction of decreased diffusion coefficients and hence smaller limiting currents. The effect is more pronounced in the cases of stirred solutions or moving electrodes because flow characteristics are strongly dependent on viscosity.

Salt effects on the electron-transfer process are in general due to some influence on the chemical or physical environment of the reacting species. Such effects can be divided into two categories: (a) effects on the initial and final products of reaction which can be treated thermodynamically, and (b) effects on the activated intermediates which affect the rates of reaction.

Effects of the first type have been known for many years with early studies by potentiometry going back to the turn of the century. One effect is the specific chemical interaction between the electrolyte and the reacting species. Complexation, acid–base interaction, and ion-pair formation are the major interactions of this type and they can be treated quantitatively by equilibrium expressions when the equilibria are fast compared to the electron's transfer, or by well known kinetic equations when they are not. Nonspecific interactions of the Debye–Hückel type are also well known and can be treated quantitatively too. Some complication is introduced in both cases because of the liquid–junction potential but experimentally this factor can be minimized and conventionally, because of problems in its treatment, it is ignored.

Effects of salts on the activated complex can be divided into two categories analogous to those for interactions in solution. Specific effects in this case are chemical interactions which can occur only at the electrode surface, i.e., bridging complexes or adsorption of the reacting species on the electrode, or interactions of such a transient nature as to be unimportant in the bulk of the solution. Nonspecific effects at the electrode surface are due to the influence of salts on the structure of the electrical double layer. In principle they can be treated in much the same fashion as Debye–Hückel interactions in solution but in practice considerable complication is involved.

The work of Taube (198A) and his co-workers on redox reactions of complex ions in solution has led to much speculation concerning the possibility of ion-bridges facilitating electron-transfer between the electrode and the reactant. The mechanism has been suggested often: Lyons (141), Delahay (40), Reilley (184) and Frumkin (55). Unfortunately, all evidence thus far has been indirect, an apparent first order dependence of the reduction on salt concentration where complexation was not probable. In fact each case could be explained on the basis of ion-pair formation between salt and reactive species without introducing the concept of a bridge at all. This is not to minimize the importance of the concept or its possible validity but merely to suggest that the present evidence for such a mechanism is by no means conclusive. The above cited work, and much other as well, seems to indicate the importance of ion-pair formation prior to reduction and also indicates that this ion-pair formation becomes more important in reduction of negatively charged species. Reilley and co-workers (147,170) have undertaken systematic studies of reductions of metal chelates of similar structure, and have rather strikingly demonstrated the importance of neutralization of charge through ion-pair formation prior to reduction when the reaction takes place at potentials at which the electrode is negative with respect to the solution, i.e., on the cathodic side of the electrocapillary maximum.

The effect of double layer structure on reduction, the nonspecific salt effect, was postulated as early as 1933 by Frumkin (52) for the hydrogen evolution reaction. The suggestion seems to have been generally overlooked or discounted until relatively recently probably because of the well justified suspicion with which all early data on the hydrogen evolution reaction were viewed. Later, Frumkin (53) applied the same idea to anions and came to the startling conclusion that on the cathodic side of the electrocapillary maximum (ecm) it is possible for rate constants of electrochemical reductions to decrease as the potential becomes more cathodic. This is so because the increasing electrostatic repulsion of electrode for anion, especially for highly charged species, more than outweighs the increased activity of the electrons in the electrode. Most of the work of Frumkin and his co-workers has dealt with the reduction of persulfate. This case is a somewhat suspicious one because of the possibility of chemical reaction between the electrode and the reducible species. Other experimental work dealing with ferricyanide has been strongly disputed by Kivalo (103). Ideas similar to those of Frumkin have been advanced by many other workers including Randles (167), Gerischer (61), Laitinen and Onstott (122), Bockris (16), de Bethune (14), Heyrovsky (80), Delahay and co-workers (23), and Rogers and co-workers (172).

The influence of salts in these cases can be of two types depending upon whether these salts are adsorbed on the electrode surface, i.e.. their plane of closest approach corresponds to an unhydrated radius, or whether they form simply a diffuse double layer, i.e., remain hydrated at the surface. In general, on the cathodic side of the ecm cations form the inner layer of the double layer and are not adsorbed. In this potential region addition of salt makes the potential at the site of reaction more positive. The effect of this change in potential at the reaction site can be arbitrarily broken into two components. First, the potential difference between the reaction site and electrode is increased, thus facilitating electron-transfer. Second, the change in potential at the surface affects the concentration of the reacting species if it is charged, adversely if it is a positive species, beneficially if it is negative. Generally these two effects are not compensatory and particularly in the case of highly charged anions the rates of reduction are markedly increased by increasing salt concentration. On the anodic side of the ecm the effect is qualitatively the same except that anions form the inner double layer and the potential becomes more negative on salt addition. Quantitatively, however, the picture changes considerably because anions are generally adsorbed and hence their effect on the potential is much greater. In addition, whereas the cation effect varies little with different cations the anion effect depends very strongly on the nature of the anion, e.g., iodide > chloride > fluoride, the more strongly sorbed species having the greater influence. Gierst (66), Delahay and co-workers (23), and Rogers and co-workers (172) have discussed the nature of this influence on polarographic halfwave potentials, the last authors also presented data for slopes of waves.

Experimentally and theoretically, interpretation of salt effect data offers many difficulties. For example, in the case of reduction of a singly charged anion with a diffuse double layer present the predicted salt effect is essentially the same whether the mechanism is a non-specific double layer effect or ion-pair formation prior to reduction. This has led Reinmuth (173) and Reiley and Martin (147,170) to question the interpretation of Delahay and co-workers for the reduction of iodate.

Quantitative comparison of theory and experiment for these inter-actions requires some estimate of the potential at the reaction site. Some authors have used the results of double layer theory to make such estimates. Frumkin (58) questions this type of treatment be-cause he feels that average potentials calculated in this fashion do not give realistic pictures of the actual potentials at the reactive site. Certainly his data in which negative ions influence the reduction of persulfate on the negative side of the ecm can not be readily inter-preted on a simple double layer picture.

VIII. SURFACE-ACTIVE AGENTS

Much interest has centered recently on the adsorption of surface active species at electrode solution interfaces. The work can be readily divided into two categories: (a) those studies dealing with the nature of the adsorption process, and (b) those dealing with the effect of adsorption on electrode reactions. Studies of adsorption equilibrium at metal–solution interfaces were first undertaken by Guoy over 50 years ago. Occasional papers have appeared in the intervening years with a noticeable quickening of the pace after World War II. Qualitatively, the behavior of neutral surface active species is as follows: they are adsorbed relatively strongly in the potential region around the ecm but are desorbed at potentials farther removed on either side because of the strong electrostatic attraction between ions of electrolytes or oriented solvent dipoles and the charged electrode surface. For charged species, the adsorp-tion curves are shifted anodically or cathodically according to the charge, e.g., tributyl amine is desorbed on the cathodic side of the ecm at -1.3 v. versus SCE, while the positively charged tetrabutylammonium ion is desorbed at -1.8 v. (15). The desorption process generally takes place over a relatively narrow potential range.

1. Methods of Study

Most studies of adsorption phenomena have been conducted at mercury electrodes because of the relative ease with which they can be prepared and manipulated. Since the principles are the same in any event, only mercury work will be discussed here. Much of the earliest work was done by measuring the interfacial tension as a function of potential. This method was later largely supplanted by bridge measurements of impedance of the electrode to small (5 to 50 mv.) a.c. potentials superimposed on d.c. (69). This type of measurement is by far the most accurate method available, but Breyer (25–29) and others have obtained similar information more conveniently by simply measuring the a.c. current produced. Loveland and Elving (140) used voltammetry with linearly changing potential with high rates of potential scan for the same purpose. It should be pointed out that neither of the last two methods gives the phase characteristics of the current through the interface, often an importance diagnostic criterion. On adsorption of surface active species, the differential capacity curve is considerably depressed from its normal value in electrolyte solutions because of the lower dielectric constant and increased separation of charge at the interface. At potentials of desorption large peaks occur in the capacity curves. These represent a pseudo-capacity (69) akin to that observed in the presence of a reversible electrode reaction. These peaks have been termed "tensammetric waves" by Breyer and Hacobian (26). The same desorption process is responsible for the polarographic pseudo-wave observed in the presence of, e.g., camphor at about -1.6 v. versus SCE. Loveland and Elving used an empirical relation between desorption potential and concentration as the basis for a quantitative determination of several alcohols. Breyer and Hacobian (26) determined tungstate from an empirical relation between concentration and tensammetric wave height.

2. Quantitative Equilibrium Studies

Despite the wealth of qualitative information, it is only very recently that the adsorption process has been characterized quantitatively. Hansen, Minturn, and Hickson (76) extended the early theory of Frumkin (54) to the calculation of adsorption isotherms from capacitance measurements. Later these same authors (77), Delahay and Trachtenberg (41), and Laitinen and Mosier (121) made measurements on a number of surface active agents.

The treatment of Hansen and co-workers (76) hinges on several simplifying assumptions. The first is that the adsorption obeys a modified Langmuir isotherm, the modification after Frumkin (52) to take account of the interactions between adsorbed molecules. The second assumption is that the coated and uncoated areas of the electrode can be considered as condensers in parallel, with no interactions. The first assumption can only be presumed to hold where energies of all adsorbed molecules are the same and thus is questionable for multilayer adsorption. Melik–Gaĭkazyan (156) has shown that, at least in some cases, multilayer adsorption does occur. On the other hand, Laitinen and Mosier (121) found that the simpler Langmuir isotherm was applicable to a wide selection of species. The second assumption is more difficult to justify. If the adsorbed layer were in the form of agglomerated two-dimensional crystals floating on an otherwise uncoated surface this picture would seem plausible. However, for gaseous films in which intermolecular distances undergo a transition from large to small values as compared with molecular diameters in the course of a coating process, it might seem more reasonable to expect a greater effect at high surface coverage than at low. It is apparent that in regions of desorption this assumption loses its meaning so that studies are restricted to regions near the ecm. Another assumption implying the same restriction is that the capacity of the coated fraction does not change with potential. Despite the difficulties, Hansen et al. obtained fair agreement between theory and experiment for adsorption of pentanoic acid.

Several workers have addressed themselves to the problem of the effect of structure of the adsorbent on adsorbability. Gerovich (64,65) found a linear relation between surface activity and the number of rings for aromatic hydrocarbons. This would appear to be a more empirical formulation of a linear relationship found by Hansen and co-workers between free energy of adsorption and the product of optical polarizability and molecular volume to the first or to the two-thirds power. As the latter authors pointed out such a simple relationship might well be expected for spherical molecules in an isotropic medium, but it is based on a much oversimplified view of the actual situation. Obedience to this equation, particularly for compounds with the wide range of functional groups studied by Hansen *et al.*, indicates that the major effect of change in structure lies in the effect on polarizability and possibility of interaction with the solvent. This is not surprising if it can be assumed, as is often done, that most surface active materials are oriented with polar groups toward the solution. On the other hand, some compounds which might be expected to have interaction with mercury, e.g., thiourea and biuret, are most probably oriented with the functional group to the surface (1). The criterion most commonly used for mode of orientation is the shift in position of the ecm on adsorption in conjunction with the dipole moment of the adsorbed compound. In cases where the dipole moment of the sorbed material is small, however, this method is questionable since there is, as yet, little reliable evidence as to orientation of water dipoles at the interface, and the effect measured is the difference between the two. The above cited work of Gerovich seems to imply that aromatic compounds can lie flat on the surface presumably gaining energy, particularly at positive potential, by means of interaction of π electrons with the surface. This view is substantiated by later studies of Gerovich and Rybalchenko (65) on saturated and unsaturated aliphatic and alicyclic hydrocarbons. Laitinen and Mosier have investigated a large number of compounds of varied structure and characterized the adsorption in terms of two parameters, namely, the "adsorption index," the reciprocal of the concentration required for half-surface coverage, and the capacitance of a completely coated layer. The first of these is a qualitative measure of surface activity, the second, of the dielectric constant in the double layer. Both of these parameters must be applied with some caution. Strictly speaking, comparisons involving the first should be made only with molecules having equal area per molecule. The magnitude of the second depends on whether the closest packed monolayer excludes foreign ions from the interface.

Miller and Grahame (158) have made a careful study of the adsorption characteristics of two polymers, polymethacrylic acid and polylycine. They concluded that the adsorbed molecules are attached to the surface at a number of points but a significant fraction of each molecule has negligible interaction with the surface and forms a "surface phase" around it.

3. Kinetics of Adsorption

From studies of the tensammetric peaks and particularly from their behavior as a function of the frequency of the applied a.c. potential, it is possible to draw inferences as to the rate of the adsorption process and its slow step. Frumkin and Melik–Gaĭkazyan (56) first developed and used this method. Generalizations of the theory were later made by Berzins and Delahay (11), and Lorenz and Mochel (135). Experimental studies of aliphatic alcohols by Melik–Gaĭkazyan (157) showed diffusion to be the limiting factor but Lorenz and Mochel determined the rate of exchange of phenol between adsorbed layer and solution as 1.6×10^{-4} mole cm.$^{-1}$ sec.$^{-1}$. This rate is at the upper limit of experimental accessibility. Schmid and Reilley (183) have given indirect evidence that the adsorption step may be much slower in other cases (*vide infra*).

In connection with studies of adsorption equilibrium and the effect of adsorption on electrode kinetics, the rates of diffusion of species to an electrode surface and the time at which the surface reaches equilibrium are of interest. Delahay and Trachtenberg (41) gave theoretical equations for the diffusion process to a plane, expanding sphere, streaming electrode and in stirred solution with the aid of several simplifying assumptions, the most damaging of which is that the adsorption obeys a linear isotherm. Later Delahay and Fike (42) attempted a more rigorous approach for the cases of stationary and expanding plane electrodes assuming a Langmuir isotherm. Testa and Reinmuth (199) have disputed the validity of these calculations and have given an alternative set for the stationary plane.

Kortya (110), Campbell (35), and Schmid and Reilley (183), considered the expanding sphere for the limiting case in which the equilibrium was completely displaced toward adsorption. They showed that the results could be well explained with a simple theoretical model.

Delahay and Trachtenberg (41) concluded that particularly at low concentrations of surface active agents and small diffusion coefficients, e.g., polymers, equilibrium is reached only very slowly, i.e., in times of the order of a half-hour. Thus, results which do not take account of this factor are suspect. The calculations of these authors show that at low concentrations the time required to reach equilibrium is independent of concentration of the species in solution. At higher concentrations the time decreases because of the limited area of the surface. The effect of free energy of adsorption is in the opposite direction, i.e., the stronger the interaction of the species with the surface, the longer is the time to reach equilibrium at a given concentration. Thus, time required to reach equilibrium is a function of concentration *and potential* for a given substance.

4. Effect of Adsorption on Reaction Kinetics

In some cases surface active agents are oxidizable or reducible within the available potential range. In this case there are several possibilities. The adsorbed species may be either more or less reactive than its unadsorbed counterpart and the reaction product may be more or less surface active than the original substance. To further complicate matters the electrode reaction may be Nernst-controlled or slow. Early studies of adsorption, prior to reduction, were made polarographically most notably by Brdicka (22) and Müller (159). Much more recently Lorenz has given a theoretical treatment for the effect of adsorption on a chronopotentiometric wave assuming a linear isotherm (133). Experimental investigation of adsorption of I_3^- on platinized platinum and other systems were given by Lorenz and Mulberg (134). Since the electroactive species is concentrated at the interface prior to electrolysis the transition time is somewhat prolonged. Probably the most unequivocal and generally useful method for such studies is impedance measurement at the electrode interface. Loshkarev, Krivstov, and Kryukova (136) first applied the method to the problem. Laitinen and Randles (123) developed the theory of this method and applied it to cobalt ethylenediamine complexes. Because of a large phase difference between the current observed in the two cases the method can readily distinguish between adsorbed and nonadsorbed reactants. Laitinen and Mosier (121) have demonstrated by impedance measurements that a number of species are adsorbed at their reduction potentials. Earlier Breyer and co-workers did this same type of study with a.c. polarography (27). Schmid and Reilley (183) have recently discussed a number of cases in which the product of an electrode reaction is surface active. Effects in these cases are similar to those of the effects of other surface active agents on reaction (*vide infra*).

A most eagerly pursued topic in recent years has been the effect of surface active agents on electrode reactions of other species. Perhaps the first systematic study of such a phenomenon was that of

Kolthoff and Barnum (109). The case they studied was one in which the reactive species was itself surface active. They added inert surface active agent which competed with it for surface sites. It soon became obvious, however, that surfactants could materially affect even simple electrode reactions.

Several mechanisms have been proposed to explain the observed effects. If reaction on a coated electrode were more difficult than on an uncoated one, the "blocking" effect of a film partially coating the electrode would cause the current density at the uncoated sites to be correspondingly greater, thus making more demands on the electrode reaction and increasing the overpotential or perhaps creating one where none had been previously observable. The presence of a surface film might well be expected to alter the potential at the reaction site, especially if the surface active species were charged—a "ψ" effect. The alteration of structure of the layer surrounding the electrode might facilitate or inhibit a chemical reaction proceding the actual charge-transfer process—a kinetic effect. The surface active species might itself react chemically with the reactive species—a specific chemical effect. The rate of penetration of a film might become the slow step in reaction—a penetration effect.

In view of the number of possibilities and the subtle experimental distinctions between them, it is not surprising that there are still major disagreements between various workers as to the predominant effect in many situations. Indeed, it is likely that in any given case several of the effects might be operative.

Each of the above forms of interference acts to inhibit or accelerate a particular step in the over-all electrode process. If the step affected is not rate determining then there is no apparent effect to the observer. Thus, very often Nernst-controlled waves are not altered by the presence of large amounts of surface active agent. On the other hand, pronounced enhancement or inhibition of reaction is possible. Experimental studies of the effect of surface active agents on kinetics are so numerous that a complete review is out of the question. Consequently, in the following we shall attempt to discuss the expected experimental consequences of an effect of each type, to give some examples of each from the literature, and then to dwell briefly on the areas of disagreement.

The blocking effect does not affect the electrode reaction per se, but only the effective area in which it can occur. Thus if correction

were made for the decrease in area the rate constant should be invariant with change in fractional surface covered. Frumkin has
implied that a suitable diagnostic criterion for cases of this type is that
the overpotential for reduction be increased without effect on the
apparent electron transfer coefficient. The reasoning being that
change in transfer coefficient will signal any change in mechanism.
This, however, is a questionable method at best, because the apparent
electron-transfer coefficient, α, reflects the change of adsorption
characteristics with potential in the presence of surfactants and consequently might be expected to change even in the absence of a
change in mechanism. Moreover, α need not change appreciably
even with a change in mechanism. A much more satisfactory
method of investigation is that chosen by Delahay and Trachtenberg
(41), namely, direct measurement of reaction rate and fractional
surface coverage. Their method rests on the as yet unproven
assumptions that blocking is directly related to fraction of surface
coverage, and that fractional surface coverage can be determined
from capacity measurements, but the results are at least consistant
with these assumptions. They concluded from their work that cyclo-
hexanol and n-amyl alcohol gave blocking effects on the titanium
(III–IV) couple in tartaric acid medium, whereas thymol produced
an effect which could not be explained so simply.

The most distinguishing characteristics of the ψ effect is that it can
act to increase as well as to decrease reactivity. Also, in contrast to
the blocking effect, it is dependent on the charge of the reducible
species as well as its size. Rogers and co-workers (84,139) have
shown the beneficial effect of tetraalkylammonium ions on the reduction of several organic halo compounds. Kryukova (113) and
Frumkin and Florianovich (55) did likewise for reduction of persulfate. On the other hand, the same salts inhibit reduction of
hydrogen ion and have no effect on reduction of nitro compounds in
the same potential regions (84). Clearly the inhibitory effect in the
case of hydrogen can not be due to blocking or penetration effect
since reactions of bulkier organic compounds are enhanced under
the same conditions. The mechanism is apparently not one of
hindering a chemical reaction leading to a supply of hydrogen ions
at the surface since such a process would also hinder the hydrogen
dependent nitro reduction. Thus, the hydrogen ion and halo cases
would seem to be ψ effects. A kinetic effect should, in principle,

be easy to distinguish. The necessary condition for its occurrence is that a chemical reaction be the method by which the electrochemically reactive species is delivered to the electrode. The polarographic and chronopotentiometric characteristics of such currents are well known. The difficulty lies in the fact that a penetration effect would be expected to result in the same apparent behavior. Thus, a priori, there is no method of distinguishing between the two. Schmid and Reilley (183), however, have offered a line of reasoning which may be of value in some cases. They note that gelatin or Triton X-100 have little effect on the polarographic reduction of $Cd(En)_3^{2+}$ but strongly depress the limiting current of $Cd(CN)_4^{2-}$. Since the cyanide complex is smaller than that of the ethylenediamine their argument is that the effect can not be one of hindered penetration for then both complexes would be equally affected. Their argument then implies that the determining factor in rate of penetration is the size of the reactive species. There is, however, little evidence except intuition to support this view. The difference in charge between the two species cited above, not to mention the difference in chemical character between the alkyl carbon and hydrogen and cyanide nitrogen, might be expected to affect the rate of penetration. There may be, however, more validity to the comparison between Cd EDTA and Pb EDTA, another example chosen by the same authors. Here the charges and chemical constitutions are very similar. Schmid and Reilley feel that the difference in effect of Triton X-100 in the two cases (30% more surface active agent required for the lead complex than the cadmium to depress the limiting current to half of diffusion controlled value) is too large to be due to difference in rates of penetration. Whatever the merits of the argument in this particular case, it is the only criterion even offered thus far to distinguish between kinetic and penetration effects. Another consideration which might aid in making this distinction would be the potential dependence of the limiting current. Gierst (66) and Breiter, Kleinerman, and Delahay (23) feel that the rates of chemical reactions occurring in the double layer should be potential dependent (*vide supra*). If so, then the limiting current in the kinetically controlled case should not be a level plateau, but rather some more complicated function of potential. The structure of the adsorbed layer, however, seems to be relatively invariant (except, of course, near potentials of desorption). If the rate of penetration could be assumed to be dependent only on structure and not also on the potential gradient within the double layer, penetration effects should show a level plateau region. This line of reasoning leads to conclusions in conflict with those of Schmid and Reilley (183) for plateau regions are in fact observed. Polarographic or chronopotentiometric techniques in which the reactive species was generated within or beneath the surface coating by electrolytic stripping might prove of value in investigations of this type.

Many years ago Heyrovsky and co-workers (78–80) first formulated the precept that the effect of surfactants on reduction was inhibition of a chemical step following the first electron-transfer. This may or may not be true in some cases, but the further pronouncement of these workers that reactions involving a single electron could not be affected by surfactants has been clearly disproven by Loshkarev (136–138) and Tamamushi (195,196).

The specific chemical effects can very often be predicted on intuitive chemical ground. In addition, as Meites and Meites pointed out (155), if the surface active agent reacts chemically with the electroactive species, it can generally be expected to affect the course of reaction even when it is not adsorbed. Many of the effects attributed to complexation by early workers, it is now obvious, are due to other courses. Coe and Rogers (36) for example, called the effect of gelatine on iodate one of complexation but the peculiarities which they observed in the current–time curves are, in retrospect, clearly associated with adsorption phenomena. Most of the specific chemical effects are ones involving complexation or other direct reaction of an electrochemically reactive species with the surfactant. There are, however, kinetic effects of the second kind (to borrow a potentiometric term) in which not the surfactant itself but a species produced by it is involved in the electrode reaction. The only examples of this type reported thus far involve hydrogen ions but donation of other species is possible, if less likely. The most obvious examples involve catalysis of hydrogen ion discharge by adsorption of certain alkaloids, e.g., quinine and cinchonine. Conway, Bockris, and Lorrecek (31) made a detailed theoretical analysis and concluded that adsorption of the alkaloid tends to increase the availability of protons but that the fact that the alkaloids are stronger bases than water tends to decrease the rate of supply of protons to the surface. Which of the effects is predominant depends on the particular case. A case which may be similar is the increase in the rate of reduction of nitro-benzene in the presence of gelatine in 80% alcoholic solution, observed by Hummelstedt and Rogers (84). Proton donation by the gelatin or water trapped in it could be responsible, although there might also be a ψ effect.

The foremost proponents of the inhibited penetration theory have been Loshkarev and his co-workers (136–138). These workers and others have presented compelling reasons why the cases they chose could not be explained in terms of blocking or ψ effects but have done little if any work which would distinguish between kinetic and penetration effects.

In view of the many conjectures as to the nature of the influence of surface active agents to reactions it seems strange that little experimental work has been devoted to the problem of the structure of the film formed by these agents. At air–water interfaces it is well known that the two dimensional analogues of solid, liquid, and gaseous films can be found. Perhaps as more work is done information from the further advanced air-solution interface studies will be of value in interpretation of solution–metal data.

An interesting line of research is that followed by Loshkarev and co-workers in mixing surface active agents in various proportions. In some cases this technique seems to yield more impenetrable (more closely packed ?) films than are obtainable from a single species. Another complex effect is that of surface active agents and inorganic ions acting in concert. The effect in some cases may be that counter-ions allow closer packing of surfactant in the adsorbed layer, or salt additions may simply alter the ψ effect in the layer. More work would be of interest.

All the criteria mentioned above for distinguishing between various types of effects rest on the assumption that equilibrium is established in the adsorption process. In most of the work prior to 1954 there is little indication that the possibility was recognized that this might not be so under polarographic conditions. Since then several workers (*vide supra*) have made theoretical and experimental studies of the rate of the adsorption process. Schmid and Reilley (183) by investigation of current–time curves at individual drops with a DME have given a very clear picture of the effect of adsorption kinetics on reaction. Depending upon the form of the current–time curve these authors were able to distinguish three major types of behavior:

(1) those in which rate of diffusion of the surfactant to surface was determinative; (2) those in which the adsorption equilibrium was reached essentially instantaneously at the drop surface; and (3) those in which the rate of the adsorption process was slow.

In theoretically treating cases of the first type they used a very simple theory due to Kortya (110). This theory assumes that a full monolayer is adsorbed as rapidly as it can arrive at the electrode surface: Schmid and Reilley showed that this simplification can be applied in a number of cases and, where independent measures of diffusion coefficients are available, it is possible to calculate area per molecule of adsorbant. Cases of type 2 are those discussed previously. That there should be cases in which the adsorption process is slow at all seems surprising in view of the work of Lorenz and Mochel (135), and Melik–Gaĭkazyan (157). Experimentally, the first two cases considered by Schmid and Reilley correspond (1) to the case in which equilibrium lies completely to the side of adsorption, and (2) to the case in which there is negligible concentration polarization during the adsorption process, i.e., the equilibrium lies very much in favor of nonadsorption or the concentration in solution is very high. Cases cited by these authors as showing rate effects in the adsorption process might well be simply intermediate equilibrium cases in which there is appreciable concentration polarization and appreciable equilibrium concentration in solution so that the use of neither of the first two limiting cases is justified. A resolution of the dilemma would be possible by comparison of the observed current-time curves with those calculated theoretically with the aid of exact theory.

References

1. Adam, N. K., *Physics and Chemistry of Surfaces*, Oxford University Press, London, 1930, p. 343.
2. Anson, F. C., and J. J. Lingane, *J. Am. Chem. Soc.*, **79**, 4901 (1957).
3. Bahary, W. A., and W. H. Reinmuth, unpublished.
4. Barker, G. C., and I. L. Jenkins, *Analyst*, **77**, 685 (1952).
5. Barker, G. C., *Anal. Chem. Acta*, **18**, 118 (1958).
6. Basu, S., *Trans. Faraday Soc.*, **52**, 6 (1956).
7. Basu, S., and R. Bhattacharya, *J. Chem. Phys.*, **25**, 596 (1956).
8. Bauer, H. H., and P. J. Elving, *Anal. Chem.*, **30**, 334, 341 (1958).
9. Baumann, F., and I. Shain, *Anal. Chem.*, **25**, 697 (1958).
10. Bergman, I., *Trans. Faraday Soc.*, **50**, 829 (1954); **52**, 690 (1956).

11. Berzins, T., and P. Delahay, *J. Chem. Phys.*, **59**, 406 (1955).
12. Berzins, T., and P. Delahay, *J. Chem. Phys.*, **23**, 972 (1955).
13. Berzins, T., and P. Delahay, *J. Am. Chem. Soc.*, **75**, 555 (1953).
14. de Bethune, A. J., *J. Am. Chem. Soc.*, **71**, 1956 (1949).
15. Bockris, J. O'M., and B. E. Conway, *J. Chem. Phys.*, **25**, 697 (1958).
16. Bockris, J. O'M., *Modern Aspects of Electrochemistry*, Academic Press, New York, 1954, p. 205.
17. Booman, G. L., E. Morgan, and A. L. Crittenden, *J. Am. Chem. Soc.*, **79**, 5533 (1957).
18. Borisova, T. I., B. V. Ershler, and A. N. Frumkin, *Zhur. Fiz. Khim.*, **22**, 925 (1949).
19. Boult, E. H., and H. R. Thirsk, *Trans. Faraday Soc.*, **50**, 404 (1954).
20. Bowden, F. P., and E. K. Rideal, *Proc. Roy. Soc. (London)*, **120A**, 59 (1928).
21. Brdicka, R., and K. Weisner, *Collection Czechoslov. Chem. Communs.*, **12**, 138 (1947).
22. Brdicka, R., *Z. Elektrochem.*, **48**, 248 (1942); *Collection Czechoslov. Chem. Communs.*, **12**, 522 (1947).
23. Breiter, M., M. Kleinerman, and P. Delahay, *J. Am. Chem. Soc.*, **80**, 511 (1958).
24. Bresle, A., *Acta Chem. Scand.*, **10**, 943 (1956).
25. Breyer, B., *Rept. Australian New Zealand Assoc. Advance. Sci., 28th Meeting*, 192 (1951).
26. Breyer, B., and S. Hacobian, *Anal. Chem. Acta.*, **16**, 497 (1957).
27. Breyer, B., and S. Hacobian, *Aust. J. Sci. Res., Ser. A*, **5**, 500 (1952).
28. Breyer, B., H. H. Bauer, and S. Hacobian, *Aust. J. Chem.*, **8**, 312 (1955).
29. Breyer, B., and S. Hacobian, *Aust. J. Chem.*, **7**, 225 (1954).
30. Brodd, R. J., and N. Hackerman, *J. Electrochem. Soc.*, **104**, 704 (1957).
31. Brown, H. C., *J. Phys. Chem.*, **56**, 818 (1952).
32. Bruss, D. B., and T. DeVries, *J. Am. Chem. Soc.*, **78**, 733 (1956).
33. Burdick, D. L., A. V. Santoro, W. McEwan, and J. Kleinberg, *J. Am. Chem. Soc.*, **79**, 5467 (1957).
34. Byrne, J. T., and L. B. Rogers, *J. Electrochem. Soc.*, **98**, 452 (1951).
35. Campbell, H., *Trans. Faraday Soc.*, **50**, 1351 (1954).
36. Coe, R. H., and L. B. Rogers, *J. Am. Chem. Soc.*, **70**, 3276 (1948).
37. Conway, B. E., J. O'M. Bockris, and B. Lorrecek, *Proc. 6th Meeting C.I.T.-C.E.* **1955**, Butterworth, London, 1955, p. 207.
38. Delahay, P., *Disc. Faraday Soc.*, **17**, 205 (1954).
39. Delahay, P., *J. Am. Chem. Soc.*, **75**, 1430 (1953).
40. Delahay, P., and C. C. Mattax, *ibid.*, **76**, 5314 (1954).
41. Delahay, P., and I. Trachtenberg, *ibid.*, **79**, 2355 (1957); **80**, 2094 (1958).
42. Delahay, P., and C. T. Fike, *ibid.*, **80**, 2628 (1952).
43. Delahay, P., *ibid.*, **75**, 1190 (1953).
44. Delahay, P., and T. Berzins, *ibid.*, **75**, 2466 (1953).
45. Delahay, P., and C. C. Mattax, *ibid.*, **76**, 874 (1954).
46. Delahay, P., C. C. Mattax, and T. Berzins, *ibid.*, **76**, 5319 (1954).
47. Elving, P. J., *Record Chem. Prog.*, **14**, 99 (1953).
48. Eyring, H., L. Marker, and T. C. Kwoh, *J. Phys. Chem.*, **53**, 1453 (1949).

49. Fernandez-Alonso, J. I., and R. Domingo, *Nature*, **179**, 229 (1957).
50. Fournier, N., *Compt. rend.*, **232**, 1673 (1951).
51. Frankenthal, R. P., and I. Shain, *J. Am. Chem. Soc.*, **78**, 2969 (1956).
52. Frumkin, A. N., *Z. Physik. Chem.*, **A164**, 121 (1933).
53. Frumkin, A. N., *Acta Physicochim.*, *U.R.S.S.*, **6**, 502 (1931); **7**, 475 (1937).
54. Frumkin, A. N., *Z. Physik.*, **35**, 792 (1926).
55. Frumkin, A. N., and G. Florianovich, *Doklady Akad. Nauk. S.S.S.R.*, **80**, 907 (1951).
56. Frumkin, A. N., and V. I. Melik–Gaïkazyan, *ibid.*, **77**, 855 (1951).
57. Frumkin, A. N., and N. Nikolajeva, *J. Chem. Phys.*, **26**, 1552 (1957).
58. Frumkin, A. N., *Can. J. Chem.*, **37**, 253 (1959).
59. Gerischer, H., and M. Krause, *Z. Physik. Chem.*, **14**, 184 (1958).
60. Gerischer, H., *Z. Physik. Chem.*, **198**, 286 (1951); **201**, 55 (1952); **202**, 292, 307 (1953).
61. Gerischer, H., *ibid.*, **202**, 293, 302 (1953).
62. Gerischer, H., and K. E. Staubach, *Z. Elektrochem.*, **61**, 789 (1957).
63. Gerischer, H., *Anal. Chem.*, **31**, 33 (1959).
64. Gerovich, M., *Doklady. Akad. Nauk.*, *S.S.S.R.*, **96**, 543 (1954); **105**, 1278 (1955).
65. Gerovich, M., and O. Rybalchenko, *Zhur. Fiz. Khim.*, **32**, 109 (1958).
66. Gierst, L., *Thesis*, University of Brussels, Belgium, 1958.
67. Gierst, L., and A. Juliard, *J. Phys. Chem.*, **57**, 701 (1953).
68. Giguere, P. A., and D. Lamantague, *Science*, **120**, 390 (1954).
69. Grahame, D. C., *Chem. Revs.*, **41**, 441 (1947).
70. Grahame, D. C., *Ann. Revs. Phys. Chem.*, **6**, 337 (1955).
71. Grahame, D. C., *Anal. Chem.*, **30**, 1736 (1958).
72. Grahame, D. C., *J. Electrochem. Soc.*, **99**, 370c (1952).
73. Haissinsky, M., and A. S. Ghosh–Mazamdan, *Bull. Electrochem. Res. Inst. Karashada*, **2**, 5 (1954).
74. Haissinsky, M., *J. Chem. Phys.*, **43**, 21 (1946).
75. Hans, W., and W. Jensch, *Z. Elektrochem.*, **56**, 648 (1952).
76. Hansen, R. S., R. E. Minturn, and D. A. Hickson, *J. Phys. Chem.*, **60**, 1185 (1956).
77. Hansen, R. S., R. E. Minturn, and D. A. Hickson, *ibid.*, **61**, 983 (1957).
78. Heyrovsky, J., F. Sorm, J. Forejt, *Collections Czechoslov. Chem. Communs.*, **12**, 11 (1947).
79. Heyrovsky, J., *Collections Chem. Communs.*, **19**, 56 (1954).
80. Heyrovsky, J., *Disc. Faraday Soc.*, **1**, 212 (1947).
81. Heyrovsky, J., *Chem. listy.*, **35**, 155 (1941).
82. Hoijtink, G. J., and R. Van Schooten, *Rev. trav. chim.*, **71**, 1089 (1952); **72**, 691, 903 (1953).
83. Hoijtnk, G. J., *ibid.*, **73**, 895 (1954); **74**, 1525 (1955); **76**, 885 (1957).
84. Hummelstedt, L. E. I. and L. B. Rogers, *J. Electrochem. Soc.*, **106**, 242 (1959).
85. Hush, N., *J. Chem. Phys.*, **28**, 962 (1958).
86. Ilkovic, D., *J. Chem. Phys.*, **35**, 129 (1938).
87. Imai, H., *Bull. Chem. Soc. Japan*, **29**, 276, 281 (1956).

88. Imai, H., and H. Sunahara, *ibid.*, **27,** 554 (1954).
89. International Colloquium on Passivity of Metals,*Z . Elektrochem.*, **62,** 619–827 (1958).
90. Iredale, T., *Nature*, **177,** 36 (1956).
91. Jaffe, H. H., *Chem. Revs.*, **53,** 191 (1953).
92. Jordan, J., E. Ackerman, and R. L Berger, *J. Am. Chem. Soc.*, **78,** 2979 (1956).
93. Jordan, J., R. A. Javick, and W. E. Ranz, *ibid.*, **80,** 3846 (1958).
94. Kalousek, J., *Collections Czechoslov. Chem. Communs.*, **13,** 105 (1948).
95. Kambara, T., *Bull. Chem. Soc. Japan*, **27,** 529 (1954).
96. Kambara, T., and I. Tachi, *ibid.*, **23,** 225 (1952).
97. Kambara, T., and I. Tachi, *J. Phys. Chem.*, **61,** 1405 (1957).
98. Kaufman, D., J. W Loveland and P. J. Elving, *ibid.*, **63,** 217 (1959).
99. Kemula, W., Z. Galus, and Z. Kublik, *Nature*, **182,** 1228 (1958).
100. Kemula, W., private communication (1958).
101. Kemula, W., and Z. Kublik, *Nature*, **182,** 793 (1958).
102. Kemula, W., and Z. Kublik, *Roczniki Chem.*, **32,** 941 (1958).
103. Kivalo, P., *J. Phys. Chem.*, **61,** 1126 (1957).
104. Kivalo, P., K. B. Oldham, and H. A. Laitinen, *J. Am. Chem. Soc.*, **75,** 4148 (1953).
105. Kivalo, P., and H. A. Laitinen, *ibid.*, **77,** 5205 (1955).
106. Kolthoff, I. M., and N. Tanaka, *Anal. Chem.*, **26,** 632 (1954).
107. Kolthoff, I. M., and E. Nightengale, *Anal. Chem. Acta.*, **17,** 329 (1957).
108. Kolthoff, I. M., and F. J. Coetzee, *J. Am. Chem. Soc.*, **79,** 870, 1852 (1957).
109. Kolthoff, I. M., and C. Barnum, *ibid.*, **63,** 520 (1941).
110. Kortya, J., *Collections Czechoslov. Chem. Communs.*, **18,** 206 (1953).
111. Koutecky, J., *Czechoslov. J. Phys.*, **2,** 50 (1953); *Collections Czechoslov. Chem. Communs.*, **18,** 597 (1953); **19,** 1045, 1083 (1954); **20,** 116 (1955); **21,** 652, 1056 (1956); **22,** 160 (1957).
112. Koutecky, J., and J. Cizik, *Collections Czechoslov. Chem. Communs.*, **21,** 836, 1013 (1956); **22,** 914 (1957).
113. Kryukova, T., *Doklady Akad. Nauk.*, *S.S.S.R.*, **80,** 907 (1951).
114. Kuta, J., *Chem. listy*, **48,** 1493 (1954).
115. Kuta, J., and J. Drabek. *ibid.*, **49,** 23 (1955).
116. Kuwana, T., and R. N. Adams, *J. Am. Chem. Soc.*, **79,** 3607 (1957).
117. Kuwana, T., and R. N. Adams, *Anal. Chem. Acta.*, **20,** 51 (1959).
118. Laitinen, H. A., and C. H. Liu, *J. Am. Chem. Soc.*, **80,** 1015 (1958).
119. Laitinen, H. A., and I. M. Kolthoff, *J. Phys. Chem.*, **45,** 1023 (1941).
120. Laitinen, H. A., and P. Kivalo, *J. Am. Chem. Soc.*, **75,** 2198 (1953).
121. Laitinen, H. A., and B. Mosier, *ibid.*, **80,** 2363 (1958).
122. Laitinen, H. A., and E. I. Onstott, *ibid.*, **72,** 4565 (1950).
123. Laitinen, H. A., and J. E. Randles, *Trans. Faraday Soc.*, **51,** 54 (1955).
124. Lambert, F. L., and K. Kobayashi, *Chem. and Ind.*, **1958,** 149.
125. Lange, E., *Z. Elektrochem.*, **55,** 761 (1951); **56,** 94 (1952).
126. Laughlin, B. D., J. Kleinberg, and A. W. Davidson, *J. Am. Chem. Soc.*, **78,** 559 (1956).
127. Lee, J. K., R. N. Adams and C. Bricker, *Anal. Chem. Acta.*, **17,** 321 (1957).
128. Lee, T. S., *J. Am. Chem. Soc.*, **74,** 5001 (1952).

129. Levich, B., *Acta. Physicochim. U.R.S.S.*, **17**, 257 (1942).
130. Libby, W. F., *J. Phys. Chem.*, **56**, 863 (1952).
131. Lingane, J. J., and B. A. Loveridge, *J. Am. Chem. Soc.*, **72**, 438 (1950).
132. Lord, S. S., and L. B. Rogers, *Anal. Chem.*, **26**, 284 (1954).
133. Lorenz, W., *Z. Elektrochem.*, **59**, 730 (1955).
134. Lorenz, W., and W. Mulberg, *ibid.*, **59**, 736 (1955).
135. Lorenz, W., and F. Mochel, *ibid.*, **59**, 906 (1955).
136. Loshkarev, M., A. Krivstov, and A. Kryukova, *Zhur. Fiz. Khim.*, **23**, 209 (1949).
137. Loshkarev, M. A., and A. A. Kryukova, *Doklady Akad. Nauk. S.S.S.R.*, **62**, 97 (1948); **72**, 919 (1950); *Zhur. Fiz. Khim.*, **22**, 805, 815 (1948); **23**, 209 (1949); **26**, 731, 737 (1952).
138. Loshkarev, M. A., *Doklady Akad. Nauk.*, *S.S.S.R.*, **72**, 729 (1950).
139. Lothe, J. J., and L. B. Rogers, *J. Electrochem. Soc.*, **101**, 268 (1954).
140. Loveland, J. W., and P. J. Elving, *J. Phys. Chem.*, **56**, 250, 255, 935, 941, 945 (1952); *Chem. Revs.*, **51**, 67 (1952).
141. Lyons, E. H., Jr., *J. Electrochem. Soc.*, **101**, 363, 376 (1954); *Z. Elektrochem.*, **59**, 766 (1955).
142. Lyons, E. H., Jr., J. C. Bailer, and H. A. Laitinen, *J. Electrochem. Soc.*, **101**, 410 (1954).
143. Maccoll, A., *Nature*, **163**, 178 (1949).
144. Marcus, R. A., *Can. J. Chem.*, **37**, 155 (1959); *J. Chem. Phys.*, **24**, 966, 979 (1956); **26**, 967, 972 (1957).
145. Markowitz, J. M., and P. J. Elving, *Chem. Revs.*, **58**, 1047 (1957).
146. Markowitz, J. M., and P. J. Elving, *J. Am. Chem. Soc.*, in press (1959).
147. Martin, E., *Ph.D. thesis*, University of North Carolina, Chapel Hill, N. C. (1959).
148. Matsuda, H., *Z. Elektrochem.*, **61**, 489 (1957).
149. Matsuda, H., and Y. Ayabe, *Bull. Chem. Soc.*, *Japan*, **28**, 422 (1955); **29**, 134 (1956).
150. Matsuda, H., and Y. Ayabe, *Z. Elektrochem.*, **59**, 494 (1955).
151. McEwen, W. E., J. Kleinberg, D. L. Burdick, W. D. Hoffman, and J. Y. Young, *J. Amer. Chem. Soc.*, **78**, 4587 (1956).
152. McGillavry, D., and E. W. Rideal, *Rec. Trav. Chim.*, **56**, 1013 (1937).
153. Mehl, W., and J. O'M. Bockris, *Can. J. Chem.*, **37**, 190 (1959).
154. Meites, L., and T. Meites, *J. Am. Chem. Soc.*, **73**, 395, 1581 (1951).
155. Meites, L., and T. Meites, *ibid.*, **73**, 177 (1951).
156. Melik–Gaĭkazyan, V. I., *Zhur. Fiz. Khim.*, **26**, 1184 (1952).
157. Melik–Gaĭkazyan, V. I., *ibid.*, **26**, 560 (1952).
158. Miller, I. R., and D. C. Grahame, *J. Am. Chem. Soc.*, **79**, 3006 (1957).
159. Müller, O. H., *Trans. Electrochem. Soc.*, **87**, 441 (1945).
160. Müller, R. H., R. L. Garman, M. E. Droz, and J. Petras, *Ind. Eng. Chem.*, *Anal. Ed.*, **10**, 339 (1938).
161. Nicholson, M. M., *J. Am. Chem. Soc.*, **79**, 7 (1957).
162. Nicholson, M. M., *ibid.*, **76**, 7539 (1954).
163. Oldham, K. B., P. Kivalo, and H. A. Laitinen, *J. Am. Chem. Soc.*, **75**, 5712 (1953).

164. Parsons, R., in J. O'M. Bockris, Ed., *Modern Aspects of Electrochemistry*, Academic Press, New York, 1954.
165. Randles, J. E. B., *Disc. Faraday Soc.*, **1**, 11 (1947).
166. Randles, J. E. B., *Can. J. Chem.*, **37**, 238 (1959).
167. Randles, J. E. B., and K. W. Somerton, *Trans. Faraday Soc.*, **48**, 957 (1952).
168. Randles, J. E. B., *ibid.*, **44**, 327 (1948).
169. Reilley, C. N., G. W. Everett, and R. H. Johns, *Anal. Chem.*, **27**, 483 (1955).
170. Reilley, C. N., and E. Martin, private communication (1959).
171. Reinmuth, W. H., *J. Am. Chem. Soc.*, **79**, 6358 (1957).
172. Reinmuth, W. H., L. B. Rogers, and L. E. I. Hummelstedt, *J. Am. Chem. Soc.*, **81**, 2947 (1959).
173. Reinmuth, W. H., *ibid.*, submitted for publication (1959).
174. Rogers, L. B., and A. F. Steheny, *J. Electrochem. Soc.*, **95**, 25 (1949).
175. Rosebrugh, T. R., and W. Lash–Miller, *J. Phys. Chem.*, **14**, 816 (1910).
176. Ross, J. W., and I. Shain, *Anal. Chem.*, **28**, 548 (1956).
177. Ross, J. W., A. D. DeMars, and I. Shain, *ibid.*, **28**, 1768 (1956).
178. Rothschild, *Proc. Roy. Soc. (London)*, **B125**, 283 (1936).
179. Rüetschi, P., and P. Delahay, *J. Chem. Phys.*, **25**, 697 (1955).
180. Sanborn, A. H., and E. F. Orleman, *J. Am. Chem. Soc.*, **78**, 4852 (1956).
181. Sarmouskis, J. N., and M. J. Prager, *J. Electrochem. Soc.*, **104**, 454 (1957).
182. Schaap, W. B., A. E. Messner, and F. C. Schmidt, *J. Am. Chem. Soc.*, **77**, 2683 (1935).
183. Schmid, R. W., and C. N. Reilley, *ibid.*, **80**, 2083 (1958).
184. Schmid, R. W., and C. N. Reilley, *ibid.*, **80**, 2101 (1958).
185. Schmid, R. W., and C. N. Reilley, *ibid.*, **78**, 2910, 5513 (1956).
186. Senda, M., and I. Tachi, *Bull. Chem. Soc., Japan*, **28**, 632 (1955).
187. Silverman, J., and A. E. Remick, *J. Electrochem. Soc.*, **97**, 335 (1950).
188. Sevcik, A., *Collections Czechoslov. Chem. Communs.*, **13**, 349 (1948).
189. Smutek, M., *Collections Czechoslov. Chem. Communs.*, **20**, 246 (1955).
190. Snead, W. K., and A. E. Remick, *J. Am. Chem. Soc.*, **79**, 6125 (1957).
191. Strehlow, H., and M. Von Stackelberg, *Z. Elektrochem.*, **54**, 51 (1950).
192. Stricks, W., and I. M. Kolthoff, *J. Am. Chem. Soc.*, **80**, 2101 (1958).
193. Tachi, I., and T. Kambara, *Bull. Chem. Soc., Japan*, **28**, 25 (1955).
194. Takemori, Y., T. Kambara, M. Senda, and I. Tachi, *J. Phys. Chem.*, **61**, 968 (1957).
195. Tamamushi, R., *Polarography*, **3**, 56 (1955).
196. Tamamushi, R., and T. Yamanaka, *Bull. Chem. Soc., Japan*, **26**, 673 (1953).
197. Tanaka, N., and R. Tamamushi, *Proc. I Pol. Congr. (Prague)*, **1**, 426 (1951).
198. Taube, H., *Chem. Revs.*, **50**, 69 (1952).
198A. Taube, H., *Record Chem. Progr.*, **17**, 25 (1956).
199. Testa, A. C., and W. H. Reinmuth, unpublished work.
200. Van Cakenberghe, J., *Bull. Soc. Chim. Belges*, **60**, 3 (1951).
201. Vetter, K. J., *Z. Physik. Chem.*, **199**, 785 (1952).
202. Vielstich, W., and P. Delahay, *J. Am. Chem. Soc.*, **79**, 1874 (1957).
203. Vlcek, A. A., *Nature*, **177**, 1045 (1956).
204. Vlcek, A. A., *Collections Czechoslov. Chem. Communs.*, **20**, 894 (1955).

205. Vlcek, A. A., *ibid.*, **22,** 948 (1957).
206. Von Stackelberg, M., and H. Fassbenden, *Z. Elektrochem.*, **62,** 834 (1958).
207. Von Stackelberg, M., W. Hans, and W. Jensch, *ibid.*, **62,** 839 (1958).
208. Wagner, C., *J. Electrochem. Soc.*, **97,** 72 (1950).
209. Watanabe, A., F. Tsuji, S. Ueda, *J. Electrochem. Soc., Japan*, **22,** 521 (1954).
210. Watson, A. T., and F. A. Matsen, *J. Chem. Phys.*, **18,** 1305 (1950).
211. Weaver, J. R., and R. W. Parry, *J. Am. Chem. Soc.*, **78,** 5542 (1956).
212. Weisner, K., *Z. Elektrochem.*, **49,** 164 (1943).

The Analytical Chemistry of Thioacetamide

Ernest H. Swift and Fred C. Anson, *California Institute of Technology, Pasadena, California*

I. INTRODUCTION

It is highly doubtful that even those few chemists who somehow managed to escape the rigors and odors of the classical courses in qualitative and quantitative analysis are unfamiliar with the properties of gaseous hydrogen sulfide. The repugnance of its odor, its extreme toxicity, the frequently colloidal and difficultly filterable sulfides which it yields, and the practical inconveniences of storing or generating the gas have resulted in many attempts to find alternative means for precipitating metal sulfides. A review of the suggestions which have been proposed for eliminating the use of gaseous hydrogen sulfide has been made by Sykes (1) and West (2) has discussed various nonsulfide systems of qualitative analysis. Those items from these reviews which are of most pertinence to a discussion of the analytical chemistry of thioacetamide have been included below.

A novel suggestion by Gaddis (3) involved saturating a slurry of an anion exchange resin (Amberlite IR-4) with hydrogen sulfide. Portions of the resulting resin, which was quite stable and contained 12% by weight hydrogen sulfide, were added to metal ion solutions and the sulfides precipitated. Recovery of the metal sulfides from the resin presents a serious limitation to the general usefulness of this process.

The most frequently occurring suggestions, however, eliminate the use of gaseous hydrogen sulfide altogether and involve the use of solid and liquid sulfur-containing compounds which can be made to yield hydrogen sulfide or sulfide ion in solution, or which can react directly to precipitate metal sulfides.   As early as 1842 the "headache-producing stench" of hydrogen sulfide led Hinly (4) to propose the use of sodium thiosulfate as a sulfide precipitant in acid solutions.   Other inorganic reagents which have been suggested include a warm solution of phosphorous pentasulfide and a fusion with sodium carbonate and sulfur.

As early as 1894 Schiff and Tarugi (5) proposed thioacetic acid as a substitute for hydrogen sulfide.   This reagent and its ammonium salt were employed for many years in numerous laboratories but few chemists find its odor much more pleasant than that of hydrogen sulfide, and since its stability and ease of preparation leave much to be desired it is seldom used today.

Thiourea, potassium ethyl xanthate and sodium amyl xanthate, mono- and dithiocarbamates, trithiocarbonates, thioglycollates, and thiosalicylates have all been proposed and tested but all suffer from drawbacks and none has achieved widespread acceptance.

Thioformamide has been used by Gagliardi (6) and co-workers with notable success as a substitute for hydrogen sulfide. Satisfactory precipitations of platinum, palladium, iridium, arsenic, copper, antimony, and tin have been achieved and a separation of copper and arsenic was accomplished under conditions where hydrogen sulfide failed.   The decomposition of thioformamide leads eventually to formic acid which can be decomposed relatively easily and removed from the solution.   This is an advantage which thioformamide would have over thioacetamide, where the decomposition leads to acetic acid or acetate ion. These may form undesirable complexes with metal ions or may alter the pH of the solution and are much more difficult to destroy than is formic acid. It is possible that thioformamide may be an advantageous means of generating hydrogen sulfide in specific instances where interference by acetate is very severe. However, the low melting point (28 to 29°C.) of thioformamide and the instability of its solutions are factors which do not favor its routine use.

At the present time by far the most widely used nongaseous reagent for precipitating metal sulfides is thioacetamide. The first reported use of thioacetamide was made by Iwanow (7) in 1935 to detect certain heavy metals in pharmaceuticals.   In 1938 Wawilow (8) used it to test for bismuth.

In spite of this early work it was 11 years before the use of thioacetamide as a substitute for gaseous hydrogen sulfide was suggested in the literature.   In 1949 Barber and Grazeskowiak (9) reported the successful use of thioacetamide in a system of qualitative analysis in place of hydrogen sulfide for the precipitation of the elements commonly precipitated by gaseous hydrogen sulfide from approximately 0.3F hydrochloric acid solutions (F indicates *volume formal*, formula weights per liter of solution), that is, lead, copper, bismuth, cadmium, mercury, arsenic, antimony, and tin.   The present interest in thioacetamide dates from the publication of this brief note.

Although the original impetus which led to the investigation of thioacetamide was the desire to eliminate the odor of hydrogen sulfide and the unwieldy equipment which is frequently a part of hydrogen sulfide generation, much of the continuing interest has resulted from the well coagulated and easily filterable sulfide precipitates which thioacetamide produces.

Precipitation of metal sulfides with gaseous hydrogen sulfide and the subsequent filtration of the precipitates is a notoriously unpleasant and difficult chore.   This is doubly true when constituents such as nickel(II) and tin(IV) are to be precipitated because of their pronounced tendency to form extremely finely divided colloidal precipitates which can be separated, at best, only after tedious coagulation.   However, by the use of thioacetamide under appropriate conditions, it is possible to initiate precipitation of nickel sulfide in the form of an adherent, shining, golden-brown mirror on the walls of a glass vessel, and the resulting particles of nickel sulfide are so large that filtration presents no problem.   The ability to yield dense, filterable precipitates is a property which thioacetamide shares with other substances that slowly react in solution to produce a species which precipitates another component of the solution.   The production of coarse, coagulated precipitates by homogeneously generating a reagent throughout a solution at a rate slow enough to allow the initial crystals to grow larger has been studied by Willard and Gordon and co-workers (10).   Under certain conditions, the rate of the hydrolysis of thioacetamide to give hydrogen sulfide can be used to control the rate at which sulfides are precipitated.   Under somewhat different conditions, as is described in the next section of this review, the sulfide precipitates are produced by a direct reaction between thioacetamide and the metal ion without prior hydrolysis of the thioacetamide to hydrogen sulfide being involved.

It is possible to control the rate of this direct reaction, which when properly controlled yields precipitates that are as well coagulated and filterable as are those resulting from the direct reaction with prior hydrolysis. Both of the mechanisms by which thioacetamide produces metal sulfides take place in homogeneous solutions and both processes are properly termed homogeneous precipitations. It is not necessary for a precipitating agent to decompose in solution to produce a species which precipitates another solution component in order to qualify as a homogeneous solution precipitant. A slow direct reaction between the substance to be precipitated and the precipitating agent can also constitute a homogeneous process. In general, any precipitation that can be carried out homogeneously will result in precipitates which "are denser, easier to filter and wash, and are less contaminated with foreign ions than is the case when ordinary precipitation methods are employed" (10). Thus, to the relatively unobjectionable odor of thioacetamide, and the relative stability of its aqueous solutions, should be added as an additional advantage the ease with which the rate of metal sulfide precipitation can be controlled by controlling the temperature and pH of the solution. Thioacetamide possesses, to an unusual degree, the desirable characteristics of a precipitant from homogeneous solutions.

Partly because thioacetamide was originally investigated for the purpose of finding a simple substitute for gaseous hydrogen sulfide, especially for instructional use, and partly because the elements usually precipitated with hydrogen sulfide seemed to be precipitated quantitatively by thioacetamide under the same solution conditions, the impression was gained rather early that thioacetamide could be substituted for hydrogen sulfide without modification of procedure and that exactly the same results would be achieved as with hydrogen sulfide gas. Subsequently certain manufacturers of thioacetamide caused this impression to become more widespread by stating explicitly in their advertising literature that such was the case. Subsequent work by Swift and co-workers (which is discussed in detail below) has shown that this statement is not tenable. Indeed, as more information is accumulated on the reactions of thioacetamide with various metals it becomes clear that the indiscriminate use of thio-

acetamide as a substitute for hydrogen sulfide is not only unjustified, but that the results of such use will seriously prejudice the future
applications of a potentially valuable reagent.

II. REACTIONS OF THIOACETAMIDE (TAA) IN AQUEOUS SOLUTIONS

After 1949 the renewed interest in the possible use of thioacetamide
(TAA) as a substitute for hydrogen sulfide resulted in the development by Flaschka and co-workers (11) of analytical procedures for
precipitating the sulfides of a large number of metals.   These studies
were very valuable in establishing the applicability of TAA to the precipitation of these elements, and the pioneering work of these investigators has been, in large measure, responsible for the subsequent
use of the reagent for quantitative procedures.   More recent work
(12) has pointed out important differences between hydrogen sulfide
and TAA which must be borne in mind if one is to employ TAA as a
precipitant with maximum effectiveness.   Therefore it seems desirable to depart from a strictly chronological treatment of the developments in the analytical chemistry of TAA and consider first the
kinetics of the fundamental reactions which are responsible for the usefulness of TAA in precipitating metal ions.   After the reactions by
which TAA precipitates various sulfides have been considered the procedures for precipitating specific elements can be more logically discussed.   In this section the reactions of TAA in acid and basic solutions and in buffer solutions will be considered.   The precipitation
of metal sulfides by TAA is discussed in the succeeding section.

1. Hydrolysis in Acid Solutions

Swift and Butler (12) studied the hydrolysis of TAA in solutions
having hydrogen ion concentrations ranging from 0.08 to 10^{-4} M
by measuring the rate at which hydrogen sulfide was evolved and
equating this rate with the rate of disappearance of TAA.   They
found that the thio group hydrolyzed at measurable rates; the hydrolysis of the amide group was too slow to be detected by the methods used.   The rate of the hydrolysis of the thio group was observed
to be first order with respect to both TAA and hydrogen ion and the
second order rate constant had a value of 0.21 $\pm$ 0.023 l. mole^{-1}
min.$^{-1}$ at 90°C.; the activation energy of the reaction was 19.1 kcal.
per mole in the temperature range from 60 to 90°C.   The hydrolysis

of the resulting acetamide to give acetic acid and ammonium ion was observed to be a much slower reaction in agreement with the data of Crocker and Lowe (13) on the rate of hydrolysis of acetamide.

A study of the hydrolysis reactions of TAA was also made by Rosenthal and Taylor (14). These authors measured the rate of disappearance of TAA spectrophotometrically in 0.3 to 6F hydrochloric and perchloric acid solutions at 35°C. The rate of the hydrolysis was again observed to be first order with respect to TAA but at acid concentrations greater than about 1F the dependence on the hydrogen ion concentration was no longer the simple first order observed by Swift and Butler (12). In analogy to the well known acid hydrolysis of acetamide, the rate of TAA hydrolysis was observed to reach a maximum in 4.5F hydrochloric acid and 4F perchloric acid and to decrease at higher and lower acid concentrations. It should be mentioned, however, that extrapolation of the Arrhenius plot determined by Swift and Butler between 90 and 60°C. to 35°C., the temperature at which Rosenthal and Taylor worked, gives second order rate constants which agree with those determined by Rosenthal and Taylor for acid concentrations up to about 1F, after which the observed rate is greater than would be expected on the basis of the acid concentration alone. Thus the second order rate constants measured by Swift and Butler are applicable throughout most of the analytically important acid range.

Rosenthal and Taylor proposed a mechanism for the hydrolysis of TAA which led to a rate equation in agreement with their experimental data. They also presented evidence for the formation of thioacetic acid as an intermediate product of TAA hydrolysis prior to acetic acid. The fact that Swift and Butler observed a strictly first order dependence of the rate of hydrolysis on the TAA concentration while following only the rate of evolution of hydrogen sulfide indicates that under the conditions employed by these authors no significant amount of TAA ended up in the form of thioacetate.

Since Swift and Butler also showed from pH measurements that only a few per cent of the TAA hydrolyzed all the way to acetic acid and ammonium ion during the time required for substantial decomposition of TAA they concluded that the hydrolysis reaction proceeds predominantly according to the equation

$$CH_3CSNH_2 + H_2O \longrightarrow CH_3CONH_2 + H_2S \qquad (1)$$

at the acid concentrations employed.

A detailed hydrolysis mechanism proposed by Rosenthal and Taylor takes into consideration the possible tautomerism of TAA,

$$
\underset{\text{I}}{\underset{\parallel}{\overset{\text{S}}{\underset{\parallel}{\text{CH}_3-\text{C}-\text{NH}_2}}}} \rightleftharpoons \underset{\text{II}}{\overset{\text{SH}}{\overset{\mid}{\text{CH}_3-\text{C}=\text{NH}}}} \tag{2}
$$

and predicts that the hydrolysis will lead to thioacetic acid when the reaction occurs via the thioamide form, I, and to acetamide when the reaction occurs via the thiolimido form, II. These authors state that the relative importance of the two routes is unknown on the basis of existing information.

Butler, Peters, and Swift (15) restudied the hydrolysis of TAA at 90°C. in $0.25F$ hydrochloric acid and made use of the spectrophotometer to follow directly the disappearance of TAA. The second order rate constant obtained was in excellent agreement with the value determined by following the rate of hydrogen sulfide evolution and no spectrophotometric evidence of the formation of thioacetic acid was obtained. The spectrophotometric study lent strong support to the previous conclusion (12) that the evolved hydrogen sulfide resulted directly from hydrolysis of TAA and that the rate of hydrolysis of TAA to give thioacetic acid and ammonium ion proceeded too slowly to be observed at the acidities employed.

Analytically, the importance of these measurements of the rate of hydrolysis of TAA in acidic solutions lies in the way the data can be used to choose the best conditions for carrying out sulfide precipitations. In precipitations of sulfides by means of the hydrogen sulfide produced by the hydrolysis of TAA one can calculate that with a solution $0.1F$ in hydrochloric acid, $0.01F$ in a metal cation of the type $M(II)$, and $0.05F$ in TAA the time required for the hydrolysis of TAA to furnish an amount of hydrogen sulfide equivalent to the metal present is 15 min. at 90°C. At 60°C. the time required becomes approximately 2 hr.

2. Hydrolysis in Alkaline Solutions

Butler, Peters, and Swift (15) also studied the hydrolysis of TAA in alkaline solutions. In 0.08 to $0.30F$ sodium hydroxide solutions they observed that two sets of reactions occur:

$$
\text{CH}_3\text{CSNH}_2 + \text{OH}^- \longrightarrow \text{CH}_3\text{CSO}^- + \text{NH}_3 \tag{3A}
$$

followed by

$$CH_3CSO^- + OH^- \longrightarrow CH_3COO^- + HS^- \tag{3B}$$

and

$$CH_3CSNH_2 + OH^- \longrightarrow CH_3CONH_2 + HS^- \tag{4A}$$

followed by

$$CH_3CONH_2 + OH^- \longrightarrow CH_3COO^- + NH_3 \tag{4B}$$

Reaction (4B) had previously been shown to be first order with respect to acetamide and hydroxide ion (13) and Butler *et al.* demonstrated that the rates of reactions (3A), (3B), and (4A) are also first-order with respect to both reactants.

The rate of the second order reaction (3A) is difficult to measure for lack of a good analytical method, but Butler *et al.* were able to estimate the constant to within about 10 % by distilling and titrating the ammonia. The resulting value for the second order constant was 5 l. mole^{-1} min.$^{-1}$ at 90°C. The rate of reaction (3B) was measured by following the rate of HS$^-$ formation titrimetrically and gave a value for the second order constant of 0.019 ± 0.0015 l. mole^{-1} min.$^{-1}$ at 90°C. The rate of reaction (4A) was estimated by observing that the total quantity of ammonia which was initially recovered by distillation from a sodium hydroxide–TAA solution amounted to about 80 % of the TAA which had been added to the solution. This indicated that reaction (3A) proceeded about four times as fast as reaction (4A) which led to a value of 1 to 2 l. mole^{-1} min.$^{-1}$ at 90°C. for the second order rate constant for reaction (4A).

The second order rate constant for reaction (4B) was measured by Crocker and Lowe (13). Its value at 90°C. was calculated from their data by Butler *et al.* to be 0.24 l. mole^{-1} min.$^{-1}$.

The rate constants evaluated by Butler, Peters, and Swift are analytically significant since by their use the rate at which sulfide can be generated, and, therefore, the rate at which metals can be precipitated from basic solutions can be calculated if only the hydrolysis of TAA leads to precipitation. Thus, these constants show that in separate solutions with equal hydrogen ion and hydroxyl ion concentrations, the hydroxide-catalyzed hydrolysis of TAA to yield sulfide and acetamide is 8 to 10 times as fast as the acid-catalyzed hydrolysis, but that in hydroxide solutions only about one-fifth of the TAA hydrolyzes directly to give sulfide. Hence, neglecting the contribution from the much slower thioacetate hydrolysis in basic solution, for equal initial TAA concentrations sulfide is produced about twice as fast in a hydroxide ion solution as in a hydrogen ion solution of the same concentration.

It is worth noting that the rate constants determined by Butler *et al.* indicate that in hydroxide solutions containing only an amount of TAA equivalent to the metal ion about 20% of the metal would be precipitated at the rate at which reaction (4A) proceeds and the remaining 80% would be precipitated as a result of reaction (3B) which proceeds at 1/50 the rate of reaction (4A).

3. Reactions in Alkaline Buffer Solutions

Since a frequently employed method of precipitating metal sulfides involves the use of buffered solutions to control the sulfide ion concentration, Peters and Swift (16) examined the reactions of thioacetamide in ammonia–ammonium ion and carbonate–hydrogen carbonate buffers. The results they obtained were quite unexpected. In ammonia–ammonium chloride solutions containing an ammonia to ammonium ion ratio of 5 to 1 and having pH values near 10, the rate of sulfide evolution was observed to be 10 to 200 times as fast as was expected on the basis of the pH and the previously evaluated second order rate constant for the hydroxide-catalyzed sulfide hydrolysis of TAA. Their measurements showed that in the presence of ammonia the rate of sulfide evolution was first order with respect to TAA and second order with respect to ammonia. The third order rate constant was calculated to be 0.055 l.^{2} mole^{-2} min.$^{-1}$ at 90°C. Ammonium ion appeared to have no effect on the rate.

In experiments with ammonia–ammonium buffers where sufficient time was allowed to elapse for essentially complete reaction of the TAA to have occurred the rate of sulfide evolution fell to a value characteristic of the hydroxide-catalyzed hydrolysis of thioacetate observed previously in sodium hydroxide solutions (15). Hence it was concluded that ammonia increased the rate of sulfide evolution from TAA but had essentially no effect on the rate of sulfide evolution from thioacetate.

In order to account for the observed second order dependence on the ammonia concentration Peters and Swift proposed the following mechanism involving the reaction of one molecule of thioacetamide and two molecules of ammonia to produce an amidine:

$$CH_3-\underset{\underset{NH_2}{|}}{\overset{\overset{NH_2}{|}}{C}}=S + NH_3 \underset{fast}{\rightleftharpoons} CH_3-\underset{\underset{NH_2}{|}}{\overset{\overset{NH_2}{|}}{C}}-SH \qquad (5A)$$

$$CH_3-\underset{\underset{NH_2}{|}}{\overset{\overset{NH_2}{|}}{C}}-SH + NH_3 \xrightarrow[determining]{rate} CH_3-\overset{\overset{NH_2}{|}}{C}=NH + HS^- + NH_4^+ \quad (5B)$$

This mechanism implies that the ammonia does not serve as a general basic catalyst but is a reactant and is stoichiometrically involved in the reaction. An experiment which could be used to verify the above mechanism would be to follow the rate of change of the concentration of ammonia in an unbuffered solution containing only ammonia and a large excess of TAA.

The relative magnitudes of the reaction rate constants for the hydroxide-catalyzed hydrolysis of TAA and the reaction with ammonia is such that the rate of sulfide evolution in ammonia–ammonium ion buffers, at a pH 9 to 10, is determined primarily by the ammonia concentration and not by the hydroxide concentration. The analytical ramifications of this fact are evident.

Peters and Swift (16) also studied the hydrolysis of TAA in carbonate–hydrogen carbonate solutions and obtained unexpected results. They found that the rate of sulfide evolution is first order with respect to the TAA and to the carbonate ion, and is inversely one-half order with respect to the hydrogen carbonate ion. No mechanism to account for these observations was proposed.

Before attempting to formulate a suitable mechanism it would be desirable to know whether or not carbonate and hydrogen carbonate are consumed during the evolution of sulfide. Experiments which followed the change in the concentration of carbonate species in the presence of an excess of TAA would help to answer this question. The specific reaction rate constant was calculated to be $0.015 \pm 0.0014 \ 1.^{1/2} \ mole^{-1/2} \ min.^{-1}$ at 90°C. The magnitude of this rate constant is such that, at the hydroxide ion concentrations of carbonate–hydrogen carbonate buffer solutions, the rates of the hydroxide-catalyzed amide and sulfide hydrolyses of TAA are very small compared to the rate of sulfide evolution from the carbonate–hydrogen carbonate solution.   Thus, in both ammonia–ammonium ion and carbonate–hydrogen carbonate buffers the rate of sulfide evolution is determined not by the pH but by the concentrations of the buffers.

The meagerness of the available experimental data on the reactions of TAA in alkaline buffer solutions makes generalizing on the sulfide-producing reactions of TAA both difficult and unwise.   However, the surprises which resulted from studying the TAA reactions in both ammonia and carbonate solutions suggest that a study of the behavior of TAA in the absence of metal ions should precede the use of any untried buffer systems with TAA to precipitate metal ions.   The experiments which have been carried out thus far suggest that the rate of hydrolysis of TAA in alkaline solutions will be generally influenced by the specific buffer constituents used.

4. Reaction of Hydrazine and TAA

The enhancement of the rate of sulfide evolution by ammonia and carbonate ion makes them valuable in sulfide precipitations in alkaline media where it is time saving to carry out the precipitation at a faster rate than would correspond to a specific hydroxide-ion catalysis of the TAA hydrolysis.   A species which would accelerate the rate of sulfide evolution in neutral and weakly acidic solutions would be even more valuable because of the larger number of sulfide precipitations which are normally carried out in such solutions.   Hydrazine has been found to be a very promising accelerator of hydrogen sulfide evolution from neutral and weakly acidic TAA solutions (17).   Preliminary studies have shown that in this acceleration the hydrazine is consumed.   Detailed kinetic studies of the TAA–N_2H_4 reaction are in progress.

III. REACTIONS INVOLVED IN THE PRECIPITATION OF METAL SULFIDES BY TAA

Once rate constants for the formation of sulfide from various solutions containing only TAA have been determined, one would expect that experiments on the rates of precipitations of metallic sulfides from solutions by TAA could be interpreted for most metals.   If the rate of reaction between a metal and sulfide is much faster than the rate of hydrolysis of TAA one would expect that, unless some specific interaction between the metal and TAA occurs, the rate of precipitation of the metal sulfide would be the same as the rate of formation of hydrogen sulfide from TAA in a similar solution in the absence of the metal. The studies which have been carried out to date contain several examples of sulfide precipitations for which this is true. These studies, however, also have shown that specific interactions between the metal and TAA occur frequently and in these cases the rate of formation of metal sulfides is not what one would calculate on the basis of the rate constants for the hydrolysis of TAA. The results of the studies of both systems are described below.

1. Precipitation of Lead Sulfide

A. HYDROLYSIS CONTROLLED PRECIPITATION

The first measurement of the rate of precipitation of a metallic sulfide from a TAA solution was made by Swift and Butler (12). They measured the rate of precipitation of lead sulfide from solutions of pH 1 to 5 by analyzing filtered aliquots for lead. They observed that when the solutions had pH values of less than 3 the rate at which lead was removed was identical to the rate at which TAA hydrolyzed. In addition, the rate of precipitation of the lead sulfide was independent of the lead ion concentration and of the presence of lead sulfide. Also, in a solution $0.01F$ in lead nitrate, $0.05F$ in TAA, and having a hydrochloric acid concentration $(0.3F)$ sufficiently high to prevent the precipitation of lead sulfide (since the gas was continually swept from the solution), the rate of evolution of hydrogen sulfide was identical to that in a similar solution which contained no lead ion. These observations led to the conclusion that any specific interaction between lead ion and TAA in solutions more acidic than pH 3 was negligible under these conditions.

B. PRECIPITATION BY A DIRECT REACTION

Between pH values of 3.5 and 5.1 Swift and Butler (12) observed that the rates of precipitation of lead sulfide from TAA solutions were considerably greater than the rates of hydrolysis of TAA at the same pH values. Experiments showed that the rate of decrease of the lead-(II) concentration was first order with respect to both the TAA and to the lead(II) concentrations and was inversely half order with respect to the hydrogen ion. The rate constant was calculated to be $1.13 \times 10^{-3} \ 1.^{1/2} \ \text{mole}^{-1/2} \ \text{min.}^{-1}$ at 90°C. in $0.081F$ sodium formate solutions, and the activation energy was calculated to be 15.5 kcal./mole.

Experiments were performed which showed that formate ion forms a complex of considerable stability with lead ion. All the kinetic experiments were carried out in $0.081F$ sodium formate solution and the reproducible rate constants observed are strictly applicable only to lead(II) solutions containing this concentration of formate. No measurement of the rate of reaction of uncomplexed lead ion has been made.

Experiments designed to determine the effect of chloride ion on the rate of the direct reaction between lead ion and TAA have shown that the addition of chloride decreases the rate of precipitation of lead sulfide (18). The decrease in rate which was observed could be accounted for by the formation of a less rapidly reactive $PbCl^+$ complex. The quantitative aspects of the chloride inhibition are still under investigation.

To account for the accelerated precipitation of lead sulfide at pH values greater than 3, Swift and Butler (12) proposed that a direct reaction between TAA and lead(II) was occurring. However, no mechanism for a direct reaction which would account for the half order inhibition by hydrogen ion was suggested. The possibility of the reaction proceeding through species such as $Pb_2(OH)^{2+}$, which could give a half order hydroxide catalysis, seems remote in view of the negligible proportion of the lead which exists in this form at the pH values involved. In addition, the observed first order dependence of the reaction rate on the concentration of lead(II) is not compatible with a mechanism involving $Pb_2(OH)^{2+}$. The kinetic data for the dependence of the direct reaction on the lead and TAA concentrations are not consistent with the possible existence of lead–TAA complexes and this type of species can be ruled out. As yet there has been no satisfactory explanation proposed for the half order inhibition by hydrogen ion.*

Kinetic experiments with lead(II) solutions of pH values greater than 5 have not been carried out. With the data of Butler, Peters, and Swift (14) on the kinetics of TAA reactions in alkaline solutions it becomes possible to interpret the results of future experiments on the rate of precipitation of lead(II) from alkaline solutions. Barber and Taylor (19) and Flaschka (20) have noted that the precipitation of lead sulfide proceeds much more rapidly in alkaline than in acid

* Recent experiments at the California Institute of Technology have indicated that the rate depression for the "direct reaction" can depend upon the number of nuclei present, and the dependence of the rate on both TAA and pH can be other than that given above. These effects are being studied.

solutions. A 5-fold increase in rate is to be expected from the more rapid basic hydrolysis of TAA but no quantitative data are available on the rates at which species such as $Pb(OH)^+$, $Pb(OH)_3{}^-$, etc., may react directly with TAA to yield lead sulfide.

2. Precipitation of the Arsenic Sulfides

A. HYDROLYSIS CONTROLLED PRECIPITATION

Arsenic(III). Butler and Swift (21) have studied the precipitation of arsenic(III) by TAA in acid solutions ranging from $6F$ hydrochloric acid to pH 6. The rate of precipitation was followed by determining the arsenic concentration in filtered aliquots from the reaction solution. Throughout this pH range there was no evidence that the precipitation proceeded by any path other than the hydrolysis of the TAA.

Arsenic(III) was precipitated as the sulfide more slowly in TAA solutions of pH 1 to 4 when nitrogen was slowly bubbled through the solution whereas passing nitrogen through lead solutions of similar pH values had no effect on the rate of precipitation of lead sulfide. This indicates that the reaction between arsenious acid and hydrogen sulfide is slower than the reaction between lead ion and hydrogen sulfide under these conditions.

As_2S_3, being extremely insoluble, is frequently precipitated with gaseous hydrogen sulfide in $6F$ hydrochloric acid solutions. At such hydrogen ion concentrations the rate of hydrolysis of TAA is quite rapid. In fact, even at 20°C. with a solution $0.1F$ in TAA and $0.01F$ in arsenic(III) one can calculate that the arsenic would be essentially completely precipitated in 25 min.; at 90°C. the precipitation would be complete in less than 30 sec.

The precipitation of arsenic affords an example of the way in which variations in the acid concentration as well as the temperature can be used to control the rate of sulfide formation. These two variables are independent and when the sulfide is sufficiently insoluble precipitations can be conveniently carried out at room temperature by appropriate increase of the acid concentration.

The chloro–arsenic(III) species which are known (22) to exist in hydrochloric acid solutions of arsenic(III) appear to have no effect on the rate at which arsenic is precipitated by TAA. The kinetic experiments indicated that all of the arsenic(III) species reacted with hydrogen sulfide rapidly as compared to the rate with which hydrogen sulfide was produced from TAA.

B. REDUCTION OF ARSENIC(V) BY TAA

Arsenic(V). Butler and Swift (21) found that in 0.3 to $1F$ hydrochloric acid solutions the initial product of the reaction between TAA and arsenic(V) was sulfur. The precipitation of arsenic sulfide commenced only subsequent to the precipitation of the sulfur and the quantity of sulfur which formed indicated that the arsenic(V) was being reduced to a considerable extent before the precipitation of a sulfide. Rate measurements were made of the reduction of arsenic(V) by TAA. In hydrochloric acid solutions of pH 1 to 2 the reduction is first order with respect to TAA, to arsenic(V), and to hydrogen ion. The third order rate constant was calculated to be 35 l.^{2} mole^{-2} min.$^{-1}$ at 90°C. and the activation energy was roughly estimated to be 20 kcal./mole.

In solutions of pH greater than about 2 the dependence of the rate on the hydrogen ion concentration is no longer first order. Because the precipitation of arsenic at pH values above about 2 is generally of minor analytical importance, no quantitative determination of the hydrogen ion dependence in this pH range was made. The observed change in hydrogen ion dependence is not unexpected, however, in view of the change in the predominant form of arsenic(V) at pH values above 2 (the first ionization constant of arsenic acid is 6×10^{-3}) (23).

The first order dependence of the rate of reduction on the arsenic(V) concentration indicates that the reduction of arsenic(V) is independent of the rate of hydrolysis of TAA and is the result of a direct reaction between arsenic(V) and TAA. Butler and Swift (21) confirmed this interpretation by showing that for at least the first half of the reaction the rate of arsenic(V) reduction is independent of whether or not the hydrogen sulfide formed by the hydrolysis of TAA is swept from the solution as fast as it is formed. As the arsenic(V) concentration and therefore the rate of the reduction reaction both decrease, the hydrogen sulfide from the hydrolysis of TAA reacts with arsenic(V) to form thioarsenic acids which slowly decompose to give sulfur and arsenic(III).

Thus the addition of TAA to acid solutions of either arsenic(III) or arsenic(V) leads to the formation of arsenic(III) sulfide. In arsenic (III) solutions the rate of precipitation is determined by the rate of hydrolysis of the TAA to give hydrogen sulfide. In arsenic(V) solutions the rate determining process is also the rate at which hydrogen sulfide is formed by hydrolysis but this slowest step must be preceded by the slightly more rapid reduction of arsenic(V) by TAA in order for the hydrogen sulfide to produce rapid precipitation of As_2S_3. Butler and Swift (21) found that the concentration of chloride ion did not affect the rate of reduction of arsenic(V); the same rate constant was obtained in chloride-free perchloric acid solutions as in solutions $0.1M$ in chloride ion.

Most analytical chemists have learned from painful experience that the precipitation of arsenic(V) from approximately $0.3F$ acid solutions by gaseous hydrogen sulfide is a slow, tedious process.   One typical procedure requires that the solution be saturated with hydrogen sulfide, placed in a pressure bottle, and heated to 100°C. for 30 min. in order to effect quantitative precipitation.   By contrast the use of TAA under similar solution conditions results in quantitative precipitation of the arsenic in less than 10 min. at 90°C. without the use of a pressure bottle.

When TAA is used to precipitate arsenic(V) it is desirable that the TAA concentration be large enough to give a reasonable rate of reduction of the arsenic(V).   In addition it is necessary that sufficient TAA remain after the reduction of arsenic(V) to provide hydrogen sulfide at a convenient rate.   The rate constants determined by Butler and Swift enable one to calculate the amount of TAA needed in order to complete the precipitation in any chosen length of time.

3. Precipitation of Nickel

A. HYDROLYSIS CONTROLLED PRECIPITATION

The precipitation of nickel sulfide from acidic solutions of TAA has been studied by Bowersox, Smith, and Swift (24).   Nickel sulfide is not precipitated with the hydrogen sulfide group elements from a $0.3F$ hydrochloric acid solution saturated with hydrogen sulfide.   Nickel sulfide can be precipitated at pH 4 to 5 with hydrogen sulfide (25) but is usually precipitated from a weakly alkaline solution by means of ammonium sulfide (26).   In TAA solutions at a pH of 4.5 the rate of the TAA hydrolysis is so small that about 3×10^4 min. are required to produce 1 mmole of hydrogen sulfide in 100 ml. of a $0.1F$ TAA solution at 90°C.   Because of this slow rate no experimental study of the hydrolysis controlled precipitation of nickel has been made.

B. PRECIPITATION BY A DIRECT REACTION

Precipitation from Acid Solution. In contrast to what was to be expected on the basis of the known behavior of nickel with hydrogen sulfide a slow precipitation of nickel sulfide was observed from solutions which were $0.10F$ in TAA, $0.01F$ in nickel(II), and 0.3 to $0.1M$ in hydrogen ion. The precipitation at these pH values is not hydrolysis controlled because only a small amount of nickel sulfide is formed during a time which is adequate for the formation of an excess of hydrogen sulfide. Also the rate of precipitation of nickel sulfide at these pH values is independent of whether or not the hydrogen sulfide is rapidly swept from the solution with a stream of nitrogen.

In solutions of pH 5 to 7 and at 90°C., nickel is precipitated at a rate which can be conveniently followed; measurements made under these conditions have shown that the precipitation is the result of a direct reaction between nickel(II) and TAA entirely analogous to the direct reaction observed with lead.

The rate of the reaction was determined to be first order with respect to nickel ion and to TAA and inversely half order with respect to hydrogen ion. Efforts to formulate a satisfactory mechanism which will explain this peculiar hydrogen ion dependence have been no more successful for the case of nickel than was true for lead. The rate constant was calculated to be $2.2 \times 10^{-4} \, 1.^{1/2} \, \text{mole}^{1/2} \, \text{min.}^{-1}$ at 90°C. and the activation energy to be 20 kcal./mole.

The occurrence of the direct reaction at higher pH values suggested that the slow precipitation observed in more acidic solutions, pH 0.8 to 2, was due to the persistence of this reaction at these hydrogen ion concentrations, where, unlike the case with lead, the much more rapid hydrolysis of TAA does not precipitate the metal ion and thereby mask any direct reaction. Comparisons of the amount of nickel precipitated in a certain time in $0.3F$ perchloric acid with the amount calculated on the basis of the measured rate constant confirmed this interpretation. When a $0.3F$ perchloric acid solution, which contained the same concentration of nickel as before, was saturated with hydrogen sulfide no nickel sulfide formed even after 70 hr. at room temperature.

The question as to why it is possible to precipitate nickel sulfide with TAA at hydrogen ion concentrations where gaseous hydrogen sulfide leads to no precipitations is of considerable interest. Two possible explanations are offered by Bowersox, Smith, and Swift. One makes use of the fact that there are supposed to be three allotropic forms of nickel sulfide. The solubility products of these α, β, and γ forms of nickel sulfide are given by Ringbom (27) as 3×10^{-19}, 1×10^{-24}, and 2×10^{-26}, respectively. If hydrogen sulfide can cause only the most soluble form to precipitate but TAA is capable of precipitating the least soluble form by a direct reaction one would expect a precipitate of nickel sulfide to form in TAA solutions with acid concentrations about 10^4 times as large as the most acidic solution from which hydrogen sulfide produces precipitation.

The second explanation offered involves the possibility that a slow step in the precipitation of nickel sulfide by hydrogen sulfide involves the reaction between nickel ion and HS^- or S^{2-} ion. The concentrations of these two sulfide species in solutions of pH 1 to 2 are much lower than in ammonium sulfide solution so that the rate of precipitation of nickel sulfide would be correspondingly slower if it is limited by the rate of reaction between, say, sulfide ion and nickel ion. The concentration of TAA is not significantly affected by pH in the range studied so that as much TAA is available for a direct reaction with nickel ion at pH 1 to 2 as at pH 4 to 5 or higher. Thus both TAA and hydrogen sulfide in acid solutions could lead to the precipitation of the same form of nickel sulfide but the rate with TAA would be much greater because its concentration is so much greater than that of HS^- or S^{2-}.

The effect of complex-forming anions on the direct reaction has not been studied but the pronounced effects produced by chloride ion on the direct reactions of lead and cadmium with TAA indicate that a similar effect for nickel is not unlikely although the smaller stability of the chloronickel species would make the effect less pronounced. In the pH range from 5 to 7 the direct reaction of nickel and TAA was studied in hydrogen phthalate–phthalate buffer solutions. There appeared to be no effect on the rate of total buffer concentration and the same rate constant applied to the reaction at lower pH values in the absence of any phthalate buffer. Thus phthalate appears to be without significant influence on the reaction.

Precipitation from Ammoniacal Solution. The kinetics of the precipitation of nickel from ammoniacal solutions of TAA have been studied by Peters, Klein, and Swift (28). It was observed that the rate of precipitation of nickel is faster than could be accounted for by the known rate of production of sulfide from the reaction of ammonia and TAA (16) (the hydroxyl catalyzed hydrolysis is negligible at these pH values). By subtracting from the observed rate of precipitation of nickel the contribution due to the production of sulfide by the ammonia–TAA reaction Peters, Klein, and Swift were able to elucidate the nature of the additional reaction which was responsible for the more rapid precipitation of nickel sulfide. It was anticipated that the second reaction was a continuation in alkaline solution of the direct reaction which was observed to occur between TAA and nickel in acidic solutions. The rate of the reaction in ammoniacal solution was observed to have a first order dependence on TAA, on total nickel, and an inverse half order dependence on hydrogen ion. Inasmuch as this is the same dependence as is observed for the direct reaction in acid solution it is almost certainly this reaction that is being observed in ammoniacal solution.

The dependence of the rate of the direct reaction on the concentration of ammonia indicated that the various nickel–ammonia complexes present react with TAA at rates which decrease uniformly as the number of ammonias in the nickel complex increases.

Analytically, the precipitation of nickel from ammoniacal TAA solutions offers several advantages. By proper choice of temperature and ammonia concentration quantitative precipitation can be achieved in 5 to 10 min. and the resulting precipitate is readily coagulated and filtered. This should be welcome news to analysts who have experienced frustration in their attempts to handle the dark nickel sulfide suspensions resulting from precipitations made in ammonium sulfide solutions.

4. Precipitation of Cadmium

A. HYDROLYSIS CONTROLLED PRECIPITATION

The kinetics of the precipitation of cadmium sulfide by the use of TAA have been studied by Bowersox and Swift (29). The experiments covered the pH range from 1 to 6.3 and the results were completely analogous to those obtained by Swift and Butler (12) for the precipitation of lead. At pH values of 2 and less, the rate of precipitation of cadmium is entirely controlled by the hydrolysis of TAA and is independent of the cadmium concentration or the presence of cadmium sulfide.

B. PRECIPITATION BY A DIRECT REACTION

At pH values between 2 and 4 the precipitation results from both the hydrolysis of TAA and a direct reaction between TAA and cadmium ion; at pH values above 4 the direct reaction predominates. As with lead and nickel, the rate of the direct reaction between cadmium ion and TAA, between pH values of 3.3 and 6.3, is first order with respect to cadmium ion and to TAA and is inversely half order with respect to hydrogen ion.

The rate constant for the direct reaction was calculated to be 8.1×10^{-4} l.$^{1/2}$ mole$^{-1/2}$ min.$^{-1}$ at 90°C. in $0.15F$ sodium formate solutions and the activation energy, 20.8 ± 1.2 kcal./mole.

The sodium formate buffer solution which was used to adjust the pH at values above 3 was found to have no effect on the rate of cadmium precipitation.

No information was obtained on the possible existence of cadmium formate complexes but the data indicate that if the complexes are formed to a significant extent they do not react with TAA at measurably different rates.

Chloride ion was observed, by Bowersox and Swift (29), to decrease the rate of the direct reaction between cadmium and TAA. Subsequent measurements by Bowersox, Owens, and Smith (30) have indicated that the effect of chloride can be accounted for on the basis of the formation of chlorocadmium complexes which react more slowly with TAA.

The ability of chloride (and presumably other complex-forming anions) to alter the rate of the direct reactions between TAA and metal ions could conceivably be taken advantage of analytically. It might be possible, for instance, to use chloride to decrease the rate of precipitation of a metal which formed strong chloride complexes to such an extent that it could be separated from a noncomplex-forming metal which would be more rapidly precipitated by the TAA.

Qualitative experiments have shown that the rate of precipitation of cadmium sulfide from ammoniacal cadmium solutions of TAA is much faster than the rate from acidic solutions. Whether this increase in rate results from the faster production of sulfide from TAA in ammoniacal solutions (16), or from a continuing increase in the rate of the direct reaction as the pH increases, or both, has not yet been determined.

5. Precipitation of Zinc

A. HYDROLYSIS CONTROLLED PRECIPITATION

Bowersox and Swift (31) have obtained data on the rate of precipitations of zinc sulfide by TAA. In solutions sufficiently acidic to cause the hydrolysis of TAA to proceed at a conveniently measurable rate, zinc sulfide is significantly soluble and such solutions tend to supersaturate. Furthermore, some of the hydrogen sulfide formed from the hydrolysis of TAA may escape from the solution without causing precipitation. For this reason, and because the rate of precipitation of zinc sulfide by hydrogen sulfide is slow in such solutions, measurements of the hydrolysis controlled precipitation have been made only at pH values where there is significant contribution of the direct reaction which is discussed below.

A direct reaction between zinc and TAA, similar in all respects to that observed with lead, cadmium, and nickel, was observed to occur in solutions of pH 1 to 7. The rate of the precipitation is first order both with respect to zinc and to TAA and is inversely half order with respect to hydrogen ion. The rate constant was calculated to be 4.2 $\times 10^{-4}$ l.$^{1/2}$ mole$^{-1/2}$ min.$^{-1}$ at 90°C. Preliminary experiments indicate that, as with nickel, zinc sulfide can be precipitated at lower pH values with TAA than with hydrogen sulfide.

Precipitation from Ammoniacal Solution. Klein (31a) has measured the rate of precipitation of zinc from ammoniacal solutions of TAA at 40°C. It was shown that zinc behaves similarly to nickel in that its precipitation results from the sulfide produced by the ammonia–TAA reaction and a direct reaction between the zinc–ammonia complex ion and TAA. The value of the rate constant for the third order ammonia–TAA reaction at 40°C. was measured to be 5.0 $\times$ 10^{-3} l.^{2} mole^{-2} min.$^{-1}$, which is in reasonable agreement with the value obtained from extrapolation of the Arrhenius plot of Peters and Swift (16).

The rates of the direct reactions between TAA and the various zinc ammonia species present in ammoniacal solutions having pH values between 8 and 9 were obtained by subtracting from the overall rate of precipitation, the rate of precipitation caused by the ammonia–TAA reaction. The resulting rate was shown to be first order with respect to the total zinc and with respect to TAA, and inverse two-thirds order with respect to hydrogen ion. The rate decreased as the concentration of ammonia increased and the dependence on the ammonia concentration indicated that the rate of reaction between TAA and each of the four zinc–ammonia species $Zn(NH_3)^{2+}$, $Zn(NH_3)_2^{2+}$, $Zn(NH_3)_3^{2+}$, and $Zn(NH_3)_4^{2+}$ decreased as the number of ammonia molecules in the complex increased. The values of the individual rate constants (in terms of liters, moles, and minutes) are indicated in the following expression which gives the over-all rate at which zinc is precipitated by TAA in ammoniacal solutions.

$$\frac{-dZn(II)}{dt} = \frac{(10^{-7})[TAA]}{[H^+]^{2/3}} \left\{ 53[Zn(NH_3)^{2+}] + 21[Zn(NH_3)_2^{2+}] + \right.$$

$$\left. 8.9[Zn(NH_3)_3^{2+}] + 3.1[Zn(NH_3)_4^{2+}] \right\} + 5.02 \times 10^{-3} [TAA][NH_3]^2$$

Klein observed some unusual behavior of ammoniacal zinc–TAA solutions when the concentrations of zinc and TAA were increased to near $0.01F$ and the ammonia concentrations were of the same order of magnitude. Under these circumstances it frequently was observed that up to four-fifths of the zinc would precipitate extremely rapidly upon addition of the TAA to the ammoniacal zinc solution. Whether or not this rapid precipitation was observed, appeared to depend on the age of the TAA solution, the rate of mixing of the resulting solution, and the presence or absence of seed crystals of ZnS in the solution. This behavior suggested that nucleation phenomena were involved, and conditions were controlled to eliminate the rapid initial precipitation in order to carry out the kinetic measurements. So long as no rapid initial precipitation occurred the rate of precipitation of zinc was adequately described by the rate expression given above.

The data which have been presented thus far constitute essentially all the quantitative kinetic information which is available on the precipitation of metal sulfides with TAA. Such studies of other elements are in progress at the California Institute of Technology and some preliminary results of four of these studies are outlined below.

6. Precipitation of Silver

The precipitation of silver with TAA occurs through both the hydrolysis of TAA and a direct reaction between TAA and silver ion (32). The former predominates at pH values of less than 2 and the latter predominates when the pH is greater than 3. Under the conditions studied, the direct reaction was inhibited by TAA, and an apparent inverse third order dependence was observed. This effect was attributed to the existence of a stable complex between silver ion and TAA and subsequent potentiometric measurements (33) have established that in solutions of pH 2 to 3 in which the concentration of TAA is 5 to 10 times the silver concentration, a complex of the type Ag-$(TAA)_4^+$ exists. The rate of the direct reaction had a first order dependence on silver ion and an inverse half order dependence on hydrogen ion.

When TAA is added to $1M$ sodium hydroxide solutions containing silver in the form of the thiosulfate complex a quite rapid formation of silver sulfide occurs. It is not known whether the silver sulfide is formed primarily by means of a direct reaction between the silver thiosulfate complex anion and TAA or as a result of this species' reacting with the sulfide produced by the hydrolysis of TAA. Regardless, Bush, Zuehlke, and Ballard (34) devised a method for the titration of silver in $1F$ sodium hydroxide containing thiosulfate with a solution of TAA. The end point was determined potentiometrically with a silver sulfide wire electrode and a calomel reference electrode.

7. Precipitation of Thallium

Unipositive thallium appears not to be precipitated by TAA at pH values below 4 (32). At 60°C. the precipitation takes place at a conveniently measurable rate only at pH values of 9 or above. The precipitation is evidently the result of a direct reaction because the rate is first order with respect to thallium.

8. Precipitation of Copper

In acidic solutions at room temperature the first interaction between Cu(II) and TAA leads to the formation of a Cu(I)–TAA complex and the precipitation of sulfur (35). When the solution is heated the complex is decomposed and copper sulfide precipitates. The kinetics of these processes have not been quantitatively investigated.

9. Precipitation of Molybdenum

The precipitation of molybdenum(VI) by TAA appears to take place through both the hydrolysis of the TAA and a direct reaction (36). The direct reaction predominates at pH values of 4 and

greater. The reduction of molybdenum(VI), which is a difficulty
encountered in the precipitation of molybdenum with hydrogen sulfide, also appeared to take place with TAA in 6 to $8M$ hydrochloric
acid solutions. As the pH increased the amount of reduction diminished until it was negligible at pH 4.

10. Analytical Aspects of the Reactions of TAA

The kinetic studies which have been carried out have demonstrated
that the use of TAA to precipitate metals involves the consideration of
points which are not encountered when gaseous hydrogen sulfide is the
precipitating agent. For example, when the hydrolysis of TAA is
utilized in an acid solution to supply hydrogen sulfide the solution
does not in general become saturated with hydrogen sulfide and this
will affect the pH at which quantitative precipitation of sulfides will
occur. A solution which is $0.1F$ in hydrochloric acid and $0.05F$ in
TAA is typical of solutions which have been recommended for precipitations. The rate constant for the hydrolysis of TAA determined
by Swift and Butler (12) enables one to calculate that at 90°C. the
time required for the hydrolysis of half of the TAA in this solution is
45 min.; even complete hydrolysis of the TAA without any loss of
hydrogen sulfide would result in a solution only half saturated with
hydrogen sulfide. This calculation makes understandable the observation of Swift and Butler that a solution at pH 2.7 containing
$0.01F$ zinc salt and $0.1F$ TAA when heated to 90°C. for 1 hr. resulted
in the precipitation of less than 1 mg. of zinc whereas saturation of the
same solution with gaseous hydrogen sulfide resulted in complete
precipitation of the zinc in 3 to 4 min.

The time and the TAA required to obtain quantitative precipitation in acid solutions can be minimized by beginning the precipitation in a small volume of solution and then diluting to the desired
final volume and acid concentration. During the pretreatment the
concentrations of TAA and acid are correspondingly greater and advantage is taken of the fact that the rate of the acid hydrolysis of the
TAA to give hydrogen sulfide is first order with respect to both the
TAA and the acid. When the solution is diluted to the final volume,
thus decreasing the acid concentration, the dissolved hydrogen sulfide
precipitates the more soluble sulfides. The solution should not be
boiled or contained in an open vessel during this pretreatment or

hydrogen sulfide will be lost. The solution should be warmed, the container stoppered and then heated in boiling water for the necessary time. In addition, care must be exercised to avoid loss of hydrogen sulfide after the pretreated solution is diluted. Thus, lead sulfide precipitates produced by such a dilution with cold water have been seen to dissolve when the solution was subsequently boiled.

Another result of the use of TAA, which is not encountered with gaseous hydrogen sulfide, is the presence of excess TAA and its decomposition products, in the supernatant solution after a precipitation; the latter include acetate, acetamide, ammonium ion, and thioacetate depending on the hydrolysis conditions. The possibility that any of these species could interfere with subsequent procedures needs to be considered when TAA is used in any but a terminal step of an analysis.

Finally, the demonstration that the precipitation of metal sulfides by TAA can proceed through hydrolysis of TAA, or by means of a direct reaction of TAA with the metal ions, or by both reactions simultaneously, coupled with the observation that chloride ion markedly affects the rate of the direct reaction for some cations makes it extremely unwise to continue to regard TAA simply as a source of hydrogen sulfide. To do so would be to disregard the possibilities for using the direct reaction and the anion effects in order to perform separations and precipitations under conditions that would be impossible with hydrogen sulfide.

A partial summary of the quantitative data on the rates of precipitation of various metal sulfides is presented in Table I. This table contains the time, in minutes, calculated to be necessary to precipitate 99% of these metals. Both the hydrolysis controlled and direct reaction mechanisms were considered in the calculations. The table is intended as a rough guide and the data will not be quantitatively applicable to solutions containing different complexing or buffering agents.

IV. ANALYTICAL PROCEDURES FOR THE PRECIPITATION OF METAL SULFIDES BY TAA

A relatively large number of procedures for precipitating the sulfides of various elements with TAA have been reported in the literature. The first application to quantitative procedures was made by Flaschka

TABLE I

Times[a] Required for Generation of Sulfide from, and Precipitation of Metals by TAA

Solution	Time, min., at various pH values													
	1	2	3	4	5	6	7	8	9	10	11	12	13	14
TAA only	6	60	600	6×10^3	6×10^4	6×10^5	1.4×10^6	1.4×10^5	1.4×10^4	1.4×10^3	140	14	1.4	0.14
Pb[b]	6	60	400	450	140	45								
Cd	6	60	470	550	190	60								
As(III)	6	60	600	—	—	—								
Ni	6.7×10^4	2.2×10^4	6.7×10^3	1.5×10^3	625	200								
Zn	—	—	520	930	360	120								

[a] Approximate time, in minutes, required at 90°C. and at various pH values to generate 1 mmole of sulfide in 100 ml. of a 0.1F TAA solution (second row of table), or to precipitate 99% of the metals shown from the same solution which also is 0.01F in the metal.

[b] Times for pH 3–6 applicable to 0.15M sodium formate solutions only.

and co-workers who developed procedures for the precipitation and determination of all of the following elements: antimony (37a), bismuth (37b), molybdenum (37c), copper (37d), arsenic (37e), cadmium (37f), lead (37g), tin (37h), mercury (37i), manganese (37j), nickel (37k), and cobalt (37k). These studies of Flaschka and co-workers established the usefulness and advantages of TAA as a sulfide precipitant. They stand as the most complete account available of solution conditions which can be used to effect quantitative precipitations.

The general conditions employed by Flaschka and co-workers for the precipitations of the metal sulfides, as well as any additional information provided by other workers on the precipitation of that particular element, are described below. One interested in the specific details of these procedures should consult the original literature cited above.

1. Antimony

Flaschka and Jakobljevich (37a) precipitated tripositive antimony by adding a 20 to 30 % excess of TAA to a boiling antimony(III) solution which was 1 to $3F$ in hydrochloric acid. A red or black sulfide was obtained, depending on the acid concentration. Pentapositive antimony was precipitated from solutions of the same composition.

Preliminary experiments by Butler and Swift (21) have shown that antimony, like arsenic, is precipitated only by means of the hydrolysis of TAA. Accordingly, if antimony reacts with hydrogen sulfide at about the same rate as does arsenic it seems advisable to use a greater excess of TAA than the 20 to 30 % recommended by Flaschka and Jakobljevich. Not only would this excess generate an amount of hydrogen sulfide equivalent to the antimony present in a shorter time, but would help insure that even after the inevitable loss of hydrogen sulfide from a boiling solution an amount in excess of the antimony remains.

Furthermore, it is highly probable that the precipitation of a sulfide from pentapositive antimony solutions involves the prior reduction of the antimony (V) by TAA. If the rate of reduction of antimony(V) is first order in TAA (in analogy to the kinetics reported by Butler and Swift (21) for the reduction of arsenic(V)) a reasonable excess of TAA would serve to increase the rate of both the reduction and the precipitation.

The amount of TAA which should be used in a precipitation of a metal depends on the mechanism by which the particular metal is precipitated. For those cases where precipitation results solely from the hydrolysis of TAA to give hydrogen sulfide, two factors determine the amount of TAA which should be used. An amount of TAA at least equivalent to the metal present must be used and in addition the concentration of TAA must be large enough for its hydrolysis to furnish an equivalent quantity of hydrogen sulfide in a reasonable time. Since the time required for a given fraction of TAA, in a solution, to hydrolyze is independent of the initial amount of TAA, specifying a given initial ratio of TAA and metal concentrations makes the time required to reduce the metal concentration to a specified fraction of its initial value independent of the amount of metal taken. In this case it is appropriate to recommend the excess TAA concentration in terms of the initial concentration of the metal.

For cases where the precipitation of the metal sulfide by TAA takes place primarily as a result of a direct reaction between TAA and the metal ion the time required to precipitate a metal sulfide will not be independent of the amount of metal present if a relatively small excess of TAA over metal is used. In this case the time required to effect a specified fractional decrease in metal concentration will increase 100-fold for every 10-fold decrease in the amount of metal because of the second order nature of the reaction. If the excess TAA is relatively large compared to the metal concentration this time will be independent of the initial metal concentration.

2. Bismuth

Flaschka and Jakobljevich (37b) state that bismuth can be quantitatively precipitated as the sulfide by TAA from $1F$ nitric or hydrochloric acid solutions and from ammoniacal solutions. The precipitate obtained from the acidic solutions was more easily filtered than that obtained from the ammoniacal solutions.

No information was given as to whether the TAA was added to a neutral bismuth solution which was then made ammoniacal or if the solution was made ammoniacal before the TAA was added. In either case the formation of bismuth sulfide would be accompanied by the formation of bismuth hydroxide or hydroxy salts which would be subsequently metathesized to the sulfide and the precipitation would not be a homogeneous process. Thus it is not surprising that the precipitates obtained from ammoniacal solutions were more difficult to filter.

In $1F$ acid solutions the precipitation of bismuth is probably by means of the hydrogen sulfide resulting from the hydrolysis of TAA. In solutions of higher pH it is not known whether a direct reaction between TAA and bismuth also takes place. It would be of interest to determine if under conditions where the $Bi(OH)^{2+}$ ion is predominant, a direct reaction takes place similar to that observed for dipositive metals such as lead and cadmium.

3. Molybdenum

Flaschka and Jakobljevich (37c) found that molybdenum(VI) could be precipitated with TAA from $1F$ hydrochloric or sulfuric acid solutions. They recommended heating the solution in a pressure flask for about 1 hr. These authors reported that in contrast to the results frequently encountered when gaseous hydrogen sulfide is used, no reduction of the molybdenum occurred in solutions of the above acidity. This result differs slightly from that obtained by Kallerud (36) who observed some reduction of molybdenum(VI) by TAA in solutions having pH values less than 4. The precipitate obtained by Flaschka and Jakobljevich was very much easier to handle than that produced by hydrogen sulfide.

A precipitation in ammoniacal solution is described by Flaschka and Jakobljevich which involves heating to boiling the ammoniacal molybdenum(VI) solution which contains a 20 to 30% excess of TAA and then acidifying the resulting yellow solution. The precipitate which is obtained is not readily filterable.

McNerney and Wagner (38) and Lehrman and Schneider (39) have used TAA to precipitate molybdenum from 1 and $0.5F$ acid respectively. Neither pair of workers found that the pressure flask recommended by Flaschka and Jakobljevich was necessary if a 5- to 10-fold excess of TAA was used.

The details of the mechanism by which TAA precipitates molybdenum(VI) have not been studied.

4. Copper

When Flaschka and Jakobljevich (37d), studied the precipitation of copper(II) with TAA in hydrochloric acid solutions they observed the formation of an insoluble white precipitate which they suggested might be a TAA–chloro complex of copper(I) in analogy to compounds which Kurnakow (40) isolated from solutions of copper(I) and TAA. The compound appeared to decompose on heating to give a dark precipitate. No further investigation of the compound was made and the analytical method for copper which was used showed that quantitative precipitation had been obtained but did not afford any information as to the nature of the precipitate.

Experiments by Booth (35) have shown that in cold acid solutions copper(II) and TAA react to form sulfur and a TAA complex of copper(I) which is quite stable towards hydrogen sulfide. On heating such a solution a black sulfide results which is presumably Cu_2S.

Flaschka and Jakobljevich precipitated copper(II) from hot 1 to $6F$ sulfuric acid solutions by adding a 20% excess of TAA. They continued to heat the mixture until its color changed from whitish green to brownish green to brown and stopped heating when a black precipitate appeared. The precipitation was essentially complete after a few minutes of standing. The precipitate was more filterable the higher the acid concentration.

Quantitative precipitation from hydrochloric acid solutions was observed by Flaschka and Jakobljevich up to acid concentrations of $2F$. The reason for the lack of success at higher acid concentrations was not discussed. The precipitate obtained from hydrochloric acid needed to be heated to coagulate it and render it readily filterable.

Nitric acid solutions up to $0.5F$ gave satisfactory results but higher concentrations led to decomposition of the TAA. This decomposition could be the result of a copper(II)–copper(I) catalyzed oxidation of TAA by nitric acid.

Amin (41) has used TAA to precipitate copper quantitatively from an ammoniacal tartrate solution. He obtained a readily filtered precipitate after 5 min. of heating on a water bath. The tartrate was used in order to effect a separation of copper from aluminum; the aluminum forms a soluble tartrate complex. The precipitation of copper should proceed equally well in ammoniacal solutions containing no tartrate. In fact Flaschka and Jakobljevich successfully carried out quantitative precipitations of copper from ammoniacal solutions. They overcame a tendency for the precipitate to become colloidal by adding ammonium salts and heating the solution. The precipitate coagulated quickly and could be readily filtered.

5. Arsenic

Flaschka and Jakobljevich (37e) quantitatively precipitated arsenic (III) and (V) from $1F$ hydrochloric acid and $6F$ sulfuric acid solutions. These authors added only a small excess of TAA to the arsenic(III) solution because they were interested in determining the arsenic by drying and weighing the precipitate and they found that the greater the excess of TAA used the larger the positive error. The source of the positive errors was not determined. The results of Butler and Swift (21) indicate, however, that a 5- to 10-fold excess of TAA would give a more rapid and quantitative precipitation of arsenic; such an excess is especially desirable when arsenic(V) is being precipitated in order to facilitate its prior reduction to arsenic(III).

Flaschka and Jakobljevich were able to arrive at a precipitate of As_2S_3 by heating an ammoniacal solution of TAA and arsenic(III) and then acidifying the solution. As would be anticipated, the resulting precipitate was not as readily coagulated or filtered as that obtained from acid solutions. This procedure is essentially equivalent to the use of an ammonium sulfide solution but has certain advantages. First, the polysulfides invariably present in stock alkaline sulfide solutions are minimized as is the sulfur which precipitates on acidification. Then the rate of decomposition of TAA is enhanced by ammonia and the resulting sulfide is much less liable to be partially lost by volatilization as hydrogen sulfide when the sulfide is produced in ammoniacal rather than strongly acidic solutions. The chief disadvantage is the less desirable characteristics of the precipitate resulting from a nonhomogeneous precipitation.

6. Cadmium

Flaschka and Jakobljevich (37f) state that in contrast to antimony, bismuth, copper, and arsenic the precipitation of cadmium sulfide with TAA from sulfuric or hydrochloric acid solutions is quantitative only if a 50 to 100% excess of TAA is employed. They further state that with the specified excess of TAA, cadmium is quantitatively precipitated from $6F$ sulfuric acid solutions and $1F$ hydrochloric acid solutions. At such acid concentrations the quantitative and rapid precipitation of cadmium by gaseous hydrogen sulfide requires that the solution be saturated with the gas (26); therefore, it is probable that the excess TAA found necessary by Flaschka and Jakobljevich was only that required to saturate the solution with hydrogen sulfide in the time allowed. The kinetic experiments of Bowersox and Swift (29) showed that at these acidities the precipitation was hydrolysis controlled and they observed no peculiarities in the precipitation. From their results one would predict that cadmium could be quantitatively precipitated from a small volume of solution containing only enough TAA to supply sufficient sulfide to precipitate the cadmium and in addition to saturate the solution with hydrogen sulfide. The presence of larger quantities of TAA would do no harm and would help to decrease the time needed to complete the precipitation, but the precipitation would still be quantitative if only the minimum quantity of TAA is used.

The precipitation of cadmium by TAA from ammoniacal solution was observed by Flaschka and Jakobljevich to be much more rapid than from acidic solutions. It is probable that the causes of this rate increase are the two effects observed by Peters and Swift (28) in their study of the precipitation of nickel from similar solutions. That is, ammonia greatly increases the rate at which sulfide is generated by TAA, and the rate of the direct reaction between the metal and TAA is increased by the increase in pH more than it is decreased due to the formation of the ammine complexes.

The cadmium sulfide precipitates obtained from both acid and ammoniacal solutions were readily coagulated and filtered.

7. Lead

Lead was precipitated from up to $0.3F$ nitric or $0.1F$ hydrochloric acid solutions by Flaschka and Jakobljevich (37g). As was true for cadmium they found that a significant excess of TAA was necessary for quantitative precipitation of lead—a 5-fold excess was recommended. The experiments of Swift and Butler (11) showed that the precipitation of lead from solutions of pH less than 3 results from the hydrogen sulfide produced by hydrolysis of the TAA. Thus the excess of TAA serves only to provide the concentration of hydrogen sulfide required to obtain quantitative precipitation; this excess will be determined by the volume, temperature, and pH of the solution. A reasonable value for the quantity of TAA which should be used can be calculated by using the hydrolysis rate constant determined by Swift and Butler (11) and considering the quantity of TAA required to provide sufficient hydrogen sulfide to precipitate all the metal, as well as to saturate the solution with hydrogen sulfide in a convenient time, say 10 min., at 90°C.

Flaschka and Jakobljevich report that lead also can be precipitated from alkaline plumbite solutions with TAA. The kinetics of this reaction have not been studied and it is not known whether the precipitation of lead from alkaline solutions results predominantly from a continuation of the direct reaction observed in acid solutions between lead and TAA or from the reaction of plumbite ion with the sulfide produced by the alkaline hydrolysis of TAA. Sulfide precipitates lead from an alkaline solution (26) so that a more rapid precipitation of lead by TAA from an alkaline plumbite solution could be expected by the addition of ammonia to take advantage of the increase in the rate of sulfide evolution which ammonia produces (16).

8. Tin

Flaschka and Jakobljevich (37h) were unable to precipitate tin(IV) quantitatively from a $1F$ hydrochloric acid solution even with the addition of large quantities of TAA. They observed a rapid formation of precipitate but the solution still contained some tin even after prolonged heating. However, by the addition of mercuric chloride to a solution from which most of the tin had precipitated the resulting precipitate of mercuric sulfide carried with it all the remaining tin. Flaschka and Jakobljevich suggested that the effect of the mercury(II) was similar to that observed by Kolthoff and Moltzau (42) in their studies of the effect of mercuric salts on the postprecipitation of zinc sulfide.

Crabbs (43) observed quantitative precipitation of about 1 mmole of tin(IV) by about 6 mmole of TAA from 100 ml. of 0.3 and $0.6F$ hydrochloric acid solutions in 10 to 15 min. at about 90°C. It is possible that temperature effects or differences in the hydrogen ion and chloride ion activities in 0.6 and $1.0F$ hydrochloric acid could account for the incomplete precipitation observed by Flaschka and Jakobljevich.

The mechanism by which TAA precipitates tin(IV) has not been studied, but experience with other metals leads one to expect that with acid concentrations between 0.1 and $1F$ the hydrolysis of TAA to give hydrogen sulfide is the rate determining reaction.

Flaschka (44) has studied the precipitation of tin(II) by TAA. He observed the slow precipitation of brown tin(II) sulfide from an ammoniacal tartrate solution of tin(II) and TAA. No mention of the possible effects of the formation of thio–tin(II) species such as SnS_2^{2-} in the alkaline solution was made but one would anticipate that the use of excess TAA in the precipitation would lead to the formation of such species and could prevent complete precipitation. This point would also apply to precipitations in alkaline stannite solutions from which Flaschka observed more rapid precipitation of tin(II) sulfide than was true for the ammoniacal tartrate solutions. The precipitation of tin(II) from acidic solutions has not been reported.

9. Mercury

The behavior of mercury(II) with TAA is similar to the behavior of copper (37d). In 0.2 to $1F$ hydrochloric acid solutions a white crystalline precipitate was observed by Flaschka and Jakobljevich (37i). This was assumed to be $HgCl_2 \cdot TAA$ since Ishikawa (45) has reported the isolation of such a compound. The precipitate decomposed when heated to give mercuric sulfide. In 3 to $7F$ hydrochloric acid solutions a yellowish white mercury sulfo–chloride, $Hg_3S_2Cl_2$, was observed to form but it was decomposed by excess TAA; similar precipitates are produced by hydrogen sulfide under such conditions. Flaschka and Jakobljevich also reported that the precipitation of mercury by TAA from $0.5F$ sulfuric or nitric acid solutions is quantitative.

Vozza (46) and Isenberg et al. (47) have observed that the reaction between Hg(II) and TAA often leads to precipitates of pure HgS of several different colors depending on the conditions of the precipitation. Vozza showed that these colored precipitates are modifications of cinnibar, the red modification of mercuric sulfide. Although the mercuric sulfide sometimes obtained with TAA is not identical with that obtained from hydrogen sulfide the analytical behavior of both sulfides is quite similar according to Isenberg et al.

The mechanism by which mercury(II) is precipitated by TAA has not been studied. However, a successful experiment by Flaschka and Jakobljevich in which mercury(II) was precipitated from a neutral TAA solution, where both the acid and base catalyzed hydrolyses of TAA are quite slow, suggests that a direct reaction between mercury and TAA occurs.

Preliminary experiments (47a) have shown that the rate of precipitation of Hg(II) by TAA in acetate buffer solution of pH 4 is decreased by increasing the concentration of TAA. It is likely that, as is true with Ag(I), this results from a Hg(II)–TAA complex.

10. Manganese

Flaschka and Abdine (37j) have shown that manganese(II) can be quantitatively precipitated by TAA from boiling ammonia–ammonium ion buffered solutions.

Experiments (48) have shown that manganese(II) is also quantitatively precipitated at 90°C. from borate buffers at pH 9 to 9.5. The rate of precipitation, however, is probably greater from solutions containing ammonia because of the increased rate of sulfide evolution from TAA. In both cases the precipitate obtained is much easier to handle and filter than is true when hydrogen sulfide is used as the precipitating agent.

Flaschka and Abdine state that it is difficult to precipitate manganese(II) from solutions containing less than about 5 mg. of manganese in 100 ml. They advocate adding known amounts of manganese to solutions containing less than 2 mg./100 ml. to bring the concentration up to about 5 mg./100 ml. before precipitation. It is not clear why the smaller amounts of manganese(II) did not precipitate unless supersaturation or colloidal phenomena are responsible.

No experiments designed to detect a direct reaction between manganese(II) and TAA have been made but such a reaction has been found with every M(II) cation studied.

11. Nickel

Flaschka and Abdine (37k) have shown that nickel is quantitatively precipitated from a hot ammonia–ammonium ion buffer solution. The precipitate is noncolloidal and readily filterable. The studies of Peters and Swift (28) have shown that the mechanism of the precipitation of nickel from ammonia solutions involves both a direct reaction between nickel and TAA and the ammonia–TAA reaction to yield sulfide which reacts with the nickel ion. The rate at which nickel will be precipitated from an ammoniacal TAA solution can be calculated from the constants evaluated by Peters and Swift.

Mention has been made of the discovery of Bowersox and Swift (24) that a slow precipitation of nickel by direct reaction with TAA took place in acid solutions in which hydrogen sulfide produced no precipitate. As yet no attempt has been made to effect a quantitative precipitation of nickel from acid solutions by this direct reaction.

The occurrence of this reaction must be borne in mind when separations involving the precipitation of other metal sulfides in the presence of nickel ion are attempted. The common separation of zinc from nickel, which is carried out by saturating a solution at pH 2 with hydrogen sulfide (26) thus precipitating zinc sulfide and leaving the nickel in solution, can be ruined by the precipitation of nickel sulfide as a result of the direct reaction between TAA and nickel ion. Even the separation at about pH 1 of the hydrogen sulfide group elements from the ammonium sulfide group elements can result in some nickel precipitating if the solution containing TAA is allowed to stand for too long a time.

12. Cobalt

Flaschka and Abdine (37k) quantitatively precipitated cobalt from ammoniacal TAA solutions under conditions similar to those that they employed for the precipitation of nickel. The precipitate was non-colloidal and easy to filter.

No kinetic experiments have been reported on the precipitation of cobalt with TAA. One would expect that the reactions involved would be similar to those observed with nickel.

13. Zinc

Flaschka (11) reported the precipitation of zinc from neutral or weakly acidic solutions of TAA to be very slow. Bowersox and Swift (38) have studied the rate of the precipitation and have shown that the mechanism of the precipitation in the pH range 3 to 7 is predominantly a direct reaction between zinc and TAA such as that found for other dipositive cations. Below this pH range the hydrolysis controlled precipitation may predominate, but supersaturation phenomena make rate measurements difficult.

Hahn and Shellington (49) have carried out a study on the effect of temperature, pressure, and concentrations of reactants on the time required for the complete precipitation of zinc by TAA. They also attempted a separation of cobalt and zinc by using TAA to precipitate the zinc from citrate or sulfate buffer solutions at pH 2. The separations were not successful; probably because of the cobalt sulfide precipitated as a result of a direct reaction between cobalt(II) and TAA.

A much more rapid precipitation of zinc was observed by Flaschka in ammoniacal or sodium hydroxide solutions of zinc and TAA. The resulting precipitates were not, however, readily filterable without digestion procedures. In his experiments Klein (31a) obtained granular, readily filterable precipitates of zinc sulfide from ammoniacal solutions at 40°C., when the precipitation was carried out under conditions designed to minimize nucleation. The precipitates which sometimes resulted when aged solutions of TAA were employed, and a major fraction of the zinc precipitated almost instantaneously were somewhat more difficult to filter. It is likely that the difficultly filterable precipitates obtained by Flaschka resulted from a similar very rapid precipitation.

14. Silver

Flaschka (44) stated that neutral and ammoniacal solutions of silver form silver sulfide with TAA even at room temperature. In nitric acid solutions the precipitation of silver sulfide was accompanied by the precipitation of sulfur. In warm sulfuric acid solutions, silver precipitated readily without the formation of sulfur.

Preliminary experiments by Moore (32) indicate that in acid solutions both a direct reaction between silver and TAA and the hydrolysis of TAA lead to the precipitation of silver sulfide. The hydrolysis reaction predominates at pH values less than about 2. The direct reaction becomes predominant at pH values greater than 3 and an apparent inverse third order dependence was observed. This dependence is attributed to the formation of a stable silver–TAA complex of the type $Ag(TAA)_4{}^+$. The existence of such a complex has been established (33). Silver and mercury(II) are the first cases observed where increasing the TAA concentration decreases rather than increases the rate of precipitation of the metal sulfide. The quantitative investigation of the kinetics of the TAA–silver reaction is still in progress and the results obtained so far must be considered tentative.

15. Thallium

Flaschka (44) reported that neither neutral nor acetic acid solutions containing TAA and thallium(I) gave a precipitate when heated. Ammoniacal solutions did give a precipitate. When weakly acidic solutions of thallium(III) and TAA were made ammoniacal thallium (I) sulfide precipitated. No information on the mechanism of this precipitation was given.

Preliminary experiments by Moore (34) have shown that the precipitation of thallous sulfide at pH 9 is first order with respect to thallium (I), therefore a direct reaction between TAA and thallium is implied. A detailed knowledge of the mechanism of the precipitation of thallium by TAA is still to be obtained.

16. Iron

Flaschka (44) has noted that the addition of TAA to an acid solution of iron(III) results in the slow reduction of the iron to iron(II) with the formation of sulfur; the reaction is more rapid in warm solutions. This reaction has been taken advantage of by Scholes (51) to reduce iron(III) prior to the titration in the determination of iron in iron ores, slags, and refractories.

Flaschka (44) reported that ammoniacal tartrate solutions of iron (III) and TAA react to give iron(II) sulfide when warmed.

17. Selenium

Flaschka (44) states that the reaction of TAA with a selenious acid solution leads to the formation of selenium and sulfur.

18. Vanadium

Experiments by Flaschka (44) show that in acid solutions vanadium (V) is reduced by TAA to vanadium(IV) with the precipitation of sulfur and that no further precipitate is obtained. Similar behavior is observed in ammoniacal solutions.

19. General Comments

The elements discussed above include all the common elements and certain of the rarer elements for which gaseous hydrogen sulfide has been used as a precipitant and TAA has been used to effect the quantitative precipitation of most of these. The conditions used for the precipitations have not, in general, been exhaustively studied and the fact that a precipitation was made from a strongly acidic solution does not mean that it could not be successfully carried out under different conditions. Four different mechanisms for the precipitation of metals have been discussed, namely, (1) acid catalyzed hydrolysis of TAA to give hydrogen sulfide which reacts with the metal; (2) base catalyzed hydrolysis of TAA to give HS^- or $S^=$ which react with the metal; (3) reaction of TAA with ammonia or constituent of the solution of yield sulfide which reacts with the metal; and (4) direct reaction between the metal and TAA to give a metal sulfide without prior hydrolysis of the TAA. Each of these mechanisms can predominate under different conditions, and these conditions can be utilized to control the precipitation of certain metals.

These varied mechanisms of precipitation can also introduce difficulties into procedures so that any new application of TAA to the precipitation of a metal must be examined experimentally before one has any assurance of an effective procedure.

Several published studies on the applications of TAA to special analytical problems have not been mentioned previously because their very specialized nature has not lent itself to a general discussion. For the sake of completeness these studies are briefly described below.

TAA has been used in a number of instances simply as a means of removing or separating certain metals as sulfides.

Pohl (52) employed TAA to precipitate the sulfides of traces of elements present as impurities in very pure aluminum prior to a spectrographic analysis.

Bartelmus and Hecht (53) devised conditions for precipitating micro quantities of germanium with TAA.

Edelman and Lipiec (54) administered TAA as an antidote for thallium poisoning.

Fainberg et al. (55) employed TAA to precipitate the sulfides of zinc, copper, and lead in the analysis of copper and lead slags.

Sun et al. (56) removed the interferences caused by nickel and copper in a polarographic analysis of starch by precipitating these metals as sulfides with TAA.

Babko and Marchenko (57) used TAA to precipitate cadmium, bismuth, and lead sulfides from ammoniacal solutions in the analysis of molybdenum–nickel and tungsten–nickel alloys.

The first analytical application of TAA was made by Iwanow in 1935 in connection with a problem in the analysis of pharmaceuticals for heavy metals, and similar applications have continued. Shvaikova (58) and Sietrzencewicz and Zwierzchowski (59) devised procedures for the substitution of TAA for hydrogen sulfide in toxicological analyses. MonteBovi (60) described in a note his satisfactory substitution of TAA for hydrogen sulfide in pharmaceutical tests for mercury, bismuth, zinc, manganese, and copper.

Häussermann and Fritz (61) give a detailed account of experiments designed to determine those places where TAA could replace hydrogen sulfide in pharmaceutical analysis.

A procedure using TAA to test for microgram quantities of lead in pharmaceuticals was given by Lipiec and Ramolowski (62).

V. SEPARATIONS BY MEANS OF TAA

Separations with TAA have not been so extensively studied as have precipitations of single elements. The few studies which have been made indicate that conditions which lead to successful separations when hydrogen sulfide is the precipitating agent will not necessarily be successful with TAA.

Procedures for separating the conventional hydrogen sulfide group elements, namely, lead, bismuth, copper, cadmium, mercury, arsenic, antimony, and tin from the other common elements by means of TAA have been given by Barber and Taylor (63) and by Lehrman and Schneider (64). They employ conditions similar to those usually used with hydrogen sulfide in that the precipitation is commenced in 0.2 to $0.3F$ hydrochloric acid and the solution is diluted with water to conclude the precipitation in about $0.1F$ acid. According to Lehrman and Schneider the procedure is satisfactory for the separation of the hydrogen sulfide group from the ammonium sulfide group except that about 25% of the zinc present may precipitate with the hydrogen sulfide group.

The experiments of Bowersox, Smith and Swift (24) have shown that a significant amount of nickel may be precipitated with the hydrogen sulfide group if the time during which the solution is at pH 1 is excessive. Thus, one can calculate that about 4 mg. of nickel would precipitate in 1000 min. at 90°C. from 100 ml. of a solution at pH 1 which was $0.1F$ in TAA and $0.01M$ in nickel ion. The rate of the reduction of arsenic(V) by TAA to the tripositive state which precedes the precipitation of this element as the sulfide has been shown by Butler and Swift to be first order with respect to the hydrogen ion concentration; antimony(V) probably behaves similarly. Thus if either of these elements is present in its higher oxidation state a high acid concentration will be helpful in decreasing the time required for precipitation. Actually there is no apparent reason why higher acid concentration, 1 to $3F$ for instance, could not be used to speed up the rate of formation of hydrogen sulfide from TAA and to thus increase both the rates of reduction of arsenic(V) and antimony(V) and of the hydrolytic production of hydrogen sulfide. After the solution becomes saturated with hydrogen sulfide it could be diluted to precipitate the more soluble sulfides. Bloemendal and Veerkamp (65) have recommended that the precipitation be commenced in a solution $2F$ in acid. After the solution is heated to boiling for 5 min. (with probable loss of hydrogen sulfide) they advise adjusting the pH to 0.5 to precipitate the hydrogen sulfide group elements. Bon (66) raised objections to the conditions recommended by Bloemendal and Veerkamp and pointed to the fact that a pH of 0.5 represents too high a hydrogen ion concentration to obtain quantitative precipitation of cadmium, bismuth (and lead).

Swift (67) recommends that the pH be raised to about 2 in order to insure the quantitative precipitation of lead by TAA.

One disadvantage to a mode of precipitation which involves neutralizing or diluting a solution is lack of homogeneity. The resulting precipitates may not be much easier to filter than those obtained when hydrogen sulfide is used. This difficulty is not often encountered because even in cases where dilution is required to obtain quantitative precipitation the major fraction of the metal is usually precipitated homogeneously.

In a procedure in which dilution is involved it must be borne in mind that the solution does not remain saturated with respect to hydrogen sulfide and after dilution care must be taken to avoid loss of hydrogen sulfide because it will be formed more slowly thereafter by the remaining TAA.

In general less coprecipitation of a more soluble metal with the sulfide of a less soluble metal is to be expected from a homogeneous precipitation in which only the less soluble sulfide is precipitated at equilibrium. Very few coprecipitation studies with TAA have been

made. Lipiec, Blaszczakiewicz, and Urbanowska (68) have compared the coprecipitation and postprecipitation of zinc with mercury
(II) and copper(II) sulfides when gaseous hydrogen sulfide and TAA
are used as the precipitating agents. The precipitations were made
from 0.35F sulfuric acid solutions. The results showed that about
1/30 of the zinc was coprecipitated when TAA was used in
place of hydrogen sulfide and the pronounced tendency for the amount
of coprecipitated zinc to increase with time of standing when hydrogen
sulfide was the precipitating agent was all but eliminated when TAA
was used. Under the conditions employed, 10 min. after the precipitation of the copper or mercury was essentially complete, the per cent of
zinc coprecipitated from solutions initially 0.05F in each of the metal
ions was 89.2% and 11.0% for the mercury and copper sulfides, respectively, with gaseous hydrogen sulfide; when TAA was used the values
were 2.4 and 1.5%.

Bowersox, Smith, and Swift (24) have studied the coprecipitation of
nickel with lead and cadmium when the latter two elements are precipitated with TAA in solutions 0.01 to 0.4M in hydrogen ion. They
found that the previously observed direct reaction between nickel and
TAA (which apparently leads to the precipitation of the most insoluble modification of nickel sulfide) proceeds during the precipitation of cadmium and/or lead. They calculated from the pH of the
solutions and the concentrations of nickel and TAA the amount of
nickel which should have been precipitated with the cadmium or
lead as a result of this reaction; the amounts found experimentally
agreed well with the calculated values. The occurrence of this direct
reaction was shown to make the separation of cadmium and lead
from nickel at pH 1 to 2 less satisfactory with TAA than with gaseous
hydrogen sulfide.

The fact that the direct reaction between nickel and TAA decreases
the effectiveness of this separation does not necessarily mean that the
analogous direct reactions which have been observed with zinc and
thallium(I), and doubtless will be observed with cobalt and man-
ganese(II), will also hinder effective separations; the direct reaction
will cause increased "coprecipitation" only in cases where the precipitation by hydrogen sulfide is slow and when the pH is such that the
direct reaction can cause significant precipitation in the time involved.
The possibility must always be borne in mind that other factors could
affect the completeness of a separation. The formation of sulfides

with TAA by direct reaction is very different from their formation by hydrogen sulfide, and supersaturation phenomena which result in slow rates of precipitation with hydrogen sulfide could be markedly different with TAA.

The much better separations of zinc from mercury and copper obtained by Lipiec, Blaszczakiewicz, and Urbanowska (68) with TAA are quite likely the result of the homogeneity of the precipitation process.

A number of procedures have been devised in which TAA is used to separate the sulfide of a single element from one or more other elements. For instance, Webb, Groenwald, and Munro (69) have used TAA to separate copper from acid solutions of iron–platinum samples containing about 50% nickel. No conditions for the precipitation were given but the times required to obtain essentially complete precipitation show that the precipitation must have been made from reasonably concentrated acid (0.1 to 1F). The data reported are not sensitive enough to small amounts of coprecipitated nickel with copper to detect the occurrence of the direct reaction between nickel and TAA.

Amin and Farrah (70) used TAA in the analysis of zinc–lead ores to separate manganese and lead as sulfides from calcium and magnesium by precipitation from ammoniacal solutions. Amin (71) separated copper from aluminum in the analysis of alloys by precipitating the copper with TAA from an ammoniacal tartrate solution in which the aluminum was kept in solution as a tartrate complex.

A separation of bismuth from uranium by means of TAA has been reported by Stoner and Finston (72). They were interested in separating microgram quantities of uranium(VI) from macro quantities of bismuth and ascertained that a precipitation of the bismuth from 2F nitric acid at 50 to 60°C. results in very little detectable coprecipitation of uranium.

McNerney and Wagner (73) used TAA to separate molybdenum from titanium alloys and reported that the normally troublesome precipitation of molybdenum(VI) sulfide was rendered much less difficult when TAA was employed instead of hydrogen sulfide. The authors called special attention to the large, easily filtered and washed particles of molybdenum sulfide that TAA produces.

Studies on the separation of nickel from zinc by precipitating the latter from ammoniacal solutions with TAA have been reported by

Bloch (74). The precipitations were made at 42 to 93°C. from ammonia–ammonium ion buffers. Both nickel and zinc should precipitate from such solutions; however, the separation is based on the fact that zinc precipitates first and the procedure given involves rapidly cooling the solution as soon as the white zinc sulfide precipitate begins to turn grey due to the precipitation of black nickel sulfide. The amount of coprecipitated nickel which was found by Bloch (1 to 5 mg. of nickel from solutions containing between 20 and 22 mg. of zinc and nickel) is surprisingly little for such a method. It is likely that the effectiveness of this separation would approach that of the conventional separation with hydrogen sulfide only in the hands of an analyst very experienced with the TAA procedure.

Flaschka(44) has pointed out that the number of successful sulfide separations of metals can be increased by using EDTA (ethylenediaminetetraacetic acid) to form metal complex ions which will be sufficiently stable to prevent precipitation of the metal sulfide.

According to Flaschka (75) EDTA prevents or greatly inhibits the precipitation from ammoniacal TAA solutions of the sulfides of the following elements: thallium(III), copper(II), cadmium(II), tin(II), cobalt(II), and nickel(II). Elements which form sulfides in the presence of EDTA include silver(I), thallium(I), mercury(II), bismuth (III), lead(II), arsenic(III), and tin(IV). Flaschka states that all of the metals which do not precipitate as sulfides in the presence of EDTA can be made to precipitate by adding a large excess of calcium ion to the ammoniacal TAA solutions, thus removing the excess EDTA. Quantitative studies of the feasibility of the separations suggested by Flaschka's experiments with EDTA have yet to be made.

Mixed chloride–TAA complexes of the type $M(TAA)_2Cl_2$ and $M-(TAA)_4Cl_2$ analogous to those which form when mercury(II) and TAA are mixed(46) in the presence of chloride have also been observed by Nardelli and Chierici (76) with iron(II), cobalt(II), nickel(II), cadmium(II) and zinc(II). An analogous compound of gold(I) was reported by Gibson (77). The exact conditions under which these compounds will precipitate have not been determined but a high concentration of chloride apparently favors their formation. The possibility of elements whose sulfides are soluble at a given acid concentration forming insoluble complex TAA precipitates must always be considered when TAA is used in place of gaseous hydrogen sulfide in gravimetric determinations or in separations.

Villadsen and Poulsen (77a) developed a procedure for separating antimony from tin by using TAA. A 1.4F hydrochloric acid solution of tin(IV) and antimony(V) which also contains 75 g./l. of oxalic acid (to prevent precipitation of the tin) is treated with TAA and heated. A red precipitate results which is claimed to be Sb_2S_5. The data presented showed that with the conditions used less than 0.5% of the tin was precipitated. It appears possible that the precipitate may have been Sb_2S_3 or a mixture of Sb_2S_3 and Sb_2S_5. In view of Butler and Swift's (21) observation that arsenic(V) and TAA react to give sulfur and arsenic(III), and then a precipitate of arsenic(III) sulfide, it seems likely that a similar reaction might occur with antimony. The colors of Sb_2S_5 and Sb_2S_3 are so similar that one could be confused with the other, especially if part of the antimony(III) precipitated in the black modification of the sulfide thus leading to a darkening of the otherwise orange-red precipitate.

Just as the untested substitution of TAA for gaseous hydrogen sulfide in precipitations is unjustified, TAA cannot be indiscriminately employed in separations which are known to succeed when hydrogen sulfide is the precipitating agent without thorough testing of the procedure.

Thus, although an only slightly modified procedure has been shown to be almost as successful as gaseous hydrogen sulfide for precipitating the hydrogen sulfide group while leaving the remaining elements in solution, it is unlikely that TAA can be used, as is hydrogen sulfide, to precipitate zinc, nickel, and cobalt sulfides while leaving chromium, aluminum, and manganese in solution as tartrate or oxalate complexes (26). The neutral solution in which the separation is carried out, pH 7 to 8, corresponds to the slowest rate of sulfide evolution by TAA since the rates of both the acid and base catalyzed hydrolysis are at minimum. Therefore the time required for the formation of an amount of hydrogen sulfide equivalent to the metals present by hydrolysis of the TAA is prohibitively great unless rapid precipitation takes place by the direct reaction. Again in the separation of zinc from nickel and cobalt by precipitating zinc sulfide at pH 1.8 (26) the time required for the hydrolysis of TAA to form enough hydrogen sulfide to precipitate the zinc is so great that a significant amount of any nickel present would be precipitated as a result of the direct reaction between TAA and nickel.

To be sure, some of the very reasons that prevent the indiscriminate substitution of TAA for hydrogen sulfide in separations suggest that different types of separations might be made. The separation of zinc from nickel and cobalt in ammoniacal solution devised by Bloch (74) is an example. Experience has shown that the capabilities of TAA for effecting sulfide separation can only be exploited by careful experimental evaluation of each proposed procedure.

VI. TITRATIONS WITH TAA

The demonstration by Bush, Zuehlke, and Ballard (33) that an alkaline thiosulfate solution of silver(I) can be titrated with a solution of TAA at room temperature to a potentiometric end point suggests many possibilities for analogous titrations of metals with a standard solution of TAA. In addition, the inverse titration of TAA with standard solutions of silver or other metals seems likely to succeed on the basis of the experiments of Bush et al. Solutions of sodium or ammonium sulfide are too unstable to be usable as standard sulfide solutions for titration purposes, but Bush et al. have shown that buffered TAA solutions containing a small amount of a bactericide can be kept for periods of several weeks without the titer of the solution decreasing by more than about 1%. Such solutions should prove valuable not only for carrying out precipitation titrations of solutions of metals with the formation of metal sulfides but also for use in oxidation–reduction titrations in which the thio group or the resulting sulfide can serve as a convenient reductant.

It is quite likely that titrations with TAA will form the basis of a new and fruitful area for analytical applications of TAA.

VII. PREPARATION, DETERMINATION, AND DESTRUCTION OF TAA

1. Preparation

TAA is presently commercially available from J. T. Baker Chemical Co., Arapahoe Chemical Co., A. I. Daigger Co., Eastman Kodak Co., and Matheson, Coleman, and Bell Chemical Co. The price range in September, 1958, for one pound was $25 to $50. This price has caused some users to prepare their own TAA. O'Connor, Cogswell, and Mariconi (78) have described a bench scale preparation that gives a 35 to 40% yield of TAA which these authors used for qualitative analysis without further purification. The preparation is a modification of the orginal preparation of Hantzsch (79) according to the reaction:

$$CH_3CONH_2 + P_2S_5 \longrightarrow CH_3CSNH_2 + P_2O_5$$

A. J. Barnard (80) has stated that the product resulting from this reaction contains impurities of organic phosphorous compounds and frequently gives poor results in qualitative analysis unless further purification is carried out.

Other methods for preparing TAA which have been described include heating aluminum sulfide and ammonium acetate in a tube (81) and reacting acetonitrile with hydrogen sulfide (82). A discussion of the relative advantages of the various methods is beyond the scope of this review. The method discussed by O'Connor *et al.* (78), in which phosphorus pentasulfide is employed, appears to be a very simple way of preparing TAA in the laboratory.

2. Determination of TAA

The direct titration of TAA with a standard iodate solution is possible at 70 to 80°C. in 0.5F sulfuric acid solutions containing excess iodide ion (83). The iodine formed from the iodate and iodide reacts rapidly at 70 to 80°C. with TAA to produce sulfur. The end point can be detected visually with practice as the point at which the very pale sulfur precipitate suddenly turns decidedly yellow. A more clear-cut end point can be obtained amperometrically by using two platinum indicator electrodes with about 200 mv. impressed across them. A very abrupt increase in the current between the two electrodes occurs when the TAA has been oxidized and an excess of iodine is present in the solution. In order to prevent errors from loss of hydrogen sulfide resulting from the acid hydrolysis of the TAA, the TAA solution to be analyzed is introduced into the solution just before the titration.

A similar method has been used (84) in which an excess of a standard iodine solution is added to a TAA solution in 0.5F acetic acid. After the reaction is complete the excess iodine is titrated with standard thiosulfate to a starch end point. Seeing the starch end point in the presence of the sulfur which is produced by the reaction of TAA and iodine is not always easy and an amperometric detection of the end point is apt to be more satisfactory in this method as well.   Of course any substance which is oxidized by iodine or can oxidize iodide will interfere with both of these determinations.

3. Destruction of TAA

Whenever TAA is used in a nonterminal step of an analysis its effect in the succeeding procedures must be considered.   Since it is frequently desired that the solution be freed of sulfide ion and sulfide ion producing substances various means for destroying any excess TAA present in a solution have been proposed.   Heating the solution after adding an excess of oxidizing agent is often recommended.   The suggested oxidants include HNO_3, $KClO_3$, $K_2S_2O_8$, or H_2O_2.

Such procedures will oxidize the sulfide but they produce acetate and sulfate, therefore the possibility that these species can interfere in subsequent steps must be considered.   If TAA is used in an analysis there is no possibility of subsequently obtaining solutions free of acetate without very vigorous oxidizing treatments.   If sulfate is undesirable in procedures following the introduction of TAA consideration should be given to the possibility of hydrolyzing the TAA by prolonged heating in concentrated nonoxidizing acid in order to remove the sulfur as hydrogen sulfide.   The rate constant given by Swift and Butler (21) indicates that a $0.1F$ TAA solution can be reduced to $0.0001F$ in about 5 min. of heating at 90°C. in $6F$ hydrochloric acid.

VIII. FUTURE OF TAA

The success with which TAA has already been applied to analytical problems assures its continued and increasing use.   However, it is quite apparent that a fuller exploitation of TAA must wait on a better knowledge of its chemical properties and reactions.   The rate of hydrolysis of TAA is inconveniently slow in any but strongly acidic or basic solutions.   The rate of precipitation of some metals has been speeded up by working in ammoniacal media to take advantage of the catalysis by ammonia of the rate of sulfide evolution but in the pH range 3 to 8 no satisfactorily rapid method for using TAA to precipitate metal sulfides is presently available.   There is no fundamental reason why the rate of metal precipitations must be limited by the rate at which protons, hydroxide ions, or the solvent water react with TAA to give sulfide.   The addition of other substances, which react with TAA to give sulfide at more convenient rates in the pH range where the hydrolysis is slow, deserves further study.   Hydrazine is one such substance and preliminary experiments are very encouraging (17).

Much more information is needed on the kinetics of the precipitation of various types of metal ions with TAA.   This is especially needed for those cases where a direct reaction between the metal and TAA occurs in order to explain the half order inhibition by hydrogen ion which is a characteristic of all direct reactions studied so far. Most of the direct reactions which have been studied to date have been between dipositive metal ions and TAA; direct reactions between TAA and ions of other types should be sought and studied.

That separations by means of TAA may involve many factors which are not encountered with hydrogen sulfide has already been noted.   It follows that a good deal remains to be discovered about the use of TAA in separations.   One can always question as to whether a cleaner separation results from taking advantage of the relative rates at which two metals are precipitated by TAA, or if the solution is better heated with TAA at a pH where neither metal precipitates and then the pH adjusted to the value that is customarily employed in separations with hydrogen sulfide.

The fact that differences in the rates of precipitation of lead and cadmium by the direct reaction with TAA were observed from solutions with and without chloride suggests many possibilities for using complexing agents to affect rates of precipitations and separations.

The rate of sulfide evolution by TAA has been shown to be markedly affected by the nature and concentration of the buffer employed in two instances.   A detailed understanding of which buffers produce this effect, and why, as well as the use of the effect for analytical applications require further investigation.

The advantages of TAA are manifest in the many successful procedures in which it has been employed.   It is to be hoped, however, that as TAA becomes more commonly used, and as it is found to be satisfactory for specific applications, the notion will not develop that the chemistry of a familiar reagent is already thoroughly understood, or that all the possibilities for its application have been thought of or tested.   Nothing could be further from the truth.

Acknowledgments

The authors are indebted to Dr. Hermann Flaschka for generously providing them with thesis material covering the series of investigations by Flaschka and Jakobljevich. Dr. A. J. Barnard of the J. T. Baker Chemical Co. and editor of the *Chemist Analyst* sent to the authors a remarkably complete bibliographic file of publications concerning thioacetamide; this cooperation has greatly reduced the labor of the authors and they are sincerely grateful. Dr. Dwight M. Smith has read the manuscript and made many helpful comments and suggestions.

References

1. Sykes, A., *Ind. Chemist*, **29**, 201, 256 (1953).
2. West, P. W., *J. Chem. Educ.*, **34**, 393 (1957).
3. Gaddis, S., *J. Chem. Educ.*, **19**, 327 (1942).
4. Hinly, H., *Ann. Chem. pharm.*, **43**, 150 (1842).
5. Schiff, R., and N. Tarugi, *Ber.*, **27**, 3, 437 (1894).
6. Gagliardi, E., and R. Pietsch, *Monatsch.*, **82**, 432, 656 (1951); *ibid.*, **83**, 487 (1952); E. Gagliardi and A. Loidl, *Z. anal. Chem.*, **132**, 33, 87, 274 (1951); A. Musil, E. Gagliardi, and K. Reischl, *Z. anal. Chem.*, **137**, 252 (1952).
7. Iwanow, F. W., *Chem. Zentr.*, **11**, 883 (1935).
8. Wawilow, N. W., *Chem. Zentr.*, **11**, 1093 (1938).
9. Barber, H. H., and E. Grazeskowiak, *Ind. Eng. Chem., Anal. Ed.*, **21**, 192 (1949).
10. Gordon, L., *Record Chem. Progr.*, **17**, 125 (1956); also see Gordon, Salutsky, and Willard, *Precipitation from Homogeneous Solution*, Wiley, New York, 1958.
11. Flaschka, H., and H. Jakobljevich, *Anal. Chim. Acta*, **4**, 247 (1950).
12. Swift, E. H., and E. A. Butler, *Anal. Chem.*, **28**, 146 (1956).
13. Crocker, J. C., and F. H. Lowe, *J. Chem. Soc.*, **91**, 593 (1907).
14. Rosenthal, D., and T. I. Taylor, *J. Am. Chem. Soc.*, **79**, 2684 (1957).
15. Butler, E. A., D. G. Peters, and E. H. Swift, *Anal. Chem.*, **30**, 1379 (1958).
16. Peters, D. G., and E. H. Swift, *Talanta*, **1**, 30 (1958).
17. King, D. M., and F. C. Anson, unpublished experiments, California Institute of Technology.
18. Moore, C. B., unpublished experiments, California Institute of Technology.
19. Barber, H. H., and T. I. Taylor, *Semimicro Qualitative Analysis*, W. C. Brown, Dubuque, Iowa, 1953.
20. Flaschka, H., *Chemist Analyst*, **44**, 2 (1955).
21. Butler, E. A., and E. H. Swift, *Anal. Chem.*, **29**, 419 (1957).
22. Arcand, G. M., *J. Am. Chem. Soc.*, **79**, 1865 (1957).
23. Hughes, W. S., *J. Chem. Soc.*, **1928**, 491.
24. Bowersox, D. F., D. M. Smith, and E. H. Swift, *Talanta*, **2**, 142 (1959).

25. Haring, M. M., and B. B. Westfall, *J. Am. Chem. Soc.*, **52,** 5141 (1930).
26. Swift, E. H., *A System of Chemical Analysis*, W. H. Freeman and Co., San Francisco, 1938.
27. Ringbom, A., *Solubilities of Sulfides*, Preliminary Report to the Commission of Physico–Chemical Data of Analytical Interest, July 1955.
28. Peters, D. G., D. H. Klein, and E. H. Swift, unpublished experiments, California Institute of Technology.
29. Bowersox, D. F., and E. H. Swift, *Anal. Chem.*, **30,** 1288 (1958).
30. Bowersox, D. F., D. V. Owens, and D. M. Smith, unpublished experiments, California Institute of Technology, 1959.
31. Bowersox, D. F., Thesis, California Institute of Technology, 1956, p. 107.
31a. Klein, D. H., unpublished experiments, California Institute of Technology, 1959.
32. Moore, C. B., Thesis, California Institute of Technology.
33. Lamb, J. D., unpublished experiments, California Institute of Technology, 1959.
34. Bush, D. G., C. W. Zuehlke, and A. E. Ballard, *Anal. Chem.*, **31,** 1368 (1959).
35. Booth, F. B., unpublished experiments, California Institute of Technology.
36. Kallerud, M. J., unpublished experiments, California Institute of Technology.
37a. Flaschka, H., and A. Jakobljevich, *Anal. Chim. Acta*, **4,** 247 (1950).
37b. *Ibid.*, 351.
37c. *Ibid.*, 356.
37d. *Ibid.*, 482.
37e. *Ibid.*, 486.
37f. *Ibid.*, 602.
37g. *Ibid.*, 606.
37h. *Ibid.*, **5,** 60 (1951).
37i. *Ibid.*, 152.
37j. Flaschka, H., and H. Abdine, *Chemist Analyst*, **44,** 8 (1955).
37k. *Ibid.*, 30.
38. McNerney, W. N., and W. F. Wagner, *Anal. Chem.*, **29,** 1177 (1957).
39. Lehrman, L., and P. Schneider, *J. Chem. Educ.*, **33,** 621 (1956).
40. Kurnakow, N., *Ber.*, **27,** ref. 46 (1894).
41. Amin, A. M., *Chemist Analyst*, **44,** 65 (1955).
42. Kolthoff, I. M., and R. Moltzau, *J. Phys. Chem.*, **40,** 779 (1936).
43. Crabbs, G., unpublished experiments, California Institute of Technology, 1952.
44. Flaschka, H., *Z. anal. Chem.*, **137,** 107 (1952).
45. Ishikawa, S., *Chem. Zentr.*, **99,** 1765 (1928).
46. Vozza, J. F., *J. Chem. Educ.*, **35,** 145 (1958).
47. Isenberg, N., E. M. Perlman, R. L. Puryear, and S. A. Sparks, *J. Chem. Educ.*, **35,** 404 (1958).
47a. Smith, D. M. and D. V. Owens, unpublished experiments, California Institute of Technology, 1959.
48. Anson, F. C., unpublished experiments, California Institute of Technology.
49. Hahn, R. B., and F. M. Shellington, *Anal. Chim. Acta*, **19,** 234 (1958).
51. Scholes, P. H., *Analyst*, **81,** 688 (1956).

52. Pohl, F. A., *Z. anal. Chem.*, **142,** 19 (1954).
53. Bartelmus, G., and F. Hecht, *Mikrochim. Acta*, **1,** 148 (1954); *Anal. Abstr.*, **1,** 2641 (1954).
54. Edelman, M., and T. Lipiec, *Bull. acad. polon. sci.*, *Classe(II)*, **3,** 95 (1955); *Chem. Abstracts*, **50,** 489 (1956).
55. Fainberg, S. J., A. B. Bljachman, and S. M. Stankova, *Z. anal. Chem.*, **160,** 441 (1958).
56. Sun, S. C., D. L. Love, and R. T. Holzmann, *Anal. Chem.*, **30,** 1074 (1958).
57. Babko, A., and P. Marchenko, *Anal. Abstr.*, **5,** 2549 (1958).
58. Shvaikova, M., *Chem. Abstracts*, **31,** 3824 (1937).
59. Sietrzencewicz, J., and E. Zwierzchowski, *Farm. Polska*, **9,** 205 (1953); *Chem. Abstracts*, **48,** 5024 (1954).
60. MonteBovi, A., *J. Am. Pharm. Assoc.*, **45,** 765 (1956).
61. Häussermann, H., and E. Fritz, *Arch. Pharm.*, **289,** 663 (1956).
62. Lipiec, T., and S. Ramolowski, *Acta Polon. Pharm.*, **14,** 185 (1957); *Chem. Abstracts*, **62,** 13191 (1958).
63. Barber, H. H., and T. I. Taylor, *Semimicro Qualitative Analysis*, W. C. Brown, Dubuque, Iowa, 1953.
64. Lehrman, L., and P. Schneider, *J. Chem. Educ.*, **32,** 474 (1955).
65. Bloemendal, H., and Th. A. Veerkamp, *Chem. Weekblad*, **49,** 147 (1953).
66. Bon, W., *Chem. Weekblad*, **51,** 677 (1955).
67. Swift, E. H., *A System of Qualitative Analysis*, Preliminary Edition, California Institute of Technology, 1956.
68. Lipiec, T., A. Blaszczakiewicz, and K. Urbanowska, *Roczniki Chem.*, **28,** 683 (1954).
69. Webb, J. A. V., I. D. Groenwald, and G. R. Munro, *S. African Ind. Chemist*, **10,** 86 (1956).
70. Amin, A. M., and M. Y. Farrah, *Chemist Analyst*, **44,** 62 (1955).
71. Amin, A. M., *Chemist Analyst*, **44,** 65 (1955).
72. Stoner, G. A., and H. L. Finston, *Anal. Chem.*, **29,** 570 (1957).
73. McNerney, W. N., and W. F. Wagner, *Anal. Chem.*, **29,** 1177 (1957).
74. Bloch, L., *Chem. Weekblad*, **54,** 384 (1958).
75. Flaschka, H., *Chemist Analyst*, **44,** 1 (1955).
76. Nardelli, M., and I. Chierici, *Gazz. chim. ital.*, **87,** 1478 (1957); *Chem. Abstracts*, **52,** 13508f (1958).
77. Gibson, C. S., *Brit. Assoc. Advance Sci.*, *Rep.*, **1938,** 35; *Chem. Abstracts*, **33,** 2838 (1939).
77a. Villadsen, J., and K. Poulsen, *Acta chem. Scand.*, **11,** 1671 (1957).
78. O'Connor, W. F., G. W. Cogswell and E. J. Mariconi, *J. Chem. Ed.*, **35,** 405 (1958).
79. Hantzsch, A., *Ann.*, **250,** 264 (1888).
80. Barnard, A. J., private communication, J. T. Baker Chemical Co.
81. Kindler, K., and F. Fenndorf, *Ber.*, **54,** 1080 (1921).
82. Kindler, K., *Ann. Chem.*, **431,** 203 (1923).
83. Anson, F. C., unpublished experiments, California Institute of Technology.
84. Waugh, T. D., private communication, Arapahoe Chemical Co.

Near-Infrared Spectrophotometry

ROBERT F. GODDU, *Hercules Powder Company,*
Wilmington, Delaware

I. INTRODUCTION

For the past 20 years, since analytical infrared spectrophotometry has been generally practiced, infrared spectroscopists normally have run spectra over the region from 2 to 15 μ. Their attention, however, was seldom directed to the end of the chart that contains the 2 to 3 μ region, with the almost single exception of the observation of hydroxyl groups at 2.7 μ. Very recently, analytical spectroscopists have commenced to take a closer look at the neglected region between 1 and 3 μ and have been pleasantly surprised by the information they have been able to obtain. This chapter discusses the qualitative and quantitative applications of near-infrared spectrophotometry to chemical analysis. The spectral region covered is that between 1 and 3 μ.

Studies of the vibrations observed in the 1 to 3 μ region are not new. The early studies of this region were made at the short wavelength end of the spectrum with glass prism spectrometers and photographic detectors. In those early days most of the work was done to investigate the overtones of the hydroxyl and amine bands observed in the region from 0.8 to 1.5 μ. This work, prior to 1952, was summarized by Lauer and Rosenbaum who also pointed out the analytical utility of the near-infrared (64). Despite the obvious potentialities of the region, few analytical spectroscopists worked with it because of a lack of convenient instrumentation. Thus, Kaye's review of near-infrared in 1954 (57) contained few more references which were concerned with analysis, than the review of Lauer and Rosenbaum. The more extensive references of this chapter and Wheeler's recent review (100b) indicate the rapid pace of current research in the near-infrared.

Lack of convenient instrumentation also delayed work in the long wavelength portion of the near-infrared. In the past few years, more work has begun to appear in the literature concerning studies in the 2.7 to 3.0 μ region using calcium fluoride or lithium fluoride prisms, or gratings, in conventional infrared instruments. As in earlier studies, these applications were primarily concerned with the hydroxyl bands at 2.7 to 2.8 μ and the N—H bands close to 3 μ.

With the advent, in 1954, of commercially available spectrophotometers which contained quartz prisms or appropriate gratings in the monochromators, and lead sulfide photoconductor cells as detectors, analytical research in the near-infrared region has now become quite active. The number of papers which can be considered to deal with near-infrared in analysis are now about 40. The majority of these papers have come from laboratories in the United States, but more are appearing in British and other foreign journals, as British instruments are developed and as American instrumentation for this region becomes used more widely.

II. INSTRUMENTAL

1. Instruments

Since exploitation of the near-infrared region has been limited by the availability and quality of instrumentation, it is probably best, initially, to review the currently available spectrophotometers. There are three commercially available American spectrophotometers designed for operation in the near-infrared region. These are the Applied Physics Corporation's Cary Model 14, the Beckman Model DK Spectrophotometer, and the Perkin–Elmer Spectracord Model

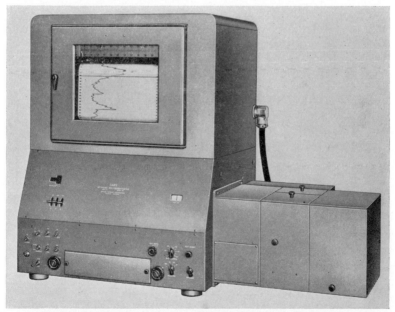

Fig. 1. Applied Physics Corp. Cary Model 14 Recording Spectrophotometer. (Courtesy of Applied Physics Corp.)

4000A.   In England, three instruments are available—the Mervyn
NPL Infrared Spectrometer, the Optica U.K. Model CF4DR, and
the Unicam SP700.   In addition, Hilger and Watts are reported to be
working on a near-infrared instrument.   Complete details on the
six commercial instruments are available from the companies which
manufacture them; consequently the following discussion is limited
to a few of the outstanding features of each.   A more complete
discussion of the general problems associated with near-infrared
spectrophotometers is available in Kaye's article on "Instrumentation
and Technique" (58).

Fig. 2.   Beckman Model DK-2 Ratio Recording Spectrophotometer with Reflectance Attachment.   (Courtesy of Beckman Instruments Inc.)

Applied Physics Corporation's Cary Model 14 (Fig. 1).   The Cary
Model 14 is an outgrowth of Cary's well-known Model 11 Ultraviolet Recording Spectrophotometer.   The Model 14 was developed
by the Applied Physics Corporation.   The monochromator is a true
double monochromator with a fused silica prism and 600 line/mm.
echelette grating.   The range of the instrument extends to 2.6 μ.
A strip chart recorder is used to record light absorption from a variety
of available slide wires including 0–1, 1–2 absorbance, 0.–0.1, 0.1–
0.2 absorbance or log absorbance.   Throughout most of the near-

Fig. 3. Perkin-Elmer Spectracord Model 4000A. (Courtesy of Perkin-Elmer Corp.)

infrared region very narrow spectral slits are obtainable, and 3 A. resolution is claimed and may be obtained. Either double- or single-beam operation is possible. The Cary is unique among the American instruments in that the light is dispersed after it passes through the sample.

Beckman Model DK (Fig. 2). This instrument is a recording version of the well-known DU manual, ultraviolet spectrophotometer. The basic recording instrument was developed by Kaye, *et al.*, at Tennessee Eastman (60,61), and has since been modified and improved by Beckman. It is available with either a strip chart (DK-1) or a plate recorder (DK-2). It has a single pass monochromator with a natural quartz prism which allows usable data to be obtained to 3.1 or 3.2 μ. (We have determined the scattered light to be less than 1% up to 3.1 μ; beyond 3.2 μ, it increases rapidly.) As in the other instruments, the detector is a lead sulfide cell. The natural quartz prism offers both advantages and disadvantages. Perhaps the greatest advantage is that the range of the DK in the near-infrared is the longest of any of the American instruments. The disadvantage is that the dispersion of quartz in the 1.2 to 1.8 μ region is poor and the resolution of the instrument suffers in this region. The water bands in the quartz which absorb in the 2.7 μ region are not extremely harmful. Either double- or single-beam operation is possible and a wide variety of transmittance and absorbance ranges are included on the basic recording instrument.

Perkin-Elmer Spectracord Model 4000A (Fig. 3). The Spectracord 4000A was developed from the earlier Spectracord manufactured by Warren Electronics, Inc. (83). It has a double monochromator with two crystal quartz prisms which allows operation up to 2.75 μ. The resolution of the 4000A in the near-infrared region is very similar to that obtained with the Beckman DK since its optics are not too different. It has a drum recorder and records 0 to 100% transmittance and from 0 to 2 absorbance. The instrument has a very low noise level and has excellent precision.

Mervyn Instruments NPL Infrared Spectrophotometer. This instrument has an NPL diffraction grating. It is designed for the range from 1 to 4 μ, with a resolution of the order of 1 to 3 cm.$^{-1}$. It indicates transmittance on a meter, has a jack for a pen recorder, and is designed for single-beam operation. The scanning may be done either mechanically or manually.

Optica U.K. Ltd.—Model CF4DR. A modification of Optica's ultraviolet instrument which has a grating monochromator is available for the near-infrared region. Its range is said to be up to 3.5 μ. In appearance it is similar to the Beckman Model DK-1 in that it has a separate relay rack with a strip chart recorder.

Unicam Model SP700. This instrument uses an NPL replica diffraction grating (300 line/mm.) for the region from 2.5 to 3.6 μ and a silica prism at shorter wavelengths. A germanium filter is used to filter out the higher orders from the grating. The instrument records absorbance on a strip chart recorder and traverses linearly with frequency.

It is possible to do work in the near-infrared region with conventional infrared spectrophotometers if special prisms (glass, silica, calcium fluoride, or lithium fluoride) and a more sensitive detector, such as a lead sulfide cell, are used. Few analytical laboratories, however, can spare the instrument or the time necessary to make these conversions. Washburn and Mahoney report that satisfactory work in this region may be done by use of conventional rock salt optics (98). For routine work in the 1 to 3 μ region the near-infrared instruments described above are more suitable because they are more rugged, generally have better resolution, photometric accuracy, and precision, and are engineered as an integrated unit. In the following discussion, there is emphasis upon the Beckman and Cary instruments since those instruments were used for obtaining the data reported. This does not imply that the Perkin–Elmer or other instruments could not be satisfactorily, or even advantageously, substituted.

2. Technique

The techniques used in near-infrared are quite similar to those used in the ultraviolet and visible regions. Cells are generally between 0.1 and 10 cm. in length and are constructed with glass or silica bodies and permanently attached windows. Glass or Corex windows may be used up to 2.4 μ. In the longer wavelength region, quartz or silica windows are necessary. A special grade of silica is available which transmits almost 90% of the incident light throughout the region between 1 and 3 μ (38). This special silica is very desirable for work in the fundamental hydroxyl region between 2.7 and 3.0 μ where ordinary silica and quartz have strong, and variable water bands. Near-infrared cells thus are quite rugged and can be readily cleaned, offering some advantages over the usual rock salt infrared cell. Also, because the cell paths are long and permanent, the path may be measured accurately by the manufacturer and does not need to be rechecked from time to time. With accurately measured and matched cells, it is possible to do excellent quality compensation work in the 1 to 3 μ region. A very practical idea for a small volume, long path length cell, useful in the hydroxyl region, was published recently by Goldberg, Meyer, and White (40). We have found a 10 cm. version of this extremely valuable since it can be made to hold but 10 ml.

The solvents which may be used for near-infrared work depend on the region of interest. For work below 2.2 μ almost anything except hydroxyl compounds can be used (see Table I). Of course, in regions of C—H vibrations there are limitations, but usually one is interested in a unique band well separated from the ordinary C—H bands in aliphatic or aromatic compounds. Carbon tetrachloride is transparent throughout the whole region and is by far the preferable solvent, especially for work with hydroxyl compounds. Carbon disulfide is also a good solvent and has but one band at 2.22 μ. Methylene chloride is often an advantageous solvent to use in the 2.7 to 2.9 μ region when samples do not dissolve in carbon tetrachloride. Further discussion of solvents and their effect on spectra is presented in subsequent sections.

One item, with respect to technique, which cannot be overemphasized is the importance of operating with a known and reproducible mechanical or spectral slit. Since the absorption bands in the near-infrared are very sharp, usually having half-height band-widths of

10 mμ or less, it is most important to have as small a spectral slit as possible, without excessive noise. In some regions and with some instruments it is impossible to obtain spectral slits narrow enough so that the true absorbance is measured (80,86). In these cases, the absorptivity of the peak is a function of slit width and reproducible results can be obtained only if a standard spectral slit is used in the region of interest.

TABLE I

Data on Solvents for Near-Infrared Spectrophotometry[a] (39a)
Numbers indicate maximum desirable path lengths in cm.
Solid lines indicate usable regions (Courtesy of *Analytical Chemistry*)

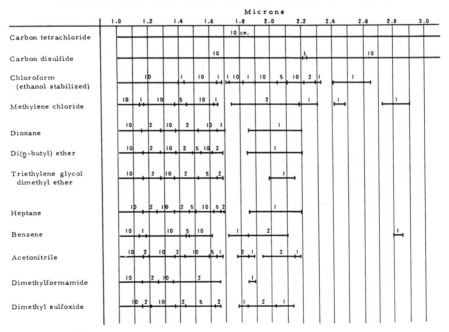

[a] Compiled from data from our laboratory.

A few other factors related to technique should be mentioned. The sensitivity of the lead sulfide detectors is very much influenced by temperature, being more sensitive at low temperatures; therefore, it is very desirable to have the spectrophotometer in a constant temperature atmosphere. For some work in the longer wavelength regions it may be desirable to cool the lead sulfide detector. (Cooled detector units are available for the Beckman DK and presumably for the other instruments if desired.) Cooling to very low temperatures loses its attractiveness, however, since the response time of the detector becomes excessively long. Large amounts of water vapor in the light path decrease the energy in the region of water vapor bands, causing rapid changes in the spectral slits. Thus in humid atmospheres, flushing the instrument and monochromator with dry air must be considered. Finally, there is very little known about the lifetime of lead sulfide cells. Our experience indicates that a detector in constant use will probably last from 1 to 2 years. The major indication of a worn-out detector is a high noise level.

The wavelength calibration of near-infrared spectrophotometers should be checked, especially in the high wavelength region. ASTM Committee E-13 has been working on this problem and made several recommendations for this region in their report given at the 61st Annual Meeting in Boston, June 22–27, 1958 (3). We have used 1,2,4-trichlorobenzene as recommended by Plyler, Blaine, and Nowak (81). It is convenient and has very sharp bands over a wide spectral region. Methanol vapor and ammonia vapor are useful for the region from 2.7 to 3.0 μ (81).

The effect of temperature on infrared absorption bands has been discussed by Hughes, Martin, and Coggeshall (54). Their work indicates that some bands, especially hydroxyl bands, are fairly temperature-sensitive, with decreases in intensity of as much as 1%/°C. rise in temperature. This variation is important in precise work, and is another indication that a constant temperature atmosphere is desirable.

III. QUALITATIVE USES OF NEAR-INFRARED SPECTRA

Infrared spectra obtained in the rock salt region have been widely used for the past two decades as important tools in organic qualitative analysis. The region from 7 to 12 μ is widely referred to as the fingerprint region. Infrared spectra are often admitted as primary evidence for defining new compositions of matter in patent cases. It is thus reasonable to look into the qualitative used of near-infrared spectra.

In order to evaluate the potentialities of the near-infrared region, it is necessary to realize that most, but not all, of the absorption bands occurring in the near-infrared region involve hydrogenic stretching vibrations or combinations of hydrogenic stretching vibrations with other modes of vibration of the molecule (57,64). Only a few of the fundamental stretching vibrations occur in the region between 1 and 3 μ, so that in general, near-infrared spectra consist of overtone spectra of the hydrogenic stretching vibrations. While these types of spectra may have many unique properties, they are not as characteristic of molecules as the spectra obtained in the regular infrared region where vibrations characteristic of the carbon skeleton of the molecules are observed. Also, there are no hydrogenic bending vibrations which are sometimes valuable in qualitative work.

Actually, it is my opinion that the near-infrared region has a very limited value in qualitative analytical work, and it is far from having the general utility of the regular infrared. It is, however, extremely valuable for detecting and then subsequently determining functional groups which contain unique hydrogen atoms. Figures 4 and 5 give the spectra of typical aliphatic and aromatic nuclei. These spectra show the regions in which aliphatic methyl and methylene groups and aromatic C—H groups can be expected to absorb. Then note the differences caused by unique hydrogen atoms in a terminal olefin group (Fig. 6), an amine group (Fig. 7), an alcohol group (Fig. 8), or a terminal epoxide group (Fig. 9). Considerable qualitative wavelength data are included in Wheeler's extensive review paper (100b).

Thus, to obtain the greatest value from near-infrared spectra, it has been our experience that a thorough knowledge of the absorption bands of the various functional groups absorbing in this region is a necessity. A large number of spectra, such as is necessary in infrared work, does not seem as desirable in near-infrared work since differences between compounds with the same functional groups are usually second order. Far more desirable, at least in our laboratory, is a large compilation of spectra–structure correlation data, coupled with molar absorptivity or intensity data. These data from the literature and from our own work are summarized in Table II. The figures given are average molar absorptivities for the functional groups and will be discussed in more detail in later sections.

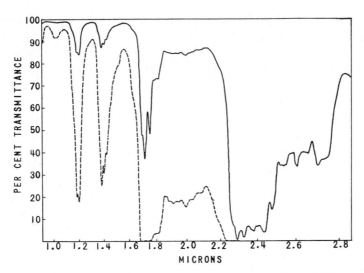

Fig.. 4. Near-infrared absorption spectrum of heptane (36). Solid line, 1 mm cell; broken line, 1 cm. cell. (Reprinted from *Anal. Chem.*, **29**, 1790 (1957).)

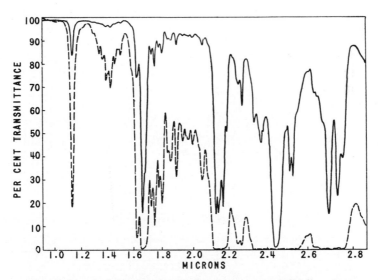

Fig. 5. Near-infrared absorption spectrum of benzene. Solid line, 1 mm. cell; broken line, 1 cm. cell.

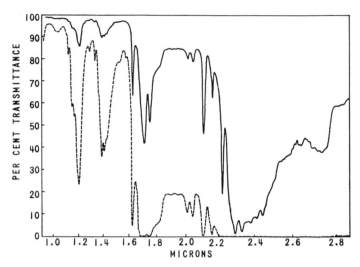

Fig. 6. Near-infrared absorption spectrum of 1-octene (36). Solid line, 1 mm. cell; broken line 1 cm. cell (Reprinted from *Anal. Chem.*, **29**, 1790 (1957).)

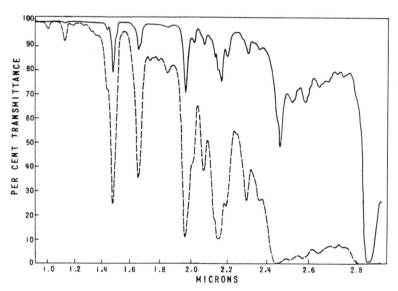

Fig. 7. Near-infrared absorption spectrum of aniline in carbon tetrachloride. Solid line, 1% solution in 1 cm. cell; broken line, 10% solution in 1 cm. cell.

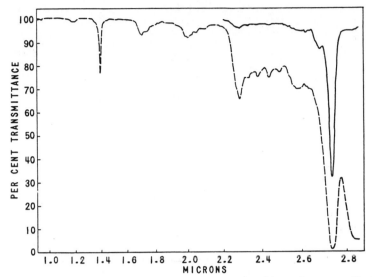

Fig. 8. Near-infrared absorption spectrum of *n*-butanol in carbon tetrachloride. Solid line, 0.1% solution in 1 cm. cell; broken line, 1.0% solution in 1 cm. cell.

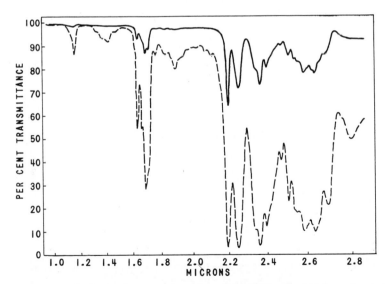

Fig. 9. Near-infrared absorption spectrum of epichlorohydrin in carbontetrachloride (39). Solid line, 1% solution in 1 cm. cell; broken line, 10% solution in 1 cm. cell. (Reprinted from *Anal. Chem.*, **30**, 2014 (1958).)

TABLE II

Spectra–Structure Correlations and Average
Molar Absorptivity Data[a] (39a) (Courtesy of *Analytical Chemistry*)

Microns

^{a} Compiled from data from our laboratory and published data, which were mostly obtained in carbon tetrachloride solution.

In addition to the qualitative use of scan-type spectra, if is often valuable to run small portions of a spectrum at high resolution. For example, one may be able to distinguish between a vinyloxy ether and an allyloxy ether in the terminal double bond region, or between various types of alcohols in the hydroxyl region. It has been our experience that a laboratory which has infrared facilities seldom will use the near-infrared for identification work but often will use it to detect various functional groups, and then do a quantitative analysis for the functional groups detected.

IV. QUANTITATIVE ORGANIC FUNCTIONAL GROUP ANALYSIS

This section is by far the largest section in this chapter, since I believe that it is in this type of work that near-infrared spectrophotometry is most valuable. With a good background knowledge of the spectra–structure correlations such as are given in Table II and an idea of the molar absorptivities of a few representative compounds, it is usually possible to reliably predict whether near-infrared is the proper tool for the particular problem. If near-infrared is applicable, it usually takes but a short time to prepare a calibration curve, if one is necessary. After that, samples can easily be analyzed at the rate of one every 10 or 15 min. Because of the relatively constant molar absorptivities in many cases, it is often possible to analyze for compounds for which standards are not available and still have reasonable accuracy. The accuracy and precision of an near-infrared analysis is usually close to that obtained in ultraviolet and visible analyses, that is, in routine work $\pm 2\%$ of the amount present. By using high absorbance reference techniques, or very carefully controlled conditions, this can be improved.

In the work reported and reviewed here, I have used molar absorptivity data as consistently as possible. In analytical work, it is seldom possible to measure other than peak absorbances with any degree of precision because of interference from bands of other compounds or because of uncertain background shapes. For these and other reasons, such as rapidity, peak absorbance measurements are generally preferable to integrated absorptivities. Much of the work in the near-infrared region, especially with hydroxyl and amine bands, has been reported in terms of integrated absorptivities.

This is true particularly of the work of T. L. Brown and H. W. Thompson. For the correlation of structure with intensity, integrated values are preferable, but work to date indicates that it is possible to get good quantitative data and acceptable adherence to the Beer–Lambert law by the use of peak absorbance measurements. The reporting of molar absorptivity, together with solvent and spectral slit width data, should be of value between laboratories, both for predicting possible applications and for quick approximations for which standards are not readily available. For example, we have two similar instruments in different laboratories in our company and have obtained molar absorptivities agreeing within a few per cent when independent calibrations were carried out. Both the tangent base line method and the difference between absorbances at two wavelengths can be used to calculate the peak intensity. In our work we generally prefer the tangent base line method.

1. C—H Vibrations

The fundamental C—H stretching vibrations of most C—H groups lie outside the near-infrared region. The single exception is the terminal alkyne vibration at about 3.0 μ. Thus, when we discuss analysis for C—H groups, we are usually concerned with combination and overtone bands. The strongest and most generally applicable combination bands occur between 2.0 and 2.4 μ, and the overtone bands occur at 1.6 to 1.8 and 1.1 to 1.2 μ. The first overtone at 1.6 to 1.8 μ is more generally used because it is more intense and appears to have no disadvantages in comparison to the weaker 1.1 to 1.2 μ bands. Weak combination bands are found at about 1.4 μ.

A. TERMINAL METHYLENE GROUPS

The bands due to a terminal methylene group stand out uniquely in almost any near-infrared spectrum. For example, compare the spectra of 1-octene (Fig. 6) and epichlorohydrin (Fig. 9) with the other spectra given in this chapter. This is very valuable to the organic analytical chemist because of the importance of compounds with terminal methylene groups, especially in the field of polymer chemistry. The bands of the terminal methylene groups are excellent for quantitative work as well as being useful qualitatively.

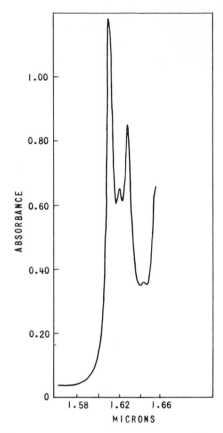

Fig. 10. Near-infrared absorption spectrum of allyl vinyl ether in the 1.6 μ region on the Cary Model 14 Recording Spectrophotometer; concentration 2.40M in carbon tetrachloride; 1 cm. cell.

a. Olefins. To date there has been one paper published giving quantitative data on the terminal methylene group (36); several authors, however, have pointed out the existence of the unique terminal olefin bands and predicted their utility (51,57,64). In addition, Miller and Willis (72) have written of using the terminal olefin band in polymer analysis, in particular, with reference to the determination of residual monomer.

The two bands which have been found most useful for quantitative work with terminal olefins have been the combination band at about

TABLE III
Effect of Structure on 1.62 μ Terminal Methylene Absorption in Carbon Tetrachloride

Compound	ν Max., cm.$^{-1}$	λ Max., μ	Mole absorptivity, ϵ, liter/mole-cm.		
			Cary model 14	Beckman DK-2	Spectracord 4000A
1-Octene	6112	1.636	0.38	0.31	0.31
1-Octadecene	6112	1.636	0.33	0.27	
Eugenol	6120	1.634	0.34		
Estragole	6124	1.633	0.34		
Allylacetaldehyde (4-pentenal)	6135	1.630	0.33		
Allyl vinyl ether	6135 (allyl)	1.630 (allyl)	0.24		
Allyl glycidyl ether	6135	1.630	0.26		
Allyl alcohol	6139	1.629		0.20	
Acrolein	6139	1.629		0.25	
Methacrolein	6139	1.629		0.20	
Butadiene monoxide	6143	1.628	0.47	0.38	
Styrene	6146	1.627		0.45	
α-Methylstyrene	6146	1.627	0.49	0.44	0.42
Allyl acetate	6150	1.626		0.24	
Allyl chloride (3-chloroproprene)	6153	1.625		0.27	
Methyl vinyl ketone	6165	1.622	0.28		
Ethyl acrylate	6169	1.621	0.37	0.32	0.30
Methyl methacrylate	6173	1.620		0.36	0.36
Acrylonitrile	6184	1.617		0.26	
Vinyl n-butyl ether	6192	1.615		0.35	
Vinyl isobutyl ether	6192	1.615		0.36	
Vinyl t-butyl ether	6192	1.615	0.45	0.35	0.35
Vinyl α-terpinyl ether	6192	1.615		0.37	
Vinyl isobornyl ether	6200	1.613		0.38	
Allyl vinyl ether	6203 (vinyl)	1.612 (vinyl)	0.40		
Butyraldehyde divinyl acetal	6203	1.612	0.86		
Vinyl acetate	6207	1.611		0.38	
Nominal slit at 1.650 μ, mm.			0.23	0.030	0.057
Half-intensity band-width, mμ			0.76	2.7	3.0

2.11 μ and the first overtone of the C—H stretching band at about 1.62 μ. (36). Other combinations or overtone bands could be used, but they are generally too close to strong C—H bands or too weak to have much sensitivity.

Table III gives typical data on a wide variety of unsaturates in the 1.62 μ region. A few generalizations relative to the effect of structure on the wavelength of the absorption maximum are possible. Vinyloxy compounds, that is, compounds with the group CH$_2$=CH—O—, absorb at the shortest wavelength—about 1.615 μ. Compounds with the group CH$_2$=C—C=O, absorb at about 1.620 μ. Unsaturated hydrocarbons generally absorb above 1.630 μ. With the resolution obtainable in the 1.62 μ region, it is often possible to make both qualitative and quantitative observations on an unknown, unsaturated compound. An idea of the resolution can be obtained from the spectrum of allyl vinyl ether in Fig. 10. The presence of a vinyl ether could be predicted from the wavelength of the short wavelength band. Few methods could be expected to differentiate the closely related functional groups so quickly and so completely. It is not difficult to obtain wavelength precision of ±0.001 μ on any of the near-infrared instruments in this region.

Molar absorptivity data are also included in Table III. These data indicate that for all compounds, the molar absorptivities are quite constant in the 1.62 μ region. For compounds of similar structure, molar absorptivities which are within experimental error are often obtained. It is thus often possible, as stated above, to do relatively good quantitative analysis for the terminal olefin content of a sample for which no standards are available.

The differences in molar absorptivities between the instruments (Table III), reflect the narrower spectral slits obtainable on the Cary Model 14 around 1.62 μ. This narrower spectral slit is mainly of importance when close adherence to Beer's law is desired or when analyses are carried out on samples in which the background changes rapidly with wavelength. Good quantitative work has been done with all the available instruments.

In the near-infrared, both vinyl (CH$_2$=CH—) and vinylidene (CH$_2$=C$\langle$) groups absorb in the same region with comparable intensities. This is different from the 10 to 12 μ region of the infrared where the two groups have very different absorption bands. This is one of many instances where near-infrared can advantageously complement conventional infrared techniques.

Table IV shows the effect of solvent on the 1.62 μ band of ethyl acrylate, a typical terminal unsaturate. To be sure, there is some effect, but it is considerably less than is observed in the case of many functional groups, such as hydroxyl or amines. As would be predicted, the highest molar absorptivities are obtained in the least polar solvents and the lowest in the polar solvents. Similar results have been obtained with other terminal unsaturates in a variety of solvents. It is thus usually possible to get order of magnitude data on unknown terminal unsaturates in an unknown solvent system. It is safe to say that by using the 1.6 μ region on unknown systems, there is a reasonable chance of getting $+10$ to 15% accuracy in the determination of terminal unsaturation, without calibration.

The terminal unsaturation band at 2.1 μ is less generally useful for terminal unsaturation because of the wider variation in molar absorp-

TABLE IV

Effect of Solvent on Terminal Methylene Absorption of Ethyl Acrylate at 1.62 μ (36)

Solvent	Molar absorptivity, ϵ, liter/mole-cm.[a]
Toluene	0.327
Decane	0.321
Carbon tetrachloride	0.314
Methyl ethyl ketone	0.289
Diethyl Cellosolve	0.279
Ethyl orthoformate	0.279
Tetrahydrofuran	0.273
Dioxane	0.265
Diethylene glycol dimethyl ether	0.263
Tri-n-butyl phosphate	0.262
Tetraethylene glycol dimethyl ether	0.251
Triethylene glycol dimethyl ether	0.250
Dimethylformamide	0.239
Hexamethylphosphoramide	0.237
γ-Butyrolactone	0.236
Methyl sulfoxide	0.228

[a] Data obtained on Beckman Model DK-2 Spectrophotometer using a constant sensitivity of 50 or half-height band-width of about 3 mμ at 1.62 μ. (Courtesy of *Analytical Chemistry*)

tivity than is observed in the 1.6 μ region. Data in Table V indicate that the molar absorptivity may vary from 0.1 to 0.6 l./mole-cm., or more. In some cases, this variation may be used to advantage in order to gain increased sensitivity or to characterize a given terminal unsaturate by comparing the 2.1 and 1.6 μ intensities.

TABLE V

Terminal Methylene Absorption at 2.1 μ in Carbon Tetrachloride

Compound	ν Max., cm.$^{-1}$	λ Max., μ	Molar absorptivity, ϵ, liter/mole-cm.		
			Cary Model 14	Beckman DK-2	Spectracord 4000
trans-Dichloroethylene[a]	4670	2.141		0.118	
cis-Dichloroethylene[a]	4673	2.140		0.116	
Acrolein	4715	2.121		0.47	
α-Methylstyrene	4724	2.117	0.34		0.29
1-Octene	4726	2.116	0.50	0.49	0.46
Allyl glycidyl ether	4735	2.112	0.45		
Allyl chloride (3-chloropropene)	4742	2.109		0.40	
Allyl acetate	4742	2.109		0.43	
3-Chloro-1-chloro-methyl-1-propene	4744	2.108		0.32	
Butadiene monoxide	4744	2.108	0.62	0.57	
Allyl alcohol	4744	2.108		0.40	
Ethyl acrylate	4746	2.107	0.68	0.63	0.57
Methyl methacrylate	4748	2.106	0.48	0.41	0.41
Pentaerythritol diacrolein acetal	4757	2.102	1.04		
Vinyl n-butyl ether	4766	2.097		0.17	
Vinyl t-butyl ether	4775	2.094	0.163		0.113
Vinyl acetate	4705	2.093		0.12[b]	
	4778	2.125			
Nominal slit at 2.200 μ, mm.			0.35	0.040	0.070
Half-intensity band-width, mμ			1.0	2.6	2.9

[a] The dichloroethylenes are not true terminal methylene compounds and behave uniquely.

[b] Vinyl acetate has no sharp peak in this region.

Because of somewhat greater background absorption, fewer solvents may be used in the 2.1 μ region, but this is not usually a very serious handicap.

In order to get high precision, it is possible to use high absorbance reference techniques in either the 1.6 or 2.1 μ regions. There is enough light available with most of the available instruments so that small slits can be maintained and better precision and accuracy achieved. In addition, because of the large amount of energy available, it is very possible to use long cell paths in order to get high sensitivity. For example, 4 mM $>$C$=$CH$_2$ (100 p.p.m.) gives an absorbance of 0.01 in a 10 cm. cell at 1.6 μ.

b. Epoxides. The spectrum of epichlorohydrin in Fig. 9 is very similar to that of 1-octene (Fig. 6) with the exception that there are

TABLE VI

Near-Infrared Absorption Data on Terminal Epoxides in Carbon Tetrachloride

	1.65 μ region				2.20 μ region			
			Molar absorptivity, ϵ, liter/ mole-cm.				Molar absorptivity, ϵ, liter/ mole-cm.	
Epoxide	ν Max., cm.$^{-1}$	λ Max., μ	Cary 14	Beckman DK-2	ν Max., cm.$^{-1}$	λ Max., μ	Cary 14	Beckman DK-2
Epichlorohydrin	6086	1.644	0.214	0.196	4531	2.207	1.65	1.59
Epibromohydrin	6079	1.645	0.208	0.185	4531	2.207	1.64	1.58
1,2-Epoxy-3-iso- propoxypropane	6068	1.648	0.208	0.192	4527	2.209	1.40	1.36
Allyl glycidyl ether	6064	1.649	0.23		4521	2.212	1.84	
Butadiene monoxide	6061	1.650	0.316	0.300	4515	2.214	2.75	2.72
1,2-Diisobutylene oxide (1,2- epoxy-2,4,4- trimethyl- pentane)	6039	1.656	0.254	0.209	4511	2.217	0.86	0.88
Styrene oxide		No sharp peak			4519	2.213	1.40	1.37
1,2-Epoxy-3-phen- oxypropane		No sharp peak			4531	2.207	1.39	1.36
Nominal slit, mm.	6061	1.650	0.27	0.030	4545	2.200	0.75	0.040
Half-intensity band-width, mμ	6061	1.650	0.89	2.7	4545	2.200	2.1	2.6

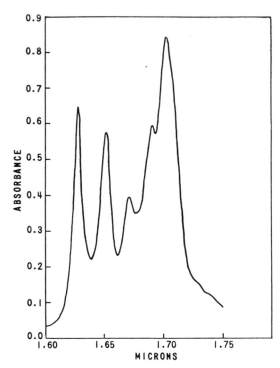

Fig. 11. Near-infrared absorption spectrum of butadiene monoxide in the 1.6 μ region on the Cary Model 14 Recording Spectrophotometer; concentration 0.158M in carbon tetrachloride; 1 cm. cell (39). (Reprinted from *Anal. Chem.*, **30**, 2015 (1958).)

somewhat fewer unique, sharp bands. The bands at 1.65 and 2.20 μ are characteristic of the terminal epoxide methylene group and have been applied to the determination of such groups (39).

Typical wavelength and intensity data for terminal epoxides are included in Table VI. The data indicate that the band at 2.20 μ is considerably more intense than the 1.65 μ band. The terminal epoxide bands lie between the terminal unsaturation bands and the aliphatic methyl and methylene bands in both the 1.6 to 1.7 and 2.1 to 2.3 μ regions. The 1.65 μ terminal epoxide band cannot be resolved from the aromatic C—H bands. However, aromatic C—H's do not interfere with the 2.20 μ band. Data quoted by Goddu and Delker (39) indicate that there is a slight dependence of molar

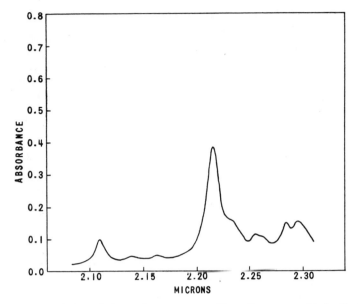

Fig. 12. Near-infrared absorption spectrum of butadiene monoxide in the 2.2 μ region on the Cary Model 14 Recording Spectrophotometer; concentration 0.158M in carbon tetrachloride; 1 cm. cell (39). (Reprinted from *Anal. Chem.*, **30**, 2015 (1958).)

absorptivity on concentration in both regions.   For a 10-fold change in concentration, the molar absorptivity decreases by 10% at 1.65 μ and 7% at 2.20 μ.   A variety of solvents may be used, especially in the 1.65 μ region.   However, the 2.20 μ band is close to bands due to other C—H groups, and some solvents were found to absorb too much to be useful (39).

It is very easy in most cases to resolve the bands due to terminal epoxides from those due to terminal unsaturation.   For example, note the spectra of butadiene monoxide in Figs. 11 and 12.   Thus, near-infrared gives a rapid method of analyzing compounds with many chemical similarities.   Most of the previous discussion on terminal unsaturation applies also to terminal epoxides, including a detection limit which is of the order of about 100 p.p.m. of $\ce{>C-CH2}$

O

in hydrocarbon samples and the possibility of using high absorbance reference techniques in order to develop assay methods.

Other oxygen rings or ethers do not interfere with the terminal epoxide band.

c. **Cyclopropanes.** A third type of terminal methylene, the terminal cyclopropyl group, has been reported by Washburn and Mahoney (99) to have bands at 1.64 and 2.24 μ. Their work was done on a conventional rock salt instrument and no intensity data were reported, except that the 2.24 μ band was more intense. It is almost certainly true that these terminal cyclopropyl bands are very similar to those found for terminal epoxides and that much of the previous discussion may be extrapolated to them. It is perhaps doubtful if they could be resolved from the terminal epoxide vibrations.

B. TERMINAL METHYNE GROUPS

The fundamental C—H stretching vibration of the terminal methyne group at about 3.0 μ is discussed in some detail by Bellamy (11). The pertinent references are also mentioned. This fundamental C—H stretching vibration is available to some near-infrared spectrophotometers, in particular the Beckman DK, while the overtone in the 1.5 μ region is accessible to all near-infrared instruments. Both the fundamental and the overtone bands are very sharp com-

TABLE VII

Near-Infrared Absorption Data on Terminal Methyne Compounds in Carbon Tetrachloride

Compound	Fundamental band			First overtone band			Instrument
	ν Max., cm.$^{-1}$	λ Max., μ	Molar absorptivity ϵ, liter/ mole-cm.[a]	ν Max., cm.$^{-1}$	λ Max., μ	Molar absorptivity ϵ, liter/ mole-cm.[a]	
Propargyl alcohol (2-propyn-1-ol)	3299	3.031	47	6527 6527	1.532 1.532	1.08 0.81	Cary 14 DK-2
1-Pentyne	3297	3.033	45	6523	1.533	0.81	DK-2

[a] Nominal slits were: DK-2, 0.33 mm. at 3.000 μ, 0.025 mm. at 1.500 μ; Cary 14, 0.21 mm. at 1.500 μ. Half-intensity band-widths: DK-2, 15 mμ at 3.000 μ, 2.4 mμ at 1.500 μ; Cary 14, 0.72 mμ at 1.500 μ. (1 cm. cells used).

pared to other bands in the respective regions and they are of good intensity. Typical molar absorptivity data obtained in our laboratory are included in Table VII. These limited data indicate that by working either at 3.0 μ or at 1.5 μ, it should be possible to determine terminal methyne groups with great sensitivity and selectivity in a wide number of systems. Because of the sharpness of these bands, it is extremely important to use narrow spectral slits. The loss in sensitivity with wide spectral slits is obvious by comparison of data from the Cary 14 and the DK-2 in Table VII. It would not be expected, that the solvent would appreciably affect these bands.

C. INTERNAL UNSATURATION

Holman and Edmondson (51) have pointed out that near-infrared bands due to cis unsaturation in nonconjugated fatty acids can be observed at 2.19, 2.14, and 1.18 μ. Subsequent work by the author (36) indicated that the 2.14 μ band was probably the most useful. Since the bands at 2.14 μ are extremely weak (see Table VIII) and since there is a high background absorption in this region, it is usually necessary to use a reference solution which approximates the sample in the number of methyl and methylene groups. For example, in work with methyl oleate, methyl palmitate was used in the reference beam.

While the sensitivity of the 2.14 μ cis unsaturation band is not high, it offers one of the few fairly specific methods for determining cis double bonds. Near-infrared determination of cis unsaturation and terminal unsaturation can complement infrared determination of trans double bonds at 10.34 μ. Trans double bonds do not adsorb at 2.14 μ, and no specific near-infrared band has been reported for them, although they may have a weak band at 1.77 μ. Holman, Ener, and Edmondson have applied near-infrared to the determination of the cis double bond content of natural fats and oils (52).

Since the cis unsaturation bands are undoubtedly due to C—H vibrations, it is quite probable that fully substituted cis double bonds will not absorb at all, and those with only one hydrogen will have bands that are considerably less intense. No study has been reported on the effect of conjugation of the cis unsaturation bands or on the effects of conjugation on near-infrared spectra, in general.

TABLE VIII

Near-Infrared Absorption Data at 2.14 μ on Compounds with Internal Double Bonds (36)

Compound	Solvent	Reference solution	ν Max., cm.$^{-1}$	λ Max., μ	Molar absorptivity, ϵ, liter/ mole-cm.	Nominal slit[a]
cis-2-Pentene	None	n-Pentane	4688	2.133	0.125, 0.121	0.028
trans-2-Pentene	None	n-Pentane		None		0.028
cis-3-Hexene	None	n-Heptane	4675	2.138	0.128	0.028
cis-4-Methyl-2-pentene	None	2-Methyl-pentane	4675	2.138	0.129, 0.135	0.028
	CCl₄	Above in CCl₄	4675	2.138	0.131	0.030
trans-4-Methyl-2-pentene	CCl₄	Above in CCl₄		None~0.004		0.030
Cyclopentene	None	Cyclopentane	4675	2.138	0.186	0.028
	CCl₄	Above in CCl₄	4675	2.138	0.199	0.028
Cyclohexene	None	Cyclohexane	4682	2.136	0.151	0.027
	CCl₄	Above in CCl₄	4682	2.136	0.153	0.027
Methyl oleate	None	Methyl palmitate in CCl₄	4669	2.142	0.108	0.079
Methyl linoleate	None	Methyl palmitate in CCl₄	4671	2.141	0.178	0.079
Oleic acid	None	Palmitic acid in CCl₄	4671	2.141	0.071 (DK-2)	0.25
			4666	2.143	0.109 (Cary)	1.8
Linoleic acid	None	Palmitic acid in CCl₄	4671	2.141	0.123 (DK-2)	0.25
			4666	2.143	0.206 (Cary)	1.8
Elaidic acid	CCl₄	Palmitic acid in CCl₄	4666	2.143	0.008 (Cary)	1.8
Crotonaldehyde	CCl₄	CCl₄	4743	2.108	0.33	0.028

[a] A nominal slit of 0.028 mm. on the Beckman DK-2 is equivalent to half-intensity band-width of 2 mμ, 0.079 mm. equals 5.5 mμ, and 0.25 mm., 17 mμ. On Cary Model 14 a nominal slit of 1.8 mm. is equivalent to half-intensity band-width of 4.7 mμ. Half-intensity band-width of these bands is 10 to 11 mμ. (Courtesy of *Analytical Chemistry*)

D. ALDEHYDIC C—H AND FORMATES

The hydrogen atom on the carbonyl carbon atom of an aldehyde, or a formate ester is unique compared to most other hydrogen atoms in common aliphatic compounds. A band, probably a combination of the C—H stretching band and the $\rangle$C=O stretching band, appears at 2.1 to 2.2 μ. This band may be readily resolved from the other C—H bands in aliphatic compounds. No quantitative use of this C—H band has been reported. Representative data in Table IX indicate that these C—H bands of formates and aldehydes are moderately strong. We have used the formate ester band successfully in quantitative work. The bands are of especial value in laboratories which have limited infrared facilities, or in unique problems where the carbonyl bands in aldehydes in the 5.5 to 6.0 μ region cannot be used.

TABLE IX

C—H Absorption of Formate Esters and Aldehydes in the 2.2 μ Region in Carbon Tetrachloride

Compound	ν Max., cm.$^{-1}$	λ Max., μ	Molar absorptivity, ϵ, liter/mole-cm.[a]
Methyl formate	4664	2.144	0.90
Ethyl formate	4655	2.148	1.03
n-Propyl formate	4655	2.148	1.00
n-Butyraldehyde	4548	2.199	0.45
Isobutyraldehyde	4543	2.201	0.45

[a] Data obtained on Beckman Model DK-2 Spectrophotometer using a nominal slit of 0.040 mm. at 2.200 μ, which gives a half-intensity band-width of 2.6 mμ.

E. METHYL AND METHYLENE VIBRATIONS

Prior to the development of the quartz prism spectrophotometer, considerable work had been done on the determination of methyl and methylene groups and even tertiary hydrogen. All of the research workers who investigated this problem agreed that the best region for the type of C—H groups in aliphatic compounds is that in the neighborhood of 1.20 μ. Rose (82), using a large spectrophotometer at the U. S. National Bureau of Standards, determined a series of molal absorptivities which allowed him to calculate the $>$CH$_3$, CH$_2$, $-\overset{\diagdown}{\underset{\diagup}{C}}-$H, and aromatic C—H content of petroleum fractions. Rose's work was extended by Hibbard et al. (27,47), who modified a Perkin-Elmer Model 12A Spectrophotometer for work in the 1.2 μ region. They were able to analyze petroleum fractions having up to 34 carbon atoms, including naphthenic as well as aromatic rings. They used simultaneous equations to determine the results and measured at 1.212 μ for aromatic C—H. They reported they could find no band due to tertiary hydrogens. They reported average deviations of 0.15 —CH$_3$ or $>$CH$_2$ group in aliphatic hydrocarbons. Results were somewhat poorer for large molecules and poorest for naphthenics. Tuot and Barchewitz (97) confirm the assignments of Rose and Hibbard et al., but give no quantitative data.

In our laboratory, we have used the 1.2 μ region to determine the methyl to methylene ratio in ketones, alcohols, and acids, as well as hydrocarbons, with some success. We did not carry out as detailed studies as those quoted above, but enough was done to show that the region has promise for most types of organic compounds, provided a variety of standards is available. The effect of molecular structure on the C—H molar absorptivities needs investigation to see whether hydrocarbons can be used as standards for other types of compounds.

Gibson has carried out similar studies in the 1.7 μ region, or first overtone region, which indicate that this region holds promise for quantitative methyl and methylene work, but that the spectra are probably more complex than are those in the 1.2 μ region (35). His work includes spectral assignments for this region.

Thus on the basis of work reported in the literature, it would appear that the bands due to C—H vibrations at 2.2 to 2.4, 1.7 (first overtone of C—H stretching), and 1.4 μ are either far less desirable than the 1.2 μ bands for the determination of methyl, methylene, and methylidene or that they have not yet been studied sufficiently.

Insufficient investigation is probably true of the 2.2 to 2.4 μ region. Buhl and Gailey (16) have found bands at 2.275 and 2.462 μ which can be correlated with the methyl content of polymers and are of some value in quantitative work. They are probably due to combination of the C—H stretching bands and the C—H deformation bands. Further work in the 2.2 to 2.4 μ region will undoubtedly uncover some interesting spectra–structure correlations, and valuable bands for quantitative work.

Recent work by Mitzner and Loori on terpenes is very encouraging (74). They report bands which appear to be indicative of various terpenoid structures and different types of bonds. These bands are mainly about 1.7 μ and in the 2.2 to 2.4 μ region. No applications to actual analyses of complex terpene mixtures were reported, but there is a possibility that such analyses may be accomplished in some cases by near-infrared.

2. N—H Vibrations

The N—H stretching vibrations are very amenable to study by the use of near-infrared spectrophotometers. The Beckman DK is quite capable of doing acceptable work in the region of the N—H fundamental stretching bands at 2.8 to 3.0 μ. All instruments perform well on the first overtone of this vibration at 1.5 μ. The second overtone at about 1 μ can also be used.

During the past 25 years, there have been extensive studies made of both the fundamental and overtone N—H stretching vibrations. The data on spectral assignments and variation of frequency relative to structure in the fundamental N—H region are reviewed in detail by Bellamy (11) and need not be reported here.

Early work on the overtone N—H bands was done by Liddel and Wulf about 25 years ago (65,108). The resolution they used was somewhat poorer than that obtainable with current instrumentation, but their work provides valuable background information and covers a wide variety of compounds.

There is little question that the quantitative determination of N—H groups will be one of near-infrared's most important applications in the future. This is despite the fact that only a few papers are available from which to obtain data to evaluate possible applications.

A. AMINES

The spectra of primary, secondary, and tertiary amines in the near-infrared region are drastically different. Primary amines have two absorption bands in the region between 2.85 and 3.05 μ, a peak, or possibly two, in the region around 2.0 μ, a doublet around 1.45 to 1.55 μ and a single peak at about 1.0 μ. These, of course, are in addition to any C—H bands or bands due to other functional groups in the molecule. Secondary amines have single absorption bands between 2.9 and 3.0 μ, 1.5 to 1.55 μ, and at about 1.0 μ. Tertiary amines have no strong bands in the near-infrared region due to the amine group.

Thus a qualitative identification of the various types of amines is usually relatively easy by near-infrared. The quantitative aspects are less well known and are discussed below.

a. Fundamental N—H Region.   Russell and Thompson (84) and Kruger and Thompson (62) have studied the intensities of the N—H bands in various amines in the fundamental N—H region and have reported a number of integrated band areas and absorption maxima. Their data indicate that aliphatic amines have, generally, a very low absorption intensity.   Aromatic amines, typified by substituted anilines, have more intense N—H bands by a factor of about 20. Various nitrogen ring systems, such as pyrrole or indole have the most intense absorption bands.

In substituted anilines, the frequency of the absorption bands were found to correlate with the Hammett σ factor.   Bellamy and Williams (12) have studied this and the relationship between the symmetric and asymmetric vibrations in various primary amines and cite a number of references to papers in which the frequencies of various fundamental N—H bands have been reported.

A very limited amount of work in our laboratory, in which we determined the molar absorptivities of a few primary and secondary amines in the 3 μ region with a Beckman Model DK-2 Spectrophotometer, confirmed the integrated intensity data of Thompson et al.; data are in Table X.   The amines were not highly purified and the wavelength data are probably not highly accurate (± 5 mμ).   The data are of value in showing the relative intensities of the weak aliphatic fundamental N—H bands compared to the stronger N—H bands in aromatic amines.   The aliphatic amines also absorb at a higher wavelength as is well known from the work of Thompson and others.   Secondary amines appear to have about half the molar absorptivity of the sum of the two molar absorptivities of the symmetric and asymmetric bands in the corresponding primary amine.

It appears that primary and secondary aromatic amines can often be advantageously determined using their fundamental N—H stretching vibrations, but that the analytical utility of the same bands in aliphatic amines is very limited.

b. 2 μ or Combination Band Region.   Both aromatic and aliphatic primary amines have fairly intense bands in the region of 2 μ.   These bands have been assigned to a combination of the N—H bending and stretching modes (57).   Secondary, and of course tertiary, amines show no absorption bands in this region.

The combination bands of primary aromatic amines have been discussed in detail in two papers by Whetsel, Roberson, and Krell

TABLE X
Fundamental N—H Stretching Bands of Several Amines in Carbon Tetrachloride

Amine	ν Max., cm.$^{-1}$	λ Max., μ	Molar absorptivity ϵ, liter/mole-cm.[a]
Primary			
t-Butylamine	3383	2.956	2.4
	3307	3.024	2.9
Cyclohexylamine	3387	2.952	2.9
	3316	3.016	1.6
Benzylamine	3406	2.936	1.7
	3332	3.001	0.8
Aniline	3499	2.858	27
	3405	2.937	31
m-Toluidine	3495	2.861	26
	3400	2.941	29
Secondary			
di-n-Butylamine	3344	2.990	0.8
N-Ethylaniline	3432	2.914	23
N-Ethyl-c-toluidine	3439	2.908	20
Diphenylamine	3442	2.905	54

[a] Data obtained on a Beckman Model DK-2 Spectrophotometer using a nominal slit at 3.000 μ of 0.25 mm., which gives a half-intensity band-width of 11.5 mμ.

(102,103). They have discussed both the use of the combination band for the determination of primary amines in mixtures with secondary and tertiary amines (102), and the relationship of the combination band to the structure of the molecules (103). In their studies of the combination bands of 40 substituted anilines, they found the frequency of the combination band to be less subject to the effect of substituent groups than the overtone, and also presumably the fundamental bands. They derived relationships between the electronic nature of the constituents and the frequency of the combination band and also between the frequencies of the overtone N—H stretching bands and the combination bands.

The intensity data and wavelength data on amines reported by Whetsel *et al.*, are in Table XI. From this, it can be seen that the wavelengths of the maxima of the combination bands of aromatic amines, range between 1.959 and 1.982 μ. The molar absorptivities are of the order of 1.75. These data are for carbon tetrachloride

TABLE XI
N—H Overtone and Combination Bands of Substituted Anilines (103)

Substituent	Combination			1st Overtone symmetric			1st Overtone asymmetric			2nd Overtone symmetric		
	νMax, cm.$^{-1}$	λMax, μ	Molar absorptivity ε liter/mole-cm.^{a}	νMax, cm.$^{-1}$	λMax, μ	Molar absorptivity ε liter/mole-cm.^{a}	νMax, cm.$^{-1}$	λMax, μ	Molar absorptivity ε liter/mole-cm.^{a}	νMax, cm.$^{-1}$	λMax, μ	Molar absorptivity ε liter/mole-cm.^{a}
Meta- and para-substituted compounds												
p-N(C$_2$H$_5$)$_2$	5046	1982.0	1.23	6656	1502.5	1.29	6850	1460.0	0.138	9737	1027.0	0.040
p-NH$_2$	5049	1980.5	1.36[b]	6656	1502.5	1.35[b]	6852	1459.5	0.158[b]	9741	1026.5	0.040[b]
p-OC$_2$H$_5$	5054	1979.0	1.41	6665	1500.5	1.31	6859	1458.0	0.154	9756	1025.0	0.041
p-OCH$_3$	5055	1978.5	1.43	6665	1500.5	1.29	6862	1457.5	0.152	9756	1025.0	0.044
p-CH$_3$	5062	1975.5	1.57	6683	1496.5	1.28	6885	1452.5	0.158	9775	1023.0	0.041
p-SCH$_3$[c]	5070	1972.5	1.51	6702	1492.0	1.32	6909	1447.5	0.165	9813	1019.0	0.035
p-CH$_2$CH$_2$OH	5070	1972.5	1.80	6693	1494.0	1.35	6897	1450.0	0.192	9804	1020.0	
None	5072	1971.5	1.63	6698	1493.0	1.21	6904	1448.5	0.156	9794	1021.0	0.038
m-CH$_3$	5074	1971.0	1.52	6693	1495.0	1.24	6897	1450.0	0.160	9794	1021.0	0.039
m-C$_6$H$_5$	5074	1971.0	1.69	6700	1492.5	1.66	6906	1448.0	0.222	9804	1020.0	0.047
3,5-(CH$_3$)$_2$	5075	1970.5	1.39	6689	1495.0	1.29	6897	1450.0	0.164	9785	1022.0	0.039
p-Cl	5075	1970.5	1.69	6705	1491.5	1.33	6906	1448.0	0.179	9813	1019.0	0.042
m-OC$_2$H$_5$	5079	1969.0	1.50	6702	1492.0	1.18	6906	1448.0	0.154	9813	1019.0	0.031
m-Br	5079	1969.0	1.66	6713	1489.5	1.32	6923	1444.5	0.199	9828	1017.5	0.043
m-COCH$_3$	5081	1968.0	1.64	6709	1490.5	1.32	6918	1445.5	0.168	9823	1018.0	0.031
m-Cl	5082	1968.0	1.71	6713	1489.5	1.32	6920	1445.0	0.192	9818	1018.5	0.040
p-SCN	5088	1965.5	1.82	6727	1486.5	1.44	6942	1440.5	0.264	9857	1014.5	0.035
m-CF$_3$	5090	1964.5	1.76	6721	1488.0	1.29	6932	1442.5	0.200	9832	1017.0	0.034
m-NO$_2$	5095	1963.0	1.88	6725	1487.0	1.47	6940	1441.0	0.242	9852	1015.0	0.032
p-COCH$_3$	5095	1963.0	2.04	6730	1486.0	1.73	6944	1440.0	0.312	9862	1014.0	0.046
p-SO$_2$CH$_3$	5096	1962.5		6739	1484.0		6954	1438.0				

Substituent												
p-COOH	5097	1962.0		6734	1485.0	1.61	6944	1440.0	0.318	9877	1012.5	0.040
p-CN	5100	1961.0	2.12	6739	1484.0	1.76	6954	1438.0	0.415				
p-NO$_2$	5104	1959.0	2.12	6745	1483.5		6964	1436.0				
Ortho-substituted compounds												
o-SCH$_3$[d]	5046	1982.0	1.57	6716	1489.0	0.58	6873	1455.0	0.148	9809	1019.5	0.019
				6609	1513.0	0.53				9662	1035.0	0.010
2-CH$_3$-4-N(C$_2$H$_5$)$_2$	5045	1982.5	1.23	6652	1503.5	1.27	6850	1460.0	0.139	9746	1026.0	0.043
o-OC$_2$H$_5$	5052	1979.5	1.70	6696	1493.5	1.24	6911	1447.0	0.140	9804	1020.0	0.029
2,5-(OC$_4$H$_9$-n)$_2$	5056	1978.0	1.98	6696	1493.5	1.31	6916	1446.0	0.138	9809	1019.5	0.033
2,5-(OC$_2$H$_5$)$_2$	5057	1977.5	1.83	6698	1493.0	1.23	6916	1446.0	0.145	9813	1019.0	0.032
o-OCH$_3$	5057	1977.5	1.71	6700	1492.5	1.24	6916	1446.0	0.129	9818	1018.5	0.026
2,5-(OCH$_3$)$_2$-4-Cl	5060	1976.5	1.84	6698	1493.0	1.40	6930	1443.0	0.167	9832	1017.0	0.032
2,5-(OCH$_3$)$_2$	5061	1976.0	1.87	6700	1492.5	1.28	6920	1445.0	0.143	9823	1018.0	0.037
2,4,6-Cl$_3$	5061	1976.0	2.95	6711	1490.0	1.53	6944	1440.0	0.326	9852	1015.0	0.031
o-SO$_2$CH$_3$	5066	1974.0	2.54	6739	1484.0	0.71	6885	1452.5	0.242	9852	1015.0	0.018
				6631	1538.0	0.75				9699	1031.0	0.012
o-Br	5068	1973.0	2.08	6695	1493.5	1.15	6925	1444.0	0.225	9823	1018.0	0.022
o-CH$_3$	5071	1972.0	1.58	6696	1493.5	1.22	6901	1449.0	0.163	9794	1021.0	0.036
2,4,5-Cl$_3$	5071	1972.0	2.18	6713	1489.5	1.47	6940	1441.0	0.298	9852	1015.0	0.035
2,4-Cl$_2$	5072	1971.5	2.01	6709	1490.5	1.42	6933	1442.5	0.258	9832	1017.0	0.021
o-Cl	5072	1971.5	2.01	6705	1491.5	1.25	6930	1443.0	0.220	9828	1017.5	0.031
o-NO$_2$	5084	1967.0	2.65	6791	1472.0	0.90	6982	1432.0	0.425	9970	1003.0	0.025
				6691	1494.5	1.16				9813	1019.0	0.015
Average	5071.5	1971.9	1.75	6701.9	1492.2	1.35	6913.4	1446.5	0.204	9810.6	1019.3	0.036
Standard deviation	16.0	6.2	0.37	21.2	4.7	0.14	31.7	6.7	0.075	34.8	3.7	0.006

[a] Dilute solutions (1% or less) in carbon tetrachloride; background absorbances at 1915, 1575, 1410–1420, and 1075 μ were subtracted from peak absorbances of combination, first overtone symmetric, first overtone asymmetric, and second overtone symmetric bands, respectively, before calculating absorptivities.

[b] Measured absorptivities divided by 2 to make these values comparable to others.

[c] Purity of this compound only 92%.

[d] Purity of this compound only 87%.   (Courtesy of *Analytical Chemistry*.)

solution only.   Data obtained in our laboratory on aniline, indicate
that there is a slight shift in the absorption maximum of the combination band when other solvents such as benzene, dioxane, methyl
ethyl ketone, or dimethylformamide are used.   The molar absorptivity changed very little, however, in these other solvents, especially
when the effect due to using a wider spectral slit is accounted for.

Primary aliphatic amines also have a strong and useful combination band at about 2 μ.   This band has not been studied extensively
and there seems to be little work on it reported in the literature.
Perhaps one reason for this is that it is very difficult to work with
aliphatic amines in carbon tetrachloride solution since they react
fairly rapidly with the solvent, especially in the more concentrated
solutions needed in the combination and overtone band regions.
Of course, other solvents, such as those listed above for aniline, can be
used equally well for analytical work with primary aliphatic amines,
but they are usually less desirable for fundamental studies.   Data
which we have obtained on a few compounds indicate that aliphatic
primary amines will absorb at 2.01 ± 0.02 μ in most solvents with a
molar absorptivity of 0.7 to 1.0 l./mole-cm.   Some amines, cyclo-
hexylamine for example, have a well resolved doublet in the 2 μ region.
The combination band region thus appears to be as attractive for the
determination of primary aliphatic amines as it has been shown to be
for the determination of the primary aromatic amines.

c. 1.5 μ or First Overtone Region.   Primary and secondary aliphatic and aromatic amines absorb in the neighborhood of 1.5 μ.
The early studies of Liddell and Wulf give some background information on the qualitative effects observed (65,108).   The more recent
work by Whetsel, Roberson, and Krell gives extensive quantitative
detail on primary aromatic amines and also limited data on secondary
aromatic amines (103).   As in the case of the combination band,
there appear to be no quantitative applications of the first overtone
region to aliphatic amines.

The data in Table XI indicate that primary aromatic amines have
two bands in the overtone region as they do in the fundamental
region.   The symmetric vibration occurs at 1.492 ± 5 μ and is about
6 or 7 times as intense as the asymmetric band which is in the region
of 1.447 μ.   The molar absorptivity of the symmetric band is about
1.3 to 1.4, which makes it very useful for a wide range of concentrations and compositions.   Whetsel et al., were able to correlate the

electronic nature and position of the substituent groups with the frequencies of the overtone bands, as well as to detect whether or not groups were present which were ortho to the amine group. While this work was done in carbon tetrachloride solution in order to eliminate intermolecular effects, it is possible to use almost any solvent except an alcohol for work in the 1.5 μ region.

Secondary aromatic amines have a single band in the 1.5 μ region. This usually occurs at a wavelength close to that of the symmetric stretching vibration of the corresponding primary amine. For example, the wavelengths of the maxima for N-ethylaniline, N-ethyl-m-toluidine, and N-ethyl-o-toluidine are from 1.492 to 1.493 μ (101,102, and data from our laboratory). The molar absorptivity of N-ethyl-o-toluidine is about 0.7 l./mole-cm. in carbon tetrachloride, which is about one-half that of the corresponding primary amine. Solvent effects on the intensity of this band are such that lower absorptivities are often found in more polar solvents such as dimethylformamide.

Beer's law is obeyed quite closely by both primary and secondary aromatic amines up to at least 2.0% concentration in carbon tetrachloride, provided a narrow enough spectral slit is used (101,102). It may be difficult to achieve a small enough spectral slit without excessive noise on some near-infrared spectrophotometers and on these, calibration curves must be used. Above 2% concentration there are very likely to be deviations from Beer's law due to intermolecular association and other solvent effects (104).

As in the case of the combination band region, there is little quantitative data relative to aliphatic amines. Whetsel et al., state that primary and secondary aliphatic amines absorb at 1.530 μ which is well resolved from the aromatic amine bands (101). This confirms the earlier data of Liddel and Wulf (65,108). It is possible to determine aromatic amines in the presence of a 10% concentration of aliphatic amines with essentially no correction (102). One would predict that all combinations of mixtures of aliphatic and aromatic primary and secondary amines could readily be analyzed by the use of simultaneous equations.

We have obtained limited data on pairs of primary and secondary aliphatic amines in the 1.5 μ region (Table XII). Only the most intense band of the primary amines was measured. These data are of interest since they show that the intensity of the first overtone band of the N—H stretching band of aliphatic amines is of the same order of magnitude as that for the fundamental band. Secondly, the wavelengths of the secondary amine bands are not the same as those for primary amines. Finally, the intensities of the secondary amine bands approach those found for the primary bands. The wavelength shift between primary and secondary makes it difficult to analyze mixtures since the absorption maximum of a mixture will shift with composition. Nevertheless, the overtone and combination band regions appear more attractive for the analysis of aliphatic amines than the fundamental region, especially when one considers the wide variety of solvents and cell paths which may be chosen.

TABLE XII

Near-Infrared Absorption Data on Aliphatic Amines at 1.5 μ in Carbon Tetrachloride

Amine	ν Max., cm.$^{-1}$ (symmetric)	λ Max., μ (symmetric)	Molar absorptivity, ϵ, liter/mole-cm.^{a}
n-Butylamine	6553	1.526	0.60
Di-n-butylamine	6494	1.540	0.61
Cyclohexylamine	6527	1.532	0.80
Dicyclohexylamine	6464	1.547	0.55

^{a} Data obtained on a Cary Model 14 Spectrophotometer using a nominal slit 0.15 mm. at 1.550 μ, which gives a half-intensity band-width of 0.52 mμ.

d. 1.0 μ or Second Overtone Region. The second overtone N—H stretching bands are very weak and for this reason are of very limited analytical utility. The intensity and position data reported by Whetsel et al., (103) are given in Table XI. Only one band, the symmetric, was reported; probably because of the extreme weakness of the asymmetric band. Aliphatic amines will absorb at longer wavelengths and presumably with somewhat less intensity.

B. AMIDES

In many ways the spectra of amides, especially with reference to their —N—H vibrations, are very similar to those of amines. The spectra of amides may be somewhat more complex, however, because of the possibility of an enol as well as a keto form, and because secondary amides can exist in either a cis or trans form. Qualitative work in the fundamental N—H stretching region is discussed fully by Bellamy (11).

Like the primary amines, most primary amides have two bands at about 2.82 and 2.92 μ due to the fundamental N—H asymmetric and symmetric stretching vibrations. The intensity of these bands determined in 0.05 M solution and extrapolated to infinite dilution is of the order of 130 l./mole-cm. for both bands, in chloroform solution (21). Although these infinite dilution values, reported by Cleverley, seem high, the few amides we have run in this region have very intense N—H stretching vibrations with absorptivities as high as 120 at a concentration of 0.5 mM.

N-Substituted or secondary amides also may have a doublet in the 3 μ region. This is attributed to the cis and trans isomers which are possible and has been used to calculate the percentage of each which is present (85).

Moccia and Thompson (70) have published data on various substituted anilides including frequency, half-intensity band-width, and integrated band intensity. Molar absorptivities, which would be more generally useful in analytical work, are not reported. Data from our laboratory on N-ethyltoluamide indicate a molar absorptivity of 45 at 2.896 μ in carbon tetrachloride. This band is somewhat more intense than the bands in aromatic amines measured under similar instrumental conditions.

Of course, tertiary of di-N-substituted amides usually have no strong absorption bands due to the amide group in the near-infrared region and it is possible to detect other amides with free N—H groups in their presence with good sensitivity.

Primary and secondary amides show two combination bands in the region of 2 μ, but qualitative or quantitative data on these have not been published. We have found a unique, strong band for primary amides at 1.96 μ which has a molar absorptivity of about 3. The band is probably due to a combination of the fundamental asymmetric N—H stretching vibration at 2.82 μ and the amide II or N—H deformation band at 6.4 μ.

Data are also sparse on the first overtone band at 1.5 μ. For one thing, carbon tetrachloride is too poor a solvent for most amides to allow data to be obtained in this region. We have used both methylene chloride and chloroform as solvents and found data such as

TABLE XIII

Near-Infrared Absorption Data on Amides in Chloroform Solution

Amides	ν Max., cm. $^{-1}$	λ Max., μ	Molar absorptivity, ϵ, liter/mole-cm.[a]		
			Cary Model 14	Beckman Model DK-2	Spectracord 4000A
Unsubstituted					
Butyramide	4998	2.001	0.56	0.46	0.36
	5102	1.960	3.27	2.93	2.46
	6743	1.483	0.81	0.78	0.73
	6831	1.464	0.83	0.75	0.70
Benzamide	4993	2.003	0.58	0.54	0.46
	5097	1.962	3.52	3.16	2.79
	6743	1.483	0.82	0.83	0.78
	6835	1.463	0.54	0.58	0.54
Monosubstituted					
N-Methyl acetamide	5003	1.999	0.45	0.42	
	6798	1.471	1.42	1.09	
Stearanilide	4963	2.015	0.94	0.91	0.79
	5033	1.987	0.37	0.34	0.31
	6711	1.490	0.86	0.76	0.75
Nominal slit at 2.00 μ, mm.		0.35	0.050	0.125[b]	
Nominal slit at 1.50 μ, mm.		0.23	0.027	0.074[b]	
Half-intensity band-width at 2.00 μ, mμ	1.1	3.7	5.8		
Half-intensity band-width at 1.50 μ, mμ	0.8	2.6	4.2		

[a] Samples run in 100 mM solution in 5 cm. cells.

[b] Spectracord was not run at as high gain to obtain these data as for that in Tables III and V.

that shown in Table XIII. It is certainly possible to use the combination and overtone regions to advantage for the determination of amides, provided that primary and secondary aromatic amines are absent. One must be careful, however, of both solvent effects and intermolecular association with resultant varying molar absorptivities. Aliphatic amines absorb at a long enough wavelength not to interfere. The N—H spectra of aliphatic and aromatic amides are quite similar and it is probably not possible to differentiate them by use of N—H bands.

Kogan reports that aryl allophanates and aryl and aryl–alkyl biurets show intramolecular N—H bonding in the 1.5 μ region (61a).

He has used the first overtone N—H stretching bands for the study of reaction rates of aryl isocyanates and ethyl carbanilates to form ethyl diaryl allophanates (61b).

More quantitative and qualitative information on the spectra of amides in the 1 to 3 μ region will be required before the potentialities of the region, for their determination, can be evaluated accurately.

C. HYDRAZINES

Hydrazines have N—H groups which also absorb in the 1 to 3 μ region. To date, very limited information is available, although with increased interest in these types of compounds more data will surely by published. Shull et al. (89) studied 1,1-dimethylhydrazine and trimethylhydrazine in the 3 μ region and found two bands for the former and one for the latter. Their work was not done in dilute solution, but the number of bands would be expected to be the same.

In addition to these fundamental N—H vibrations, hydrazines usually have combination bands in the 2 μ region, and overtone bands in the 1.5 μ region. Data are not available on the combination band region. The limited data we have obtained on the 1.5 μ bands are given in Table XIV. Chloroform was used as a solvent since hydrazines are very slightly soluble in carbon tetrachloride. The spectra are quite complex, but certainly of value in analytical work. Aliphatic amines would interfere with some, but not all, of the hydrazine bands.

TABLE XIV
Near-Infrared Absorption Data on Hydrazines in the 1.5 μ Region in Chloroform

Compound	ν Max., cm.$^{-1}$	λ Max., μ	Molar absorptivity, ϵ, liter/mole-cm.[a]
Hydrazine	6553	1.526	0.59
	6506	1.537	1.34
	6423	1.557	1.20
Methylhydrazine	6510	1.536	0.30
(questionable purity)	6468	1.546	0.21
1,1-Dimethylhydrazine	6562	1.524	0.50
	6443	1.552	0.46

[a] Data obtained on a Cary 14 Spectrophotometer using a nominal slit of 0.15 mm. at 1.550 μ which corresponds to a half-height band-width of 0.52 mμ.

Aromatic amines would be innocuous.   The analysis of mixtures of hydrazines presents an interesting problem, which may be capable of solution by near-infrared alone.

D. MISCELLANEOUS N—H CONTAINING COMPOUNDS

There are other types of compounds which contain an N—H or NH_2 grouping and which absorb in the 3 μ region and in the overtone and combination band regions.   Among these are various hetero-cyclic ring systems which have very intense N—H bands (84), peptides (46), alkaloids, and other natural products, and possibly hydroxamic acids.   There is not enough information on these to go into detail at this time.

3. O—H Vibrations

Many aspects of the fundamental hydroxyl stretching vibrations in the 2.7 to 3.0 μ region are rather completely covered by previous authors, in particular by Bellamy (11), and Jones and Sandorfy (56) in their excellent reviews of the infrared field.   Nevertheless, new applications, new data, and new papers keep appearing, so that the last words are far from said.   In particular, the applications of the quartz prism or grating instruments for routine, medium resolu-tion, analytical work are just beginning.   Although mention will be made of some of the papers included in the above reviews, the major part of this section is on new work and on analytical applications of hydroxyl spectra.   In particular, the discussion is restricted to work carried out in dilute solution under conditions which ensure almost complete elimination of intermolecular interaction.   The best opportunities to make quantitative use of the O—H stretching vibrations appear to come from dilute solution work, at least this has been the experience in our laboratory.

Most of the discussion concerns the fundamental O—H stretching band region between 2.7 and 3.0 μ, since it is in this region that most of the work has been done.   It is also my opinion that this region offers the greatest potential for quantitative analytical work. In general the discussion is limited to work in carbon tetrachloride solution; however, some other solvents, in particular methylene chloride, will be mentioned.

A. ALCOHOLS

The fundamental free hydroxyl stretching vibration in alcohols is generally observed at 2.75 to 2.77 μ in dilute carbon tetrachloride solution (92). Typical alcoholic hydroxyl spectra in this region are given in Fig. 13. Data on the wavelengths of the maxima and molar absorptivities of some representative alcohols are listed in Table XV.

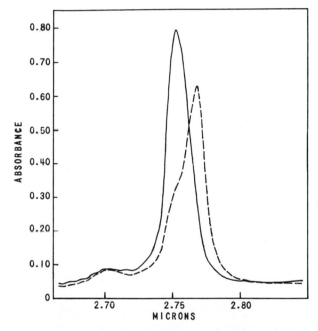

Fig. 13. Near-infrared absorption spectrum of n-octanol and benzyl alcohol in the 2.7 to 2.8 μ region on the Beckman Model DK-2 Recording Spectrophotometer; 1 cm. cell. Solid line 13.0mM n-octanol in carbon tetrachloride; broken line 10.2mM benzyl alcohol in carbon tetrachloride.

The primary aliphatic alcohols absorb at about 2.750 ± 0.002 μ; most secondary aliphatic alcohols at 2.760 ± 0.002 μ; and the tertiary aliphatic alcohols at 2.766 ± 0.003 μ. This shift of wavelength with alcohol type has been noted by many others including Kuhn (63), Anet and Bavin (4), and Cole and Jeffries (23). The peak intensity of the alcoholic hydroxyl band is usually constant to

TABLE XV

Near-Infrared Absorption Data on Alcohols in the 2.7 to 3.0 μ Region in Carbon Tetrachloride Solution

Alcohol	ν Max., cm. $^{-1}$	λ Max., μ	Molar absorptivity, ε, liter/mole-cm.^{a}	
			15 mM solution, 1 cm. cell	1 mM solution, 10 cm. cell
Primary Aliphatic				
Methyl	3612	2.746	59	59
Ethyl	3632	2.753	50	50
n-Propyl	3635	2.751	50	50
Butyl	3634	2.752	54	56
Isobutyl	3636	2.750	58	61
Isoamyl	3635	2.751	57	56
n-Octyl	3634	2.752	56	57
n-Nonyl	3636	2.750	57	57
Undecyl	3634	2.752	50	52
Tetradecyl	3635	2.751	56	55
Dehydroabietyl	3639	2.748	70	71
Secondary Aliphatic				
Isopropyl	3623	2.760	50	52
sec-Butyl	3625	2.759	44	45
sec-Amyl	3625	2.759	43	45
Cyclohexyl	3621	2.762	53	56
4-Methylcyclohexyl	3621	2.762	51	55
2-Octyl	3625	2.759	47	47
Bornyl	3627	2.757	53	54
α-Fenchyl	3631	2.754	61	61
Menthyl	3622	2.761	39	40
Tertiary Aliphatic				
t-Butyl	3613	2.768	50	52
t-Amyl	3611	2.769	44	45
1-Methylcyclohexyl	3611	2.769	41	44
α-Terpinyl	3617	2.765	47	47
cis-Dihydro-α-terpinyl	3618	2.764	44	46
Miscellaneous Alcohols				
Propargyl	3619	2.763	80	81
Allyl	3618	2.764	51	51
2-Buten-1-yl	3617	2.765	52	52
Methallyl	3615	2.766	54	55
Benzyl	3615	2.766	58	62
p-Methylbenzyl	3615	2.766	60	64
α,α-Dimethylbenzyl	3605	2.774	59	63

TABLE XV (*Continued*)

Alcohol	ν Max., cm.$^{-1}$	λ Max., μ	Molar absorptivity, ϵ, liter/mole-cm.^{a} 15 mM solution, 1 cm. cell	1 mM solution, 10 cm. cell
8-*p*-Cymyl	3605	2.774	48	48
1-Phenylcyclohexyl	3602	2.776	60	62
m-Isopropyl-α,α-dimethyl-benzyl	3602	2.776	54	54
p-Isopropyl-α,α-dimethyl-benzyl	3604	2.775	57	58
$\alpha,\alpha,\alpha',\alpha'$-tetramethyl-*m*-xylene-$\alpha$-$\alpha'$-diol	3591	2.785	129	
Triphenylmethyl	3606	2.773	80	94
Furfuryl	3615	2.766	73	78
Tetrahydrofurfuryl	3596	2.781	40	44
Diethylene glycol	3634	2.752	26	35
	3610	2.770	53	73
cis-2-Nitrocyclohexyl	3605	2.774	45	
trans-2-Nitrocyclohexyl	3609	2.771	56	
m-Nitrobenzyl	3630	2.755	62	64
	3615	2.766	54	57
p-Nitrobenzyl	3630	2.755	70	69
	3615	2.766	56	53
m-Nitrocumyl (*m*-nitro-α-α-dimethylbenzyl)	3613	2.768	28	29
	3602	2.776	27	29
p-Nitrocumyl (*p*-Nitro-α-α-dimethylbenzyl)	3610	2.770	54	55
	3602	2.776	50	51
1-(*p*-Nitrophenyl)cyclohexyl	3596	2.781	60	
2-Chloroethyl	3623	2.760	25	26
	3592	2.784	51	52
3-Chloropropyl	3632	2.753	59	60
2,2,2-Trichloroethyl	3595	2.782	111	130
1,3-Dichloro-2-propyl	3589	2.788	44	44
	3563	2.806	49	48
1,1,1-Trichloro-2-methyl-2-propyl	3583	2.791	114	121
Pentaerythritol trichloride	3634	2.752	102	100
2,3-Dibromo-1-propyl	3625	2.759	24	26
	3588	2.787	52	53
1,3-Dibromo-2-propyl	3606	2.773	15	12
	3571	2.800	34	34
	3551	2.816	48	47
3-Bromo-1-propyl	3636	2.750	126	126

^{a} Data obtained on Beckman Model DK-2 Spectrophotometer using a nominal slit of 0.12 mm. at 2.763 μ, which gives a half-intensity band-width of 6.2 mμ.

at least $\pm 10\%$ in alcohols of similar structure.   This enables the analyst to use analogs for calibration work on new or unknown compounds with some degree of confidence.   Unusual effects of various groups on the spectrum and intensity are discussed below.   Dilution of the alcohols by factors up to 50 causes very little increase in molar absorptivity as shown by the data in Table XV.   Data on integrated intensities of free hydroxyl stretching bands have been published by Brown *et al.*, (14,15), and Moccia and Thompson (75).   Marion, Ramsay, and Jones have published frequency and molar absorptivity data on the hydroxyl groups of a variety of alkaloids (69).   They report molar absorptivities mostly of the order of 50 to 80, with extremes of 30 and 160.

Figure 13 shows the hydroxyl spectrum of benzyl alcohol compared with that of *n*-octanol.   The spectrum of the benzyl alcohol appears to have a shoulder at the wavelength for primary alcohols, 2.750 μ, yet the maximum is at 2.766 μ.   Such spectra are typical of the unsaturated alcohols and aromatic alcohols mentioned in Table XV. In the case of the benzyl alcohols, such spectra have been attributed to the interaction of the π electrons in the center of unsaturation with the hydrogen atom on the hydroxyl group (4,9,30).   It is most reasonable to extend this interpretation to the other α-, β-unsaturated alcohols in Table XV.   Buswell, Rodebush, and Whitney have reported similar work on β-mesityl-substituted vinyl alcohols (17).   Schleyer, Trifan, and Bacskai have extended the work to a wide variety of proton acceptors such as triple bonds and cyclopropane rings (87).   Confirmation of this is obtainable from the data on nitrobenzyl alcohols (Table XV).   Although two peaks are still obtained for these compounds, the shorter wavelength peak is more well-defined and more intense.   This is because the electron-donating power of the ring is decreased by the substitution of the electron-attracting nitro group.

Intramolecular hydrogen bonding between a nitro group and an adjacent hydroxyl group can cause a shift of the hydroxyl band to a longer wavelength as in the 2-nitrocyclohexanols.   If Badger's rule (5) is obeyed, the bonding is probably stronger in the cis compound, hence the greater wavelength shift.

Extensive work on the configuration of alcohols, cis and trans, and axial and equatorial, has been done by Kuhn (63), Ambelang and Binder (2), Sicher, Horak, and Svoboda (89a), and Cole and co-

workers (1a,23,23b).   While it is difficult, if not impossible, to make
generalizations as to the wavelengths of the bands for various cis or
trans, or axial or equatorial hydroxyl groups, it appears that the.
fundamental hydroxyl region is very promising as a qualitative tool
for the determination of absolute configuration.   Good resolution is a
necessity for this type of work.   Anet and Bavin have also used this
region to show the preference of some molecules for certain rotational
isomers (4).

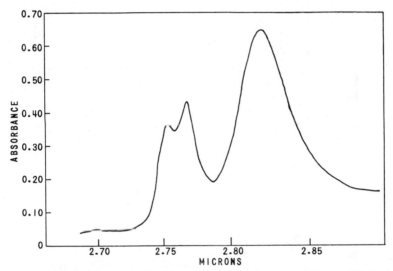

Fig. 14. Near-infrared absorption spectrum of 3-methyl-1-3,butanediol in the
2.7 to 2.9 μ region on the Beckman Model DK-2 Recording Spectrophotometer;
9.22mM solution in carbon tetrachloride; 1 cm. cell.

Substitution of halogen atoms close to the hydroxyl groups
in alcohols may give rise to rather extensive changes in the hydroxyl
spectrum (Table XV).   The band may be shifted as in 1,1,1-tri-
chloroethanol; it may be split as in 1,3-dichloro-2-propanol; it
may be intensified as in pentaerythritol trichloride; or all may
occur.   In general, from the data we have obtained, it appears that
halogen substitution on the carbon atom either α or β to an alcoholic
hydroxyl group will intensify the hydroxyl band.   Substitution on the
α-carbon atom will shift the absorption band to longer wavelengths.
Splitting of the band may occur if more than one carbon atom is

TABLE XVI

Data on Polyhydroxyl Alcohols in the 2.7 to 3.0 μ Region in Carbon Tetrachloride

Polyhydroxy alcohol	Free hydroxyl band				Intramolecularly bonded hydroxyl band					ΔFree $\frac{\Delta\text{Free}}{\Delta\text{Free}+\Delta\text{Bonded}}$
	νMax., cm.$^{-1}$	λMax., μ	Molar absorptivity, ϵ, liter/mole-cm.^{a}		νMax., cm.$^{-1}$	λMax., μ	Molar absorptivity, ϵ, liter/mole-cm.^{a}		$\Delta\nu$, Free − Bonded, cm.$^{-1}$	
			1 cm. cell 10–15 mM	0.5–1 mM 10 cm. cell			1 cm. cell 10–15 mM	10 cm. cell 0.5–1 mM		
1,2-Propanediol	3635	2.751	47	49	3595	2.782	45	48	40	0.50
2,3-Butanediol	3631	2.754	53	54	3587	2.788	55	56	44	0.49
Chloral hydrate (2,2,2-trichloro-1,1-ethanediol)	3604	2.775	92	91	3559	2.810	83	83	45	0.54
3-Chloro-1,2-propanediol^b	3638	2.749	43	41	3597	2.780	79	79	41	0.34
1,3-Propanediol^b	3635	2.751	67	70	3557	2.811	31	36	78	0.68
1,3-Butanediol	3628	2.756	57	48	3547	2.819	42	40	81	0.57
3-Methyl-1,3-butanediol	3622, 3613	2.753, 2.768	33, 40	49, 58	3544	2.822	62	90	88, 69	0.57
2-Methyl-2,4-pentanediol (hexylene glycol)	3614	2.767	43	43	3531	2.832	80	70	83	0.37
2,2-Diethyl-1,3-propanediol	3636	2.750	102	102	3549	2.818	46	36	87	0.70
Pentaerythritol monoformal^b	3636	2.750	138		3541	2.824	47		95	0.25
1,4-Butanediol^b	3621	2.762	57	77	3487	2.868		6	134	0.93
2,5-Hexanediol	3625	2.759	63	78	3460	2.890	25	33	165	0.72

^{a} Data obtained on Beckman Model DK-2 Spectrophotometer using a nominal slit of 0.12 mm. at 2.763 μ, which gives half-intensity band-width of 6.2 mμ.

^{b} This sample may not have been completely in solution.

substituted with halogen. Possibilities for the analytical differentiation and determination of halo alcohols are obvious.

Perhaps the most interesting case of intramolecular interaction in alcohols is that found in glycols (Table XVI). The hydroxyl spectrum of a typical glycol is given in Fig. 14. The bands at 2.753 and 2.768 μ are due to the free hydroxyl bands of the primary and tertiary alcohol, respectively. The 2.822 μ band is due to intramolecularly bonded hydroxyl groups. The shift of the intramolecularly bonded band is about 40 cm.$^{-1}$ for 1,2-glycols. For 1,2-glycols both the free and intramolecularly bonded bands have about the same intensity. In 1,3-glycols the bonded band is generally less intense and the shift is about 80 cm.$^{-1}$. While the data reported in Table XVI are from our laboratory, similar work has been carried out by Kuhn (63), Cole and Jeffries (23), and Flett (29). The 2.7 to 3.0 μ region thus offers good possibilities for the differentiation and analysis of mixtures of alcohols and glycols. Also, because of the high intensity of the free hydroxyl band, it is often possible to get enough of the relatively insoluble glycols into solution, in carbon tetrachloride, for analytical work.

Additional work on intramolecular interaction in alcohols is reported and summarized by Flett (29). He points out that in addition to the functional groups mentioned above, amino, nitrilo, carbonyl, ether, and ester groups may interact with alcoholic groups, if close enough in space, and cause a shifting or splitting of the free hydroxyl band. Such shifts can often be used to advantage in analytical work.

Some compounds or mixtures encountered in analytical work are not soluble in carbon tetrachloride. For this reason it is desirable to have other solvents available. However, there are very few solvents which do not have either absorption bands or strong background absorption in the 2.7 to 3.0 μ region. In addition, most good solvents hydrogen bond extensively with hydroxyl groups, thus rendering them rather useless for free hydroxyl work. To date, the only solvent we have been able to find which is a useful substitute for carbon tetrachloride (other than carbon disulfide) is methylene chloride. It is quite transparent from 2.71 to 2.90 μ so that a 1 cm. absorption cell can be used without sacrificing too much resolution. The nominal and spectral slit used with 1 cm. of methylene chloride is not quite twice as great as that with carbon tetrachloride at the same wavelength (2.763 μ). Water is more soluble in methylene chloride which leads to some problems which will be discussed later. Commercial methylene chloride has been found satisfactory without purification other than drying. Chloroform might well be a useful solvent (it has been used by some investigators) but the usual reagent material is stabilized with ethanol, which necessitates purification and careful storage. Tetrachloroethylene may occasionally be used to advantage. Other good solvents for this region are badly needed.

Some data we have obtained on alcohols in methylene chloride are listed in Tables XVII and XVIII. They show that methylene chloride generally causes a shift of the hydroxyl band to longer wavelengths, or smaller frequency by about 20 cm.$^{-1}$ In addition, in spite of the wide slits used with methylene chloride, the alcoholic hydroxyl bands are generally 20 to 30% more intense. The cause for this has not been proved. We have postulated weak intermolecular bonding or electrostatic interaction between the hydroxyl hydrogen and one of the chlorines on the methylene chloride, which may have some electronegative character due to a structure such as [CH_2Cl]$^+Cl^-$. Such structures have been cited for methylene fluoride (79).

Barrow has studied ethyl ether and triethylamine solvents for alcohols in the 2.7 to 3.0 μ region and has studied bonding to the solvent (10). He was forced to use 1 mm. cells and found very intense bands for the hydroxyl group ($\epsilon = 300$ to 800). This is a possible approach to the use of other solvents, but of course one is no longer dealing with a free hydroxyl band as measurements are made at about 2.85 μ in ethyl ether and at about 3.1 μ in triethylamine. Additional studies on the effect of various electron donors on the intensity of hydroxyl bands have been made by Tsubomura (95, 96), Kaye (59), Cole and Macritchie (23a), West (100a), and Moccia and Califano (74a).

A few alcohols have absorption bands at about 1.9 to 2.0 μ, probably due to a combination band. Little information is available on the use or properties of the band. We have made some use of this region for analysis of the hydroxyl content of very strongly intramolecularly bonded hydroxyl groups such as those in esters of pentaerythritol, or possibly glycerol or ethylene glycol. No solvent is used, so intermolecular bonding may also occur; however, this is not too likely. Good sensitivity, down to 0.1% hydroxyl or less, has been achieved.

TABLE XVII
Near-Infrared Absorption Data on Alcohols in the 2.7 to 3.0 μ Region in Methylene Chloride

Alcohol	ν Max., cm.$^{-1}$	λ Max., μ	Molar absorptivity, ϵ, liter/mole-cm.[a]
Methanol	3622	2.761	85
Butanol	3611	2.769	61
Dehydroabietyl alcohol	3615	2.766	74
Benzyl alcohol	3600	2.778	62
sec-Butanol	3605	2.774	51
Borneol	3604	2.775	66
t-Butanol	3597	2.780	47
1,3-Butanediol	3605	2.744	87
	3522	2.839[b]	42[b]
Pentaerythritol monoformal	3615	2.766	129
	3529	2.834[b]	38[b]
Pentaerythritol dichloride	3603	2.775	171

[a] Data obtained on Beckman Model DK-2 Spectrophotometer using a nominal slit of 0.20 mm. at 2.763 μ, which gives a half-intensity band-width of 10.2 mμ.
[b] Intramolecularly bonded bands.

TABLE XVIII
Comparison of Fundamental Hydroxyl Stretching Band Data on Alcohols in Carbon Tetrachloride and Methylene Chloride

Alcohol	Frequency shift ν CCl$_4$–ν CH$_2$Cl$_2$ (cm.$^{-1}$)	Ratio of absorptivities, CH$_2$Cl$_2$/CCl$_4$
Methanol	20	1.44
Butanol	23	1.28
Dehydroabietyl alcohol	24	1.07
Benzyl alcohol	15	1.14
sec-Butanol	20	1.22
Borneol	23	1.26
t-Butanol	16	1.22

The first overtone of the hydroxyl stretching band at 1.4 μ has been studied extensively (41,48,49,65,71,108). The region is of great value for qualitative or structural identification work, especially when studies can be made with the resolution obtainable on the Cary Model 14 Spectrophotometer or equivalent instruments. The information obtained is, in general, very similar to that discussed in

TABLE XVIIIA Near-Infrared Absorption Data on Alcohols at 1.4 μ (24)

Alcohol	ν Max., cm.$^{-1}$	λ Max., μ	Molar absorptivity, ε, liter/ mole-cm.^{a}
Primary			
Methanol	7119	1.405	2.16
1-Butanol	7110	1.407	1.86
1-Pentanol	7110	1.407	1.88
2-Methyl-1-butanol	7110	1.407	1.94
3-Methyl-1-butanol	7110	1.407	1.87
1-Hexanol	7110	1.407	1.86
1-Heptanol	7110	1.407	1.85
2-Ethyl-1-butanol	7110	1.407	1.90
2-Ethyl-1-hexanol	7110	1.407	1.99
Fatty alcohols	7110	1.407	1.86
Allyl alcohol	7068	1.415	1.74
Tetrahydrofurfuryl alcohol	7032	1.422	.99
Benzyl alcohol	7059	1.417	1.89
2-Phenylethanol	7037, 7100	1.421, 1.409	1.42
3-Phenyl-1-propanol	7110	1.407	1.88
2-Phenyl-1-propanol	7110, 7032	1.407, 1.422	1.02
2-(2-Methylphenyl) ethanol) (*o*-methylphenethyl alcohol)	7100, 7032	1.409, 1.422	1.21
2-(4-Methoxyphenyl) ethanol) (*p*-(methoxy)phenethyl alcohol)	7100, 7032	1.409, 1.422	1.11
Secondary			
2-Propanol	7082	1.412	2.17
2-Butanol	7087	1.411	1.88
3-Pentanol	7092	1.410	1.61
1-Phenylethanol (α-Methylbenzyl alcohol)	7063	1.416	2.13
1-Phenyl-2-propanol (α-methylphenethyl alcohol)	7082, 7023	1.412, 1.424	.99
1,2-Diphenylethanol	7059	1.417	1.54
2-Methylcyclohexanol	7087	1.411	1.65
4-*t*-Butylcyclohexanol	7082	1.412	1.83
Borneol	7087	1.411	1.91
Isoborneol	7082	1.412	2.73
Menthol	7082	1.412	1.62
Cholesterol	7073	1.414	2.32
Tertiary			
t-Amyl alcohol	7063	1.416	1.91
α-Terpineol	7068	1.415	2.06
cis-Dihydroterpineol	7068	1.415	2.08

^{a} Data obtained on a Cary Model 14 Spectrophotometer using a nominal slit of 0.1 mm. at 1.4 μ or a half height band width of 0.35 mμ. Ten cm. cells were used for the carbon tetrachloride solutions.

more detail under the fundamental hydroxyl band. For example, intramolecular effects can be well characterized in this region. Goldman and Crisler (41) show that the interaction of the π electrons in the benzene ring in 2-phenylethyl alcohol with the hydroxyl group leads to two bands, a free hydroxyl band at 1.4084 μ and an intramolecularly bonded hydroxyl band at 1.4209 μ. They observed single bands in benzyl and 3-phenyl-1-propyl alcohols. Winstein reports that this region is excellent for determining the absolute configuration in a wide variety of cis–trans, syn–anti, or axial–equatorial problems (107), and shows that many of the hydroxyl bands of saturated alcohols are in fact doublets (80a). Any electron-rich system such as a double bond, a cyclopropyl ring, a benzene or other aromatic-type ring, a halogen atom, etc., will interact with a hydroxyl group close enough in space and will cause splitting of the hydroxyl band in dilute solution.

Little quantitative work has been reported to date using the 1.4 μ region. The molar absorptivities of most alcohols are between 1 and 3, which means that in order to have solutions dilute enough to have only free hydroxyl groups, one must use 10 cm. cells exclusively. Even so, the calibration curves are usually not linear, as for example, in the work reported by Whetsel, Roberson, and Krell (101). Excellent quantitative work can certainly be done in this region, as reported by Crisler and Burrill (24). Their data on the free hydroxyl bands of alcohols are in Table XVIIIA. However, because high concentrations of alcohol are needed, it is less flexible than the 2.7 to 3.0 μ region and is certainly far less valuable for the determination of small amounts of alcohols. A compensation is the fact that a rather wide variety of solvents may be used in this region, as can be seen from Table I. As a matter of fact, Mecke has used some 18 different solvents to obtain interesting results in the second overtone region just below 1 μ (71). He found interesting effects due to the orientation of solvent molecules, in particular benzene, relative to the hydroxyl group. Similar studies have been made at 1.4 μ as well as at 1 μ by Bell and Barrow, in studying the double minimum potential of hydroxyl bands due to hydrogen bonding (10a).

B. PHENOLS

The hydroxyl group in monohydroxyphenols has an extremely intense, sharp band in dilute solution at about 2.77 μ due to the free

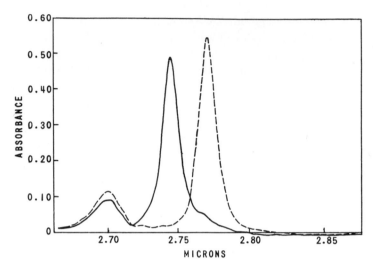

Fig. 15. Near-infrared absorption spectra of *p*-cresol and 2,6-di-tert-butyl-*p*-cresol in the 2.7 to 2.8 μ region on the Beckman Model DK -2 Recording Spectrophotometer; 10 cm. cells (38). Broken line, 0.261mM *p*-cresol in carbon tetrachloride; solid line, 0.262mM 2,6-di-*tert*-butyl-*p*-cresol in carbon tetrachloride. (Reprinted from *Anal. Chem.*, **30**, 2012 (1958).)

hydroxyl stretching vibration (see Fig. 15). Data on phenols previously published by the author are in Table XIX (38). Many other authors have also reported data, both qualitative and quantitative, on the free hydroxyl band of simple phenols (13,22,32,43,75, 93). In addition, the well-known bromination method for traces of phenols in waste water is based on this band (90).

The data in Table XIX, as well as that obtained by others, indicate that the phenols have roughly 3 to 4 times the molar absorptivities that alcohols have. Most phenols absorb at 2.772 ± 0.003 μ. Exceptions, are compounds which are 2,6-substituted with rather bulky aliphatic groups, usually called hindered phenols, e.g., 2,6-di-tert-butyl-*p*-cresol (Fig. 15) and compounds in which intramolecular interaction is possible, as in *o*-phenylphenol (88). The former absorb at shorter wavelengths, the latter at longer wavelengths, thus generally allowing the determination of other phenolic constituents in their presence. The molar absorptivities of most of the phenols vary between 170 and 200, with exceptions being compounds which are highly activated, such as phenols with aromatic

TABLE XIX
Near-Infrared Absorption Data on Phenols (38)

Phenol	ν Max., cm.$^{-1}$	λ Max., μ	Molar Absorptivity, ϵ, liter/mole-cm.^{a} 2–5 mM	0.1–0.3 mM
Phenol	3609	2.771	194	192
p-Cresol	3609	2.771	192	196
p-Isopropylphenol	3609	2.771	195	
p-Nonylphenol	3609	2.771	200	215
p-Phenylphenol	3605	2.774	245	256
4,4'-Isopropylidenediphenol (bis-phenol A)	3608	2.772	425	460 (2 OH's)
m-Cresol	3606	2.773	202	206
m-Isopropylphenol	3606	2.773	186	185
Mono-ortho-Substituted Phenols				
o-Cresol	3609	2.771	172	171
2-tert-Butyl-p-cresol	3611	2.769	173	175
	3643	2.745	14	14
2-tert-Butyl-4-methoxyphenol	3611	2.769	168	
	3644	2.744	14	
2,5-Di-tert-butyl-p-cresol	3604	2.775	169	
	3642	2.746	16	
2-Isobornyl-p-cresol	3608	2.772	160	157
o-Phenylphenol	3561	2.808	196	201
	3602	2.776	27	21
2-(α,α-Dimethylbenzyl)-p-cresol	3530	2.833	222	220
Diortho-Substituted Phenols				
2-tert-Butyl-o-cresol	3611	2.769	168	169
2,4-Di-tert-butyl-o-cresol^b	3613	2.768	150	153
2,6-Diisopropylphenol^b	3615	2.766	147	147
2,6-Di-tert-butylphenol	3642	2.746	210	214
2,6-Di-tert-butyl-p-cresol	3644	2.744	180	183
2,4,6-Tri-tert-butylphenol	3642	2.746	186	189
2,6-Diisobornyl-p-cresol	3609	2.771	143	144
2,6-Bis-(α,α-dimethylbenzyl)-p-cresol	3517	2.843	290	280

^{a} Data obtained on Beckman Model D-2 spectrophotometer using a nominal slit of 0.12 mm. at 2.763 μ or a half-height band-width of 6.2 mμ.

^{b} Sample of questionable purity. (Courtesy of *Analytical Chemistry*.)

substituents. The high molar absorptivities in phenolics allow the determination of 25 p.p.m. phenolic hydroxyl, or less, in most samples (38). Other hydroxyl compounds, e.g., tertiary alcohols, aromatic alcohols, and oximes, may interfere in the determination of monofunctional phenols.

The hydroxyl spectra of halogenated, nitrated, and polyfunctional phenols resemble the hydroxyl spectra of alcohols in many ways. A considerable number of studies have been made of the intramolecular interactions in phenols and from these a great deal has been learned about the structure of these compounds Perhaps the first such studies were those in the 1930's of Liddel, Wulf *et al.*, in the first overtone region (49,109,110). This initial work was on *o*-halophenols and it lead to Pauling's postulation of a cis or trans orientation of the hydroxyl group in a phenol (78). The effect of this cis or trans orientation is to split the hydroxyl band with the frequency shift increasing in the order F < Cl < Br < I. Recently Baker has published data on this effect in *o*-halophenols in the fundamental stretching region (6). Meta- and para-substitution have a very slight effect on the wavelength of the absorption of the hydroxyl group. This latter statement is quite generally true with all types of intramolecular interactions in phenols. That is, it is generally easy to differentiate and determine ortho isomers in the presence of meta- and para-substituted phenols where the substituents are capable of interacting with the hydroxyl group.

Flett's recent review is an excellent reference source for the effect of a wide variety of functional groups on phenolic hydroxyl absorptions (29). Baker also has recently studied intramolecular interaction in *o*-allylic phenols (8), Schiff's bases (8a), and a wide variety of functional groups in meta- and para-substituted phenols (7). The author has reported studies of various types of bisphenols which are often used as antioxidants and has given wavelength and molar absorptivity data on them (38). Other work of this nature has been reported by Ingraham *et al.*, (55), Flett (28), Moccia and Califano (74a), and Davies (25). The hydroxyl spectrum of a typical ortho-substituted phenol is given in Fig. 16. The 2.77 μ band is due to free hydroxyl and that at 2.84 μ is due to intramolecular bonding.

To summarize the work discussed above, it can be said that orthosubstitution of halogen, amino, ether, thioether, allyl, hydroxyl, benzyl, or substituted benzyl, as well as phenyl groups, all lead to intramolecularly bonded hydroxyl bands of one type or another. The frequency difference between the free and intramolecularly bonded bands is very characteristic of the groups involved, and is of value in qualitative or proof-of-structure work. The ratio of the

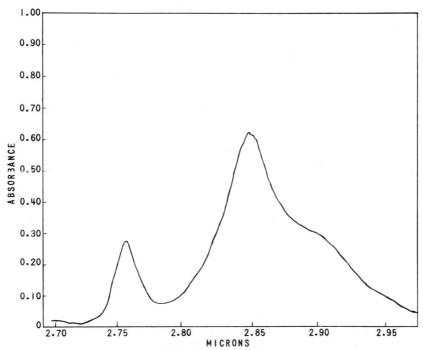

Fig. 16. Near-infrared absorption spectrum of a 2.73mM solution of 2,2′-methylene bis(4-methyl-6-*tert*-butyl-phenol) in carbon tetrachloride in the 2.7 to 3.0 μ region on the Beckman Model DK-2 Recording Spectrophotometer; 1 cm. cell (38). (Reprinted from *Anal. Chem.*, **30**, 2010 (1958).)

intensities of the free and bonded bands in dilute solution (less than 20 mM) is also qualitatively useful.

Since the intramolecularly bonded hydroxyl bands of various types of ortho-substituted isomers come at different places, it is often possible to perform quantitative analysis of very complex mixtures in this region, without separations. We have successfully determined four components, all various types of related phenols, simultaneously, in the same solution using but a single 3 min. scan of the region from 3.0 to 2.7 μ.

When the groups which cause intramolecular hydrogen bonding were mentioned above, no carbonyl function was listed. The reason is that the intramolecular hydrogen bonding in phenols with ortho-substitution of aldehyde, ketone, ester, amide, acid, etc., is so strong that the hydroxyl band is often shifted well beyond 3.1 μ and it is usually extremely broad. Other groups which have a very strong hydrogen bonding ability, such as amines, may also cause a similar shift.

As in the case of alcohols, all of the work on phenols discussed above was carried out in carbon tetrachloride or in a few cases in carbon disulfide. We have used methylene chloride successfully for a few phenols and have included our data in Tables XX and XXI. These data indicate again a shift to longer wavelengths, but this shift is less in the case of the more hindered phenols. The intensity of the hydroxyl band is less, but this is probably primarily because of the wider slits. At any rate, there appears to be no enhancement of sensitivity such as was noted for alcohols.

The interaction of phenols with other compounds present in a solution, may cause large shifts of the hydroxyl stretching band, as has been shown by West in his studies of the intermolecular hydrogen bonding of phenols to olefins and other unsaturates (100a).

Phenols have an absorption band at 2.07 μ, presumably due to a combination band (51,57). This band is weaker than the first overtone of the hydroxyl stretching band at 1.46 μ and has not been studied extensively to date.

Most of the work in the region of 1.4 μ, the first overtone region, is that of Liddel, Wulf et al., referred to earlier. Many of the same phenomena are found in this region as are observed in the fundamental region. Data reported by Crisler and Burrill in this region are in Table XXIA (24). It is possible that because of the extremely high resolution obtainable in the 1.4 μ region with some of the commercially available instruments, this region may be a better one to use for proof-of-structure work than the 2.7 to 3.0 μ region. The advantages, however, of the fundamental region for quantitative work with alcohols, apply to phenols as well. The extent of deviations of calibration curves for phenols from linearity in the overtone region has not been reported.

TABLE XX

Near-Infrared Absorption Data on Phenols in the 2.7 to 3.0 μ Region in
Methylene Chloride

Phenols	ν Max., cm.$^{-1}$	λ Max., μ	Molar absorptivity, ϵ, liter/mole-cm.[a]
Phenol	3579	2.794	156
o-Cresol	3597	2.870	131
m-Cresol	3577	2.795	144
p-Cresol	3579	2.794	146
2,6-Di-t-butyl-p-cresol	3635	2.751	173
Eugenol	3636[b]	2.828[b]	134[b]
2,2'-Methylenebis(6-t-butyl-4-methyl-phenol)	3613	2.768	113
	3499[b]	2.858[b]	74[b]
	3420[b]	2.925[b]	90[b]
2,2'-Isopropylidenebis(6-t-butyl-4-methyl-phenol)	2878[b]	2.878[b]	591[b]

[a] Data obtained on Beckman Model DK-2 Spectrophotometer using a nominal
slit width of 0.20 mm. at 2.763 μ or a half-intensity band-width of 10.2 mμ.
[b] Intramolecularly bonded hydroxyl.

TABLE XXI

Comparison of Fundamental Hydroxyl Stretching Band Data on Phenols in
Carbon Tetrachloride and Methylene Chloride

Phenols	Frequency shift ν CCl$_4$–ν CH$_2$Cl$_2$ (cm.$^{-1}$)	Ratio of molar absorptivities, ϵCH$_2$Cl$_2$/ϵCCl$_4$
Phenol	30	0.80
o-Cresol	12	0.76
m-Cresol	29	0.71
p-Cresol	30	0.76
2,6-Di-t-butyl-p-cresol	9	0.96
Eugenol	21	0.71
2,2'-Isopropylidenebis(6-t-butyl-4-methyl-phenol)	0	0.57

Studies of the second overtone of the phenolic hydroxyl band have
been made by Luttke and Mecke (66). Their observations in this
region are similar to those in the fundamental and first overtone
regions.

TABLE XXIA
Near-Infrared Absorption Data on Phenols at 1.4 μ (24)

Phenols	ν Max., cm.$^{-1}$	λ Max., μ	Molar absorptivity, ϵ, liter/ mole-cm.[a]
Phenol	7054	1.418	3.11
β-Naphthol	7042	1.420	3.30
Isoeugenol	6939	1.441	2.39
p-Bromophenol	7049	1.419	2.95
2-t-Butyl-4-methoxyphenol	7054	1.418	3.29
Thymol	7059	1.417	3.08
2,6-Di-t-butyl-4-Methyl phenol	7124	1.404	2.23

[a] Data obtained on a Cary Model 14 Spectrophotometer using a nominal slit of 0.1 mm. at 1.4 μ or a half height band width of 0.35 mμ. Ten cm. cells were used for the carbon tetrachloride solutions.

C. HYDROPEROXIDES

Hydroperoxide hydroxyl is a less common functional group, but one very attractive for analytical work in the 2.7 to 3.0 μ region. A few papers have been published in recent years which have used the free hydroxyl band of the hydroperoxide group to study the acid strengths of hydroperoxides (9) and to study problems related to the autoxidation of fats (53,91).

The fundamental hydroxyl stretching vibration of the hydroperoxide group occurs at about 2.81 to 2.84 μ. Data obtained on a few representative hydroperoxides in our laboratory are listed in Table XXII. The hydroxyl spectra of an aliphatic and an aromatic hydroperoxide are given in Fig. 17. The fact that the hydroxyl band of aralkyl hydroperoxides is split into a doublet was reported by Barnard, Hargrave, and Higgins (9). They postulated that this was caused by the interaction of the hydroxyl group with the π electrons on the benzene ring when the hydroperoxide group had a certain orientation; an analogous case to a similar interaction discussed under Section IV-3A. The intensities of the two hydroperoxide bands in aralkyl compounds are roughly equal to the intensity of a single peak in aliphatic hydroperoxides.

These hydroperoxide hydroxyl bands are well separated from those of alcohols and phenols and are therefore very useful when analyses of

TABLE XXII
Near-Infrared Absorption Data on Hydroperoxides at 2.8 μ in Carbon Tetrachloride

Hydroperoxide	ν Max., cm.$^{-1}$	λ Max., μ	Molar absorptivity, ϵ, liter/ mole-cm.^{a}
Alkyl or Alicyclic			
t-Butyl	3552	2.815	86
p-Menthane	3550	2.817	88
Pinane	3549	2.818	79
Methyl 9-hydroperoxydehydroabietate	3542	2.823	6
	3432	2.914	96
Aralkyl			
Cumene	3547	2.819	40
(α,α-dimethylbenzyl)	3521	2.840	33
p-Cymene	3544	2.822	36
	3516	2.844	30
p-Diisopropylbenzene monohydroperoxide	3546	2.820	38
	3517	2.843	38
p-Diisopropylbenzene dihydroperoxide	3545	2.821	$\sim$86
	3522	2.839	$\sim$58
p-Chlorocumene	3545	2.821	56
3,4-Dichlorocumene	3542	2.823	73
p-Nitrocumene	3544	2.822	91

^{a} Data obtained on Beckman Model DK-2 Spectrophotometer using a nominal slit of 0.12 mm. at 2.763 μ, which gives a half-intensity band-width of 6.2 mμ.

mixtures of these hydroxyl-containing compounds are desired. This is especially true of decomposition studies of hydroperoxides. The molar absorptivities of hydroperoxides are extremely constant over a concentration range from 0.2 to 20 mM.

The same types of intramolecular interactions are found in hydroperoxides as were mentioned for alcohols and phenols. There are several examples in Table XXII. The hydroperoxyabietic acid derivative has bands at 2.823 μ due to free hydroxyl and at 2.914 μ due to intramolecular hydrogen bonding with the carbonyl of the acid group which appears to be relatively far away, but actually is quite close in space. The nitro group in p-nitrocumene hydroperoxide or the chlorine atoms in the chlorocumene hydroperoxides

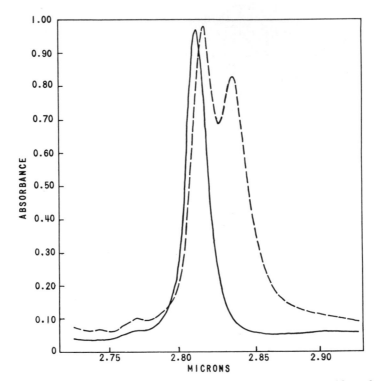

Fig. 17. Near-infrared absorption spectra of *tert*-butyl hydroperoxide and cumene hydroperoxide (α,α-dimethylbenzyl hydroperoxide) in the 2.7 to 2.9 μ region, on the Beckman Model DK-2 Recording Spectrophotometer; 1 cm. cell. Solid line, 10.9mM *tert*-butyl hydroperoxide in carbon tetrachloride; broken line 23.1mM cumene hydroperoxide in carbon tetrachloride.

are such strong electron-attracting groups, that they withdraw electrons from the benzene ring and eliminate the splitting of the hydroperoxide hydroxyl. Extension of this type of work to the determination of absolute configurations and the potential values of the intramolecular interaction in analytical work are obvious.

The fundamental hydroxyl spectra of hydroperoxides can also be run quite successfully in methylene chloride. The molar absorptivities for aliphatic hydroperoxides are of the same order of magnitude as for those found in carbon tetrachloride and the band is shifted to a lower frequency by about 20 cm.$^{-1}$. The hydroxyl spectra of aromatic hydroperoxides are altered as the doublet in carbon tetrachloride is changed into a singlet in methylene chloride. The single peak, which is roughly the same intensity as the sum of the intensities of the doublet, is probably caused by the bonding of the hydroperoxide hydroxyl to the solvent in preference to the benzene ring. The single peak of an aromatic hydroperoxide in methylene chloride is shifted about 20 cm.$^{-1}$ from the "free" hydroxyl peak in carbon tetrachloride. The enhanced sensitivity for aromatic hydroperoxides in methylene chloride is worthy of note. However, in return for the enhanced sensitivity, one has to sacrifice the long wavelength peak of the doublet in carbon tetrachloride which allows the detection and determination of aliphatic and aralkyl hydroperoxides in mixtures.

In addition to the valuable fundamental hydroxyl band, hydroperoxides have two other potentially useful bands at 2.05 to 2.07 μ and 1.45 to 1.47 μ (53). Holman et al., have reported the approximate molar absorptivities at these wavelengths to be about 0.5 and 0.5 to 1.5, respectively. Work in our laboratory using somewhat higher resolution in the 1.46 μ region gave absorptivities of about 2 for aliphatic hydroperoxides and 1 for each of the two bands of aralkyl hydroperoxides. Both types of hydroperoxides have single bands at about 2.09 μ with molar absorptivities of about 1.3 for aromatic and 0.8 for aliphatic hydroperoxides. These intensities are high enough to be of value if the 2.8 μ region is not available. As was stated earlier, I believe the greater flexibility in the fundamental region is its best recommendation.

D. CARBOXYLIC ACIDS

The hydroxyl group of a carboxylic acid has several bands in the region from 2.7 to 3.0 μ, depending on the state of association of the acid. Goulden has reported the monomer hydroxyl vibration frequencies of a variety of carboxylic acids and phenols and correlated them with their respective acid ionization constants (43). Harris and Hobbs have studied the association of carboxylic acids by the use of the monomer and dimer hydroxyl bands (45). A more recent paper by Wenograd and Spurr reports the integrated intensity of the hydroxyl bands in conjugated acids (100). All of these papers give reliable frequency or wavelength data on a variety of carboxylic acids.

Because of the extensive monomer–dimer equilibrium in carboxylic acids, even in extremely dilute solution, the hydroxyl region does not appear promising for good quantitative work. For example, in our laboratory we have found that the molar absorptivity of the monomer hydroxyl band at 2.830 μ in either acetic or benzoic acids increased from 10 to 100 as the concentration was varied from 30 to 0.2 mM. Thus, any calibration curve would be extremely nonlinear. Although it is possible to do work with nonlinear curves, deviations as extensive as these seldom lead to very precise or accurate work.

In short, we have found the acid hydroxyl bands to be mainly of qualitative value. The hydroxyl bands of other groups vary little in intensity as a function of concentration when the concentration is 20 mM or less. Thus in an unknown sample, a carboxylic acid may be readily detected by running the hydroxyl spectrum in a 1 cm. cell, diluting 10-fold, and repeating the spectrum in a 10 cm. cell. If the height of one of the hydroxyl bands between 2.82 and 2.86 μ is markedly increased, it undoubtedly is due to a carboxylic acid.

Carboxylic acids also have sharp absorption bands at 2.1 and 1.45 μ in dilute solution due to a combination band and the first overtone of the monomer hydroxyl stretching vibration. No analytical studies have been reported in which these bands were used. It might be predicted that their intensity would be as dependent on the concentration as that of the fundamental band.

E. OXIMES

A few studies of the hydroxyl band of oximes in the fundamental and overtone regions have been made. Califano and Luttke have studied the association of oximes (18) and studied the spectra of formaldehyde oxime and acetone oxime in detail (19). Their results indicate appreciable association between oxime molecules at concentrations as low as 5 mM. From their data they calculated the molar absorptivities of several oximes at infinite dilution. Palm and Werbin also studied the spectra of oximes and determined that α-oximes absorb at a lower frequency than β-oximes (77). In a recent note the author reported data on oximes at 2.78 μ and also on their molar absorptivities (37). The data (Table XXIII) indicate appreciable association leading to an increasing molar absorptivity with decreasing concentration. The increase in absorptivity is greatest for oximes of ketones. The deviations from linearity are not as serious as those found for carboxylic acids and should not detract from the use of the bands in quantitative analysis.

TABLE XXIII

Near-Infrared Absorption Data on Oximes at 2.78 μ (37)

Oxime	ν Max., cm.$^{-1}$	λ Max., μ	Molar absorptivity, ϵ, liter/mole-cm.^{a}	
			2–5 mM	0.1–1.3 mM
Cyclohexanone	3602	2.776	183	222
2-Butanone	3602	2.776	172	206
n-Butyraldehyde	3598	2.779	188	205
Acetophenone	3593	2.783	200	244
Benzaldehyde	3591	2.785	238	254

^{a} Data obtained on Beckman DK-2 Spectrophotometer, using a nominal slit width of 0.12 mm. at 2.763 μ or a half-intensity band-width of 6.2 mμ. (Courtesy of *Analytical Chemistry*.)

The first overtone of the fundamental hydroxyl band of oximes was studied by Wulf, Liddel, and co-workers (48). They also reported differences between α- and β-oximes in this region. The bands occur at about 1.45 μ. No subsequent work or analytical use of the bands has been reported.

F. WATER

In dilute carbon tetrachloride solution, water has four absorption bands in the near-infrared region. They occur at about 2.76, 2.70, 1.90, and 1.39 μ. In most other media they are shifted to longer wavelengths because of various types of hydrogen bonding. The molar absorptivities of these bands are about 7, 30, 1.2, and 0.7 l./mole-cm., respectively, in carbon tetrachloride.

The high absorptivity at 2.7 μ would appear to be very advantageous for the determination of traces of water, but we have not found this to be the case. Water has such a strong tendency to hydrogen-bond with any other electron donor that it is necessary to use extremely dilute solutions for analysis, and as a consequence most of the great sensitivity is lost. Furthermore, at high dilutions of sample and with the great sensitivity for water, it is extremely difficult to handle both the reference carbon tetrachloride and the sample diluent reproducibly enough to get high precision.

The near-infrared looks attractive for the determination of water in instances where the Karl Fischer method does not work. Since the hydroxyl bands of water are so profoundly affected by the medium in which they are present, it is, however, very difficult to find independent methods of standardization in these cases. Of course, a reference sample can always be said to be dry, or taken as containing no water, but then all analyses are relative to an unknown standard.

Despite these difficulties in determining water by near-infrared methods, several successful applications have been made. In general, the applications have used the bonded hydroxyl bands and have not attempted the dilutions necessary for work with the free hydroxyl band. An exception is Diamond's method for the determination of water in Freon-22 with use of the 2.67 μ free hydroxyl stretching band (26a).

Gordes and Tait used the 1.9 μ band to determine from 0.1 to 15% water in hydrazine and substituted hydrazines (42). Water-free hydrazine was used as a reference material. Chapman and Nacey used a similar technique to determine from 1 to 10% water in glycerol (20). The difficult problem of determining as little as 0.1% water in fuming nitric acid was solved by White and Barrett by the use of a 1.423 μ water band (105). In our laboratory we have successfully used the 1.9 μ water band to determine traces of water in hydroperoxides and a few other compounds.

Gaunt has determined water and HOD in deuterium oxide over a wide variety of concentration ranges from 99% deuterium oxide to 50% deuterium oxide using HOD bands at 1.66 and 2.95 μ and the water band at 1.445 μ (33,34). Willis and Miller report the determination of as little as 0.005% water in acetone by the use of difference spectroscopy in the 1.9 and 3.0 μ regions (106).

The 1.9 μ band is perhaps the best band for use in determining water since it is not generally close to other hydroxyl bands and it is more intense than the 1.4 μ band. However, both bands appear to be more generally useful than is the fundamental band.

It is worth pointing out that it is possible to correct for any interference of the 2.76 μ water band in alcohol or phenol determinations by determining the height of the 2.70 μ water band and making a correction from a plot of absorbance of water at 2.70 μ versus absorbance of water at various wavelengths close to 2.76 μ. These plots are quite reproducible for a given medium and have been very useful in our laboratory for work in 10 cm. cells with wet samples or in humid weather. Even though carbon tetrachloride is dried, it is most difficult to keep it from picking up a few p.p.m. water difference between the reference and sample solutions. About 1 p.p.m. water in carbon tetrachloride has an absorbance of 0.03 in a 10 cm. cell at 2.70 μ.

In methylene chloride, water has bands at 2.73 and 2.78 μ. These bands are strong since water is more soluble in methylene chloride (1500 p.p.m.) than it is in carbon tetrachloride (100 p.p.m.). They are troublesome even in 1 cm. cells. A correction graph for the absorbance of water at 2.73 μ versus absorbance from water at the wavelengths close to 2.78 μ is very desirable. Greinacher, Luttke, and Mecke have studied the complete infrared spectra of water in ten different solvents (44).

4. Thiols and P—H Groups

The first overtone of the weak 3.9 μ S—H stretching band of thiols occurs at 1.97 to 1.98 μ. It is extremely weak, the molar absorptivities of benzenethiol and 1-butanethiol being 0.081 and 0.044, respectively. It thus appears to be of relatively little analytical value.

A band due to the P—H vibration at 1.891 μ has been reported by McIvor et al., (70). It has a molar absorptivity of about 0.24 in the four compounds reported. This would appear to be the first overtone of the P—H stretching band in the 4.0 μ region and it is intense enough to be useful for analytical work.

5. Carbonyls

The first overtone of the fundamental C=O stretching vibration of esters, ketones, aldehydes, acids, and other compounds with carbonyl groups appears at 2.8 to 3.0 μ. Some representative data, we have obtained, are given in Table XXIV. The molar absorptivities are generally of the order of 2 to 4. Aliphatic esters absorb at the shortest wavelengths and aromatic ketones at the highest.

TABLE XXIV
Near-Infrared Absorption Data on Carbonyls in the 2.8 to 3.0 μ Region in
Carbon Tetrachloride

Compound	ν Max., cm.$^{-1}$	λ Max., μ	Molar absorptivity, ϵ, liter/mole-cm.[a]
Esters of Aliphatic Acids			
γ-Butyrolactone	3549	2.818	4.5
Pentaerythritol trichloride monoacetate	3497	2.860	3.6
Pentaerythritol tetraacetate	3482	2.872	12.6
Ethyl acetate	3463	2.888	2.7
Dimethyl adipate	3463	2.888	5.9
Amyl butyrate	3446	2.902	2.4
Ethyl acrylate	3433	2.913	3.1
Esters of Aromatic Acids			
Diethyl phthalate	3436	2.910	5.1
Methyl p-toluate	3427	2.918	3.0
Benzyl benzoate	3422	2.922	2.8
Aliphatic Aldehydes			
Butyraldehyde	3434	2.912	2.5
Isobutyraldehyde	3433	2.913	2.6
Aliphatic Ketones			
Methyl ethyl ketone	3414	2.929	3.3
Acetone	3413	2.930	3.8
Mesityl oxide	3367	2.970	1.4
Aromatic Aldehydes			
Benzaldehyde	3394	2.946	2.7
Aromatic Ketones			
Acetophenone	3358	2.978	4.0
Benzophenone	3313	3.018	2.8

[a] Data obtained on Beckmen Model DK-2 Spectrophotometer with a nominal slit of 0.22 mm. at 2.91 μ, which gives a half-intensity band-width of 11 mμ.

Absorptivities were generally independent of concentration between 2 and 0.1M in carbon tetrachloride. Thompson and Jameson, in a recent publication (94), have reported the frequency and intensity of this overtone band as compared with the fundamental band.

It is certain that the 2.8 to 3.0 μ region is no substitute for the 5.5 to 6.0 μ region for the detection, identification, and determination of carbonyl compounds.   It may be useful, however, for laboratories which do not have infrared facilities.   We have also used it to detect and determine large amounts of carbonyl compounds in the presence of small amounts of hydroxyl compounds from the same scan. Naturally, large amounts of the various types of intramolecularly bonded hydroxyl groups will interfere with work in this carbonyl overtone region   Amines also will interfere.   Carbon tetrachloride and carbon disulfide are about the only solvents useful in this region.

The second overtone of the carbonyl band is at 1.9 to 2.0 μ and is probably too weak to be of much analytical utility.

6. Nitriles

In our laboratory we have observed two weak bands due to nitriles in the region from 1.8 to 2.1 μ.   It is not clear to what vibrations of overtones they could be assigned, but they have been found in some ten different nitrile compounds.   The first overtone of the $C\equiv N$ stretching vibration would be expected at about 2.25 μ and the second overtone at 1.5 μ.   The bands are, most likely, the over-tones of combination bands.   The molar absorptivity of the bands are about 0.02 for aromatic nitriles and 0.08 for aliphatic nitriles. Their shape and intensity vary with the length and type of the hydrocarbon chain.   Although the bands are too weak for use in trace analysis, they occur in a relatively open region and may have some potential analytical application.

7. Miscellaneous

In their article on the spectra of organophosphorus compounds in the 1 to 2.6 μ region, McIvor, Hubley, Grant, and Grey discuss assignment of a large number of bands to larger structural units than are discussed above (70)   They particularly emphasize the region around 1.7 μ and that between 2.2 and 2.5 μ.   They quote both wavelength and absorptivity data for the very complex bands observed in these regions.   The functional groups to which they assign bands include MeO—, MeS—, EtO—, EtS—, iso-PrO—, n-PrO—, n-BuO—, MeP—, MeI, EtP—, EtI, Me$_2$N—, Et$_2$N—, iso-Pr$_2$N—, and a number of miscellaneous groups.   From their data they are able to predict near-infrared spectra in the 1.6 to 1.9 and 2.2 and to 2.6 μ regions with fair accuracy. There may be some possible analytical applications that may come out of this and similar work in these two regions.

A compound in which we were quite surprised to find a unique and usable near-infrared band was tetranitromethane, which has no hydrogen atoms. It has a strong ($\epsilon = 0.6$) and unique band at 2.086 μ, which is valuable in quantitative work. We do not know the origin of the band.

Another compound which has a strong absorption band is formaldehyde, or at least 36% aqueous formaldehyde in carbon tetrachloride. A band of molar absorptivity of 24 is observed at 2.770 μ. The band is definitely not due to water itself, but may well be due to a hydrate of formaldehyde. One must be aware of its possible interference in analyses for alcohols in the presence of traces of formaldehyde and water.

There are undoubtedly many other compounds and a few other functional groups which have unique bands in the near-infrared, so that it pays the analyst to scan each new type of compound over the region from 1 to 3 μ so he will not pass over a potentially valuable absorption band.

8. Applications

Although a good many applications of near-infrared spectrophotometry have been mentioned above, in relation to specific functional groups, there are several others which should also be discussed.

Mitchell, Bockman, and Lee report the determination of the acetyl content of cellulose acetate by near-infrared spectrophotometry (73). They found that by using pyrrole as a solvent they could dissolve the cellulose acetate and determine the residual hydroxyl content from the hydroxyl band in the 1.4 μ region.

Freeman reports the determination of 0.1 to 1% allethrolone, a keto alcohol, in allethrin using an intramolecularly bonded hydroxyl band at 2.85 μ (31).

Various oxidation processes are ideally suited to near-infrared analysis. Both Slover and Dugan (91) and Holman *et al.* (53) have followed the oxidation of fats and oils by measuring the hydroperoxide band at 2.8 μ. In addition, Slover and Dugan also detected the other functional groups which are formed as a result of oxidation and decomposition—alcohols, acids, and carbonyls—all by use of the 2.7 to 3.0 μ region. We have done similar work in our laboratory on following the oxidation of hydrocarbons to hydroperoxides and determining the rate of decomposition of the hydroperoxides to alcohols, phenols, or ketones.

Processes which involve vinylation or epoxidation are well suited to control by the near-infrared. For example, in the vinylation of alcohols (see Reaction (1)) the original alcohol content of the solvent is readily determined by near-infrared as well as the alcohol content of the end product and the purified vinyl ether. The vinyl ether content of the reaction mixture is determined easily at 1.6 μ. In addition, the isolated vinyl ether may be analyzed for purity either directly or more accurately by using high absorbance reference techniques.

$$\underset{\text{(alcohol)}}{\text{ROH}} + \underset{\text{(acetylene)}}{\text{HC}\equiv\text{CH}} \xrightarrow[\text{donor solvent}]{\text{catalyst}} \underset{\text{(vinyl ether)}}{\text{ROCH}=\text{CH}_2} \qquad (1)$$

A similar process in which reactants and products are determined by near-infrared is:

$$\underset{\text{(alcohol)}}{\text{ROH}} + \underset{\text{(carbon monoxide)}}{\text{CO}} + \underset{\text{(acetylene)}}{\text{HC}\equiv\text{CH}} \xrightarrow[\text{donor solvent}]{\text{catalyst}} \underset{\text{(acrylate ester)}}{\text{ROOCCH}=\text{CH}_2} \quad (2)$$

Hilton reported excellent accuracy and precision in determining the hydroxyl content of polyesters and polyethers using a hydroxyl band at about 2.8 μ (50). Chloroform (10%) in carbon tetrachloride was used as a solvent. Precision and accuracy of better than 0.5% of the amount present were reported after corrections had been made for background absorption and absorption due to free acid hydroxyl. Burns and Muraca reported the determination of the hydroxyl content of polypropylene glycols by use of the 2.84 μ hydroxyl band (16a).

Excellent articles pointing out possible uses of near-infrared in the synthetic polymer field have been published by Miller and Willis (72,106). They discuss the determination of endgroups, in particular the hydroxyl group in polyepoxides, using the 2.1 μ combination band. They follow the polymerization of unsaturated monomers, for example, methyl methacrylate, by using the 1.6 μ terminal unsaturation band and the use of the same band to determine monomers in the polymer. The detection limit in the latter case is about 0.1%

monomer using a $1/2$ in. thick piece of film.   This might be somewhat less successful on other polymers which are not as transparent as methyl methacrylate.   Another application was the composition of butadiene–styrene copolymers using combination bands at 2.2 and 2.4 μ for the aromatic and aliphatic contents of polymer, respectively.   We have done some work on polymers in our laboratory and have been successful in some cases.   If the polymer can be gotten into solution, usually the work is successful.   However, work with the thick films necessary to get sensitivity for residual monomer or endgroup analyses is often a problem because of the large amount of scattered light.

A device for mounting crystals and fibers for near-infrared study was recently reported by Malcolm (67).   In the future, there will undoubtedly be many applications of near-infrared to the polymer and fiber field.

V. INORGANIC APPLICATIONS

To date very little has been reported on the application of near-infrared spectrophotometry to inorganic compounds.   A method for the determination of hydrogen acids, in particular hydrogen fluoride in aqueous solutions using thin sapphire-window cells, at 1.835 μ has been published (1).   Davis and Hershenson reported the determination of copper at 940 mμ on a Beckman DU spectrophotometer (26).

In considering the near-infrared for inorganic work, one should not expect to find any strong bands due to vibrations involving metal atoms because the masses of these atoms generally cause the vibration to occur in the rock salt region and, perhaps more often, in the potassium or cesium bromide regions.   Even the first overtones of metal–hydrogen stretching bands generally occur in the region beyond 3 μ.

For inorganic compounds, solvents would present a problem only beyond 2.2 μ, and potassium bromide disks could undoubtedly be used over the entire region.

The most rewarding work with inorganic compounds in the near-infrared region might well be expected from work on various chelate compounds and inorganic complexes.   The ease with which intramolecular hydrogen bonding is picked up in this region makes it desirable for the study of chelation and the interaction of amine, oxime, and hydroxyl groups with metal atoms. Since most chelates are soluble in carbon tetrachloride, studies can be made throughout the region. In addition to chelates and similar complexes, it might be possible to do work on various complexes of unsaturates with metal atoms, e.g., the platinum–ethylene complexes, by observing effects on the terminal olefin band.

In short, the potential of near-infrared for inorganic analytical work or inorganic research has not been evaluated yet. It probably will not be generally useful, but may be of value in a few important instances, which is in many ways the same situation as is found for the conventional 2 to 15 μ region.

VI. APPLICATIONS TO SOLIDS

Applications of near-infrared to solids, and in particular to polymer films, was discussed in some detail above (Section IV-8). In addition to solid films, solids can be investigated by the use of potassium bromide disks and reflectance techniques. Since a large number of molecules are needed in the beam to obtain good overtone spectra, it is necessary to use rather thick films or disks. In the use of these thick films or disks (1 to 10 mm.) the scattering of light may become a problem which could limit the quantitative accuracy and sensitivity. In the 2.7 to 3.0 μ region it will probably be necessary to work with partially or fully bonded hydroxyl bands rather than with the free hydroxyl bands referred to earlier. Despite these possible problems, investigation of films and especially potassium bromide disks in the near-infrared region should prove extremely valuable.

Near-infrared reflectance spectra reported by Manning (68) indicate that usable spectra can be obtained using the integrating sphere technique up to 2.6 μ with commercially available equipment. The spectra are similar to transmission spectra, but less well resolved. Further work is necessary and desirable to determine their value.

VII. APPLICATIONS TO GASES

Gases give very sharp and unique spectra in the near-infrared region. To date, however, little analytical use has been made of this because of the limited path lengths available in the commercial instruments and the resultant limited sensitivity, especially for the weaker overtone vibrations. We have run the near-infrared spectra of a few gases, but have not used the region because of the sensitivity limitation. For the analysis of mixtures of gases in reasonable percentages, say greater than 1 or 2%, near-infrared is certainly a good possibility. The same functional groups mentioned in Table II can probably be determined in the gas phase, but there will undoubtedly be some slight shifts of wavelength. For example, the terminal methylene groups in allene have strong absorption bands at 1.626 and 1.633 μ. Usable cells may be fabricated easily for trial and possible applications.

VIII. FUTURE TRENDS

From the preceding pages it is evident that the near-infrared region should join the ultraviolet, visible, and infrared as a valuable region for analytical work. It will not put any region or method of analysis out of business, but it may allow one to accomplish a variety of analytical jobs more easily and more accurately. Its main value, to date, has been in quantitative organic functional group analyses and it appears reasonable to predict that it will stay this way in the future. Another value of the region, especially for hydroxyl and amino compounds, is the sensitivity for detecting intramolecular and also intermolecular interactions especially solvent–solute interactions in dilute solutions. These phenomena can be put to analytical advantage in the determination of organic structures and in the characterizing of a variety of organic systems. In addition, it is possible to obtain new information easily on a variety of combination and overtone bands which can be used in spectral assignment work and in elucidating the nature of specific molecular vibrations.

The simplicity of the technique (exclusive of the instruments), together with the speed and accuracy which are available, make near-infrared spectrophotometry a very desirable analytical tool. As any other analytical tool it has its limitations and advantages. In general, it is perhaps a little more specific than ultraviolet, but also generally less sensitive. It is less specific than conventional infrared, but is more reproducible for compounds of similar structure. The future will undoubtedly see a large number of successful applications of the region to functional group analysis.

More detailed work in the near-infrared will tell us of its value with potassium bromide disks, inorganic compounds, and gases. Near-infrared data should become as common in papers dealing with organic structures as infrared data have been for the past ten years. More equipment, with higher resolution, will become more generally available, but probably not at lower cost.

The near-infrared should be viewed by the analyst as a spectral region which he can utilize at a modest cash outlay and which is potentially of equivalent value to the ultraviolet and conventional infrared regions.   It should be viewed as a new entity, and not as a substitute for the ultraviolet or infrared.

Acknowledgment

I wish to express my appreciation to Miss Dorothy A. Delker for her most willing and helpful assistance both in obtaining and evaluating much of the near-infrared data included in this chapter.   I also wish to thank Mr. Westcott C. Kenyon and Dr. Robert T. Hall for their encouragement and assistance in this work.

References

1. Allan, W. J., and A. R. Gahler, *Anal. Chem.*, **31**, 1778 (1959).

1a. Alsop, I. L., A. R. H. Cole, D. E. White, and R. L. S. Willix, *J. Chem. Soc.*, **1956**, 4868.

2. Ambelang, J. C., and J. L. Binder, *J. Am. Chem. Soc.*, **75**, 977 (1953).

3. American Society for Testing Materials *Proposed Methods for Evaluation of Spectrophotometers*, June 1958.

4. Anet, F. A. L., and P. M. G. Bavin, *Can. J. Chem.*, **34**, 1756 (1956).

5. Badger, R. M., *J. Chem. Phys.*, **8**, 288 (1940).

6. Baker, A. W., *J. Am. Chem. Soc.*, **80**, 3598 (1958).

7. Baker, A. W., *J. Phys. Chem.*, **62**, 744 (1958).

8. Baker, A. W., and A. T. Shulgin, *J. Am. Chem. Soc.*, **80**, 5358 (1958).

8a. Baker, A. W., and A. T. Shulgin, *J. Am. Chem. Soc.*, **81**, 1533 (1959).

9. Barnard, D., K. R. Hargrave, and G. M. C. Higgins, *J. Chem. Soc.*, **1956**, 2845.

10. Barrow, G. M., *J. Phys. Chem.*, **59**, 1129 (1955).

10a. Bell, C. L., and G. M. Barrow, *J. Chem. Phys.*, **31**, 300 (1959).

11. Bellamy, L. J., *Infrared Spectra of Complex Molecules*, 2nd ed., Methuen and Co., London, 1958.

12. Bellamy, L. J., and R. F. Williams, *Spectrochim. Acta*, **9**, 341 (1957).

13. Brown, T. L., *J. Phys. Chem.*, **61**, 820 (1957).

14. Brown, T. L., and M. T. Roger, *J. Am. Chem. Soc.*, **79**, 577 (1957).

15. Brown, T. L., J. M. Sandri, and H. Hart, *J. Phys. Chem.*, **61**, 698 (1957).

16. Buhl, F. C., and J. A. Gailey, unpublished results.

16a. Burns, E. A., and R. E. Muraca, *Anal. Chem.*, **31**, 397 (1959).

17. Buswell, A. M., W. H. Rodebush, and R. M. Whitney, *J. Am. Chem. Soc.*, **69**, 770 (1947).
18. Califano, S., and W. Luttke, *Z. physik. Chem (Frankfurt)*, **5**, 240 (1955).
19. Califaho, S., and W. Luttke, *Z. physik. Chem. (Frankfurt)*, **6**, 83 (1956).
20. Chapman, D., and J. F. Nacey, *Analyst*, **83**, 377 (1958).
21. Cleverly, B., quoted in R. N. Jones and C. Sandorfy, "Infrared and Raman Spectroscopy—Applications" in A. Weissberger, Ed. *Chemical Applications of Spectroscopy (Technique of Organic Chemistry, Vol. IX)*, Interscience, New York, 1956.
22. Coggeshall, N. D., *J. Am. Chem. Soc.*, **69**, 1620 (1947).
23. Cole, A. R. H., and P. R. Jeffries, *J. Chem. Soc.*, **1956**, 4391.
23a. Cole, A. R. H., and F. Macritchie, *Spectrochim. Acta*, **15**, 6 (1959).
23b. Cole, A. R. H., and M. T. Mitchell, *J. Chem. Soc.*, **1959**, 2005.
24. Crisler, R. O., and A. M. Burrill, *Anal. Chem.*, **31**, 2055 (1959).
25. Davies, M. M., *Trans. Faraday Soc.*, **36**, 1114 (1940).
26. Davis, D. G., and H. M. Hershenson, *Anal. Chim. Acta*, **13**, 150 (1955).
26a. Diamond, W. J., *Appl. Spectroscopy*, **13**, 77 (1959).
27. Evans, A., R. R. Hibbard, and A. S. Powell, *Anal. Chem.*, **23**, 1604 (1951).
28. Flett, M. St. C., *J. Chem. Soc.*, **1948**, 441.
29. Flett, M. St. C., *Spectrochim. Acta*, **10**, 21 (1957).
30. Fox, J. J., and A. E. Martin, *Trans. Faraday Soc.*, **36**, 897 (1950).
31. Freeman, S. K., *Anal. Chem.*, **27**, 1268 (1955).
32. Friedel, R. A., *J. Am. Chem. Soc.*, **73**, 2881 (1951).
33. Gaunt, J., *Analyst*, **79**, 580 (1954).
34. Gaunt, J., *Spectrochim. Acta*, **8**, 57 (1956).
35. Gibson, J. H., *Analytical Applications of Near-Infrared Spectra*, Ph.D. Thesis, Cornell University, Ithaca, 1957.
36. Goddu, R. F., *Anal. Chem.*, **29**, 1790 (1957).
37. Goddu, R. F., *Anal. Chem.*, **30**, 1707 (1958).
38. Goddu, R. F., *Anal. Chem.*, **30**, 2009 (1958).
39. Goddu, R. F., and D. A. Delker, *Anal. Chem.*, **30**, 2013 (1958).
39a. Goddu, R. F., and D. A. Delker, *Anal. Chem.*, **32**, 140 (1960).
40. Goldberg, G., A. S. Meyer, Jr., and J. C. White, *Anal Chem.*, **30**, 1163 (1958).
41. Goldman, J. M., and R. O. Crisler, *J. Org. Chem.*, **23**, 751 (1958).
42. Gordes, H. F., and C. W. Tait, *Anal. Chem.*, **28**, 1538 (1956).
43. Goulden, J. D. S., *Spectrochim. Acta*, **6**, 129 (1954).
44. Greinacher, E., W. Luttke, and R. Mecke, *Z. Elektrochem.*, **59**, 23 (1955).
45. Harris, J. T., Jr., and M. E. Hobbs, *J. Am. Chem. Soc.*, **76**, 1419 (1954).
46. Hecht, K. T., and D. L. Wood, *Proc. Roy. Soc. (London)*, **A235**, 174 (1956).
47. Hibbard, R. R., and A. P. Cleaves, *Anal. Chem.*, **21**, 486 (1949).
48. Hibbert, G. E., O. R. Wulf, S. B. Hendricks, and U. Liddel, *J. Am. Chem. Soc.*, **58**, 548 (1936).
49. Hibbert, G. E., O. R. Wulf, S. B. Hendricks, and U. Liddel, *J. Am. Chem. Soc.*, **58**, 1991 (1936).
50. Hilton, C. L., *Anal. Chem.*, **31**, 1610 (1959).
51. Holman, R. T., and P. R. Edmondson, *Anal. Chem.*, **28**, 1533 (1956).

52. Holman, R. T., S. Ener, and P. R. Edmondson, *Arch. Biochem. Biophys.*, **80**, 72 (1959).
53. Holman, R. T., C. Nickell, O. S. Privett and P. R. Edmondson, *J. Am. Oil Chemists' Soc.*, **35**, 422 (1958).
54. Hughes, R. H., R. J. Martin, and N. D. Coggeshall, *J. Chem. Phys.*, **24**, 489 (1956).
55. Ingraham, L. L., J. Corse, G. E. Bailey, and F. Stitt, *J. Am. Chem. Soc.*, **74**, 2297 (1952).
56. Jones, R. N., and C. Sandorfy, "Infrared and Raman Spectroscopy—Applications" in A. Weissberger, Ed., *Chemical Applications of Spectroscopy (Technique of Organic Chemistry, Vol. IX)*, Interscience, New York, 1956.
57. Kaye, W., *Spectrochim. Acta*, **6**, 257 (1954).
58. Kaye, W., *Spectrochim. Acta*, **7**, 181 (1955).
59. Kaye, W., Paper presented at Pittsburgh Conference on Analytical Chemistry and Applied Spectroscopy, March 2–6, 1959.
60. Kaye, W., C. Canon, and R. G. Devaney, *J. Opt. Soc. Am.*, **41**, 658 (1951).
61. Kaye, W., and R. G. Devaney, *J. Opt. Soc. Am.*, **42**, 567 (1952).
61a. Kogan, I. C., *J. Am. Chem. Soc.*, **79**, 2253 (1957).
61b. Kogan, I. C., *J. Org. Chem.*, **24**, 83 (1959).
62. Kruger, P. J., and H. W. Thompson, *Proc. Roy. Soc. (London)*, **A243**, 143 (1957).
63. Kuhn, L. P., *J. Am. Chem. Soc.*, **74**, 2492 (1952).
64. Lauer, J., and E. J. Rosenbaum, *Appl. Spectroscopy*, **6**, No. 529 (1952).
65. Liddel, U., and O. R. Wulf, *J. Am. Chem. Soc.*, **55**, 3574 (1933).
66. Luttke, W., and R. Mecke, *Z. physik. Chem. (Leipzig)*, **196**, 56 (1950).
67. Malcolm, B. P., *J. Sci. Instr.*, **35**, 423 (1958).
68. Manning, R. J., Paper presented at Pittsburgh Conference on Analytical Chemistry and Applied Spectroscopy, March 2–6, 1959.
69. Marion, L., D. A. Ramsay, and R. N. Jones, *J. Am. Chem. Soc.*, **73**, 305 (1951).
70. McIvor, R. A., E. E. Hubley, L. A. Grant, and A. A. Grey, *Can. J. Chem.*, **36**, 820 (1958).
71. Mecke, R., *Discussions Faraday Soc., No. 9*, 161 (1950).
72. Miller, R. J. G., and H. A. Willis, *J. Appl. Chem. (London)*, **6**, 385 (1956).
73. Mitchell, J. A., C. D. Bockman, Jr., and A. V. Lee, *Anal. Chem.*, **29**, 499 (1957).
74. Mitzner, B. M., and J. Loori, Paper presented at Pittsburgh Conference on Analytical Chemistry and Applied Spectroscopy, March 2–6, 1959.
74a. Moccia, R., and S. Califano, *Gazz. chim. ital.*, **48**, 342 (1958).
75. Moccia, R., and H. W. Thompson, *Proc. Roy. Soc. (London)*, **A235**, 154 (1957).
76. Moccia, R., and H. W. Thompson, *Spectrochim. Acta*, **10**, 240 (1957).
77. Palm, A., and H. Werbin, *Can. J. Chem.*, **31**, 1004 (1953).
78. Pauling, L., *J. Am. Chem. Soc.*, **58**, 94 (1936).
79. Pauling, L., *Nature of the Chemical Bond*, 2nd ed., Cornell University Press, Ithaca, 1948, p. 235.
80. Philpotts, A. R., W. Shain, and P. G. Smith, *Anal. Chem.*, **23**, 268 (1951).

80a. Piccolini, R., and S. Winstein, *Tetrahedron Letters,* **No. 13,** 4 (1959).
81. Plyler, E. K., L. R. Blaine, and M. J. Nowak, *J. Research Natl. Bureau Standards,* **58,** 195 (1957).
82. Rose, F. W., Jr., *J. Research Natl. Bureau Standards,* **20,** 129 (1938).
83. Royer, G. L., H. C. Lawrence, S. P. Kodama, and C. W. Warren, 134th Meeting American Chemical Society, Chicago, Ill., Sept. 6–11, 1953, Abstracts of Meeting, p. 18B.
84. Russell, R. A., and H. W. Thompson, *J. Chem. Soc.,* **1955,** 483.
85. Russell, R. A., and H. W. Thompson, *Spectrochim. Acta,* **8,** 138 (1956).
86. Russell, R. A., and H. W. Thompson, *Spectrochim. Acta,* **9,** 133 (1957).
87. Schleyer, P. V. R., D. S. Trifan, and R. Bacskai, *J. Am. Chem. Soc.,* **80,** 6691 (1958).
88. Sears, W. C., and L. J. Kitchen, *J. Am. Chem. Soc.,* **71,** 4110 (1949).
89. Shull, E. R., J. L. Wood, J. G. Aston, and D. H. Rank, *J. Chem. Phys.,* **22** 1191 (1954).
89a. Sicher, J., M. Horak, and M. Svoboda, *Collection Czechoslov. Chem. Communs.,* **24,** 950 (1959).
90. Simard, R. G., I. Hasegawa, W. Bandaruk, and C. E. Headington, *Anal. Chem.,* **23,** 1384 (1951).
91. Slover, H. T., and L. R. Dugan, *J. Am. Oil Chemists' Soc.,* **35,** 350 (1958).
92. Smith, L. A., and E. C. Creitz, *J. Research Natl Bureau Standards,* **46,** 145 (1951).
93. Stone, P. J., and H. W. Thompson, *Spectrochim. Acta,* **10,** 17 (1957).
94. Thompson, H. W., and D. A. Jameson, *Spectrochim. Acta,* **13,** 236 (1958).
95. Tsubomura, H., *J. Chem. Phys.,* **23,** 2130 (1955).
96. Tsubomura, H., *J. Chem. Phys.,* **24,** 927 (1956).
97. Tuot, M., and P. Barchewitz, *Bull. soc. chim. France,* **1950,** 851.
98. Washburn, W. H., and M. J. Mahoney, *Appl. Spectroscopy,* **12,** 127 (1958).
99. Washburn, W. H., and M. J. Mahoney, *J. Am. Chem. Soc.,* **80,** 504 (1958).
100. Wenograd, J., and R. A. Spurr, *J. Am. Chem. Soc.,* **79,** 5844 (1957).
100a. West, R., *J. Amer. Chem. Soc.,* **81,** 1614 (1959).
100b. Wheeler, O. H., *Chem. Revs.,* **59,** 629 (1959).
101. Whetsel, K. B., W. E. Roberson, and M. W. Krell, *Anal. Chem.,* **29,** 1006 (1957).
102. Whetsel, K. B., W. E. Roberson, and M. W. Krell, *Anal. Chem.,* **30,** 1594 (1958).
103. Whetsel, K. B., W. C. Roberson, and M. W. Krell, *Anal. Chem.,* **30,** 1598 (1958).
104. Whetsel, K. B., W. C. Roberson, and M. W. Krell, *Anal. Chem.,* in press.
105. White, L., Jr., and W. J. Barrett, *Anal. Chem.,* **28,** 1538 (1956).
106. Willis, H. A., and R. G. J. Miller, *Spectrochim. Acta,* **14,** 119 (1959).
107. Winstein, S., personal communication.
108. Wulf, O. R., and U. Liddel, *J. Am. Chem. Soc.,* **57,** 1464 (1935).
109. Wulf, O. R., U. Liddel, and S. B. Hendricks, *J. Am. Chem. Soc.,* **58,** 2287 (1936).
110. Wulf, O. R., E. J. Jones, and L. S. Deming, *J. Chem. Phys.,* **8,** 753 (1940).

INDEX

F

Fast reactions, techniques for, 252–8

Feldspar, determination of potassium in, 53

Ferric chloride, as titrant in fluoride determination, 166

Fertilizers, analysis of, 71

Fixatives, for ashing organic fluorides, 177–8

Flame ionization detector, carrier gas for, 131
  electrodes for, 130
  for gas chromatography, 129–31
  sensitivity of, 131

Flame measuring devices, as gas chromatography detectors, 125–31

Flow-proportioned counter, for full-flow detection, 132

Fluoride, determination of, with aluminum as titrant, 156, 166
  chemical methods for, 160
  by colorimetric methods, 159, 169–75
    buffers for, 186
    difficulties in, 180–2
  by direct methods, 156–8, 166–7, 183–5
    difficulties in, 180–2
  with disodium ethylenedinitrilotetraacetate as titrant, 167–8
  fluorometric methods for, 159–60, 175
  by fluosilicate reactions, 158–9, 168–9
  by gravimetric methods, 155–6, 165
  by hydrofluoric acid reactions, 159, 169
  by indirect methods, 158, 167–8
  by instrumental methods, difficulties in, 182
  with iron(III) as titrant, 156, 166
  by lanthanum fluoride precipitation, 165
  as lead chlorofluoride, 155
  by miscellaneous methods, 175–6, 187–8
  by neutralization methods, 158–9, 168–9
  with permanganate as titrant, 158
  physical methods for, 160–1, 186–7
    difficulties in, 182
  with potassium ferrocyanide as titrant, 168
  by quantitative infrared spectrophotometry, 187
  with rare earth metals as titrants, 157, 166
  with scandium chelates, 185
  with silver as titrant, 158
  spectrographic methods for, 160
  with thorium as titrant, 157, 167
  as triphenyltin fluoride, 156, 165
  by volumetric methods, 156–9, 166–9
    buffers for, 186
    difficulties in, 180–2
  with zirconium as titrant, 156, 166
  with zirconium chelates to reduce anion interference, 181
  recovery of, effect of contaminants, 155
  separation of, by adsorption, 164
    by ashing, 177–8
    by direct methods avoiding separations, 183–5
    future investigations, 183–8
    by gas chromatography, 165
    as hexafluosilicic acid, 155, 162
    by ion exchange, 164
    by paper chromatography, 165
    preparation of samples, 154, 161–2, 177–8
    by pyrolysis, 163–4, 185
    by solvent extraction of tetraphenylstibonium fluoride, 165
    by volatilization, 155, 162–4, 178–9
    by Willard-Winter technique, 155, 162

Fluoride complexes, relative solubility of, 179–80
  stability of, 179–80